Praise for *The Myth of Normal*

"In *The Myth of Normal*, Gabor Maté takes us on an epic journey of discovery about how our emotional well-being and our social connectivity (in short, how we live) are intimately intertwined with health, disease, and addictions. Chronic mental and physical illnesses may not be separate and distinct diseases but intricate, multilayered processes that reflect (mal)adaptations to the cultural context that we live in and the values we live by. This riveting and beautifully written tale has profound implications for all of our lives, including the practice of medicine and mental health."

—Bessel A. van der Kolk, MD, president, Trauma Research Foundation, professor of psychiatry, Boston University School of Medicine, and author of the #1 *New York Times* bestseller *The Body Keeps the Score: Brain, Mind, and Body in the Healing of Trauma*

"Gabor and Daniel Maté have created a magnificent resource for us all in *The Myth of Normal*, a powerful, in-depth, science-packed, inspiring story–filled opus that helps us see how stress within our culture shapes our well-being in all its facets. By carefully reviewing medical and mental health through a wide lens of inquiry, they challenge simplistic views of disease and disorder to offer instead a wider perspective on human flourishing that has direct implications for how we live individually, at home, and as a larger human family. A thorough and inspiring work of the heart, this book urges us to question our assumptions and think deeply about who we are and how we can live more fully and freely, harnessing the power of the mind to bring healing and wholeness into our shared lives on Earth."

—Daniel J. Siegel, MD, clinical professor, UCLA School of Medicine, executive director, Mindsight Institute, and *New York Times* bestselling author of *IntraConnected: MWe (Me + We) as the Integration of Self, Identity, and Belonging*

"Wise, sophisticated, rigorous, and creative: an intellectual and compassionate investigation of who we are and who we may become. Essential reading for anyone with a past and a future."

—Tara Westover, *New York Times* bestselling author of *Educated*

"Gabor and Daniel Maté have delivered a book in which readers can seek refuge and solace during moments of profound personal and social crisis. *The Myth of Normal* is an essential compass during disorienting times."

—Esther Perel, psychotherapist, author, and host of *Where Should We Begin?*

"Gabor Maté articulates bluntly, brilliantly, and passionately what all of us instinctively know but none of us really want to face: The entire social construct of the world we're living in is deeply flawed, with toxicities on every level. Yet though the book makes clear what's so terribly wrong, it also points to how we can make it right. Maté is a guide through the dangerous forest of our minds and our society, not letting us ignore the darkness but ultimately showing us the light. *The Myth of Normal* is exactly what we need."

—Marianne Williamson, *New York Times* bestselling author of *A Return to Love*

"*The Myth of Normal* is an astonishing achievement, epic in scope and yet profoundly down-to-earth and practical. I believe it will open the gates to a new time when we come to understand that our emotions, culture, bodies, and spirits are not separate, and wellness can only come about if we treat the whole being. I will read this book again and again."

—V (formerly Eve Ensler), author of *The Vagina Monologues* and *The Apology*

"*The Myth of Normal* may forever change the way you view your life experiences and how they can shape your biology. But more important, Gabor Maté points us to a path of desperately needed communal healing."

—Elissa Epel, PhD, professor, University of California, San Francisco, and co-author of the bestseller *The Telomere Effect*

"In this brilliant, compelling, and groundbreaking book, Gabor Maté unveils the societal trance that has blinded us to the death grip of pervasive trauma in our world. He shows that this is not our personal trauma. It is sourced in a culture that undermines meeting our basic needs for connection, authenticity, and meaning. Drawing on his decades of pioneering clinical work, fascinating contemporary science, and contemplative wisdom, Maté offers us a way to bring clear seeing and a greatness of heart to the crisis of our times."

—Tara Brach, author of *Radical Acceptance* and *Radical Compassion*

"Gabor and Daniel Maté offer a powerful and surprising redemptive path out of the toxic illusion of 'normalcy.' This remarkable and revolutionary book will profoundly impact the well-being of self, society, and our earth at a time when wisdom and compassion are essential for our common survival."

—Reverend Joan Jiko Halifax, abbot, Upaya Zen Center

"At a time when so many of us are struggling physically and psychically, Gabor Maté's *The Myth of Normal* is a godsend, providing wisdom and realistic hope. Maté is a revolutionary thinker and gifted writer whose work has always inspired me. *The Myth of Normal* is no exception. It's no exaggeration to say that this groundbreaking book can help us heal as individuals, families, and a society."

—David Sheff, author of the #1 *New York Times* bestseller *Beautiful Boy*

"As if Gabor Maté hasn't done enough already by depathologizing addiction, autoimmune diseases, and ADHD, now, in this magnum opus, he challenges us to expand our minds even further. In *The Myth of Normal*, he asserts that those problems, and the many other social ills that plague us, are not only related to the traumas we've suffered but are also symptoms of the toxic nature of our materialistic, isolating, patriarchal, and racist culture. What's remarkable about this beautifully written book is not just that he makes that bold contention, but how well he backs it up with an amazing amount of scientific research, compelling stories of his patients, and moving disclosures from his own life. Our culture is indeed very sick and I don't know of a better diagnostician of and physician for it than Gabor Maté. This book contains a prescription that, if we have the courage to follow it, will heal us all."

—Richard Schwartz, PhD, creator of the Internal Family Systems model of psychotherapy

"*The Myth of Normal* is a book literally everyone will be enriched by—a wise, profound, and healing work that is the culmination of Dr. Maté's many years of deep and painfully accumulated wisdom."

—Johann Hari, *New York Times* bestselling author of *Stolen Focus*

"This gripping book builds upon two key truths for our time—that everything is connected, including psychic wounds and physical illnesses, and that these are not anomalies but ordinary, even epidemic, in the society we've built. *The Myth of Normal* is a powerful call for change in how we live with, love, understand, treat, and think about one another, by someone ideally situated to map the terrain and to give us some valuable tools with which to navigate it."

—Rebecca Solnit, author of *Men Explain Things to Me*

"In this wide-ranging and beautifully written book, Gabor Maté and his co-writer son Daniel offer an acute diagnosis of what ails our culture and a blueprint for personal healing, while pointing the way to what is required to create a more hospitable, human-friendly world for ourselves and our children."

—Dr. Shefali, *New York Times* bestselling author and clinical psychologist

"Gabor Maté's latest book is a guide to self-awareness, social insight, and healing that is deeply personal and utterly transparent. Written with fluid, crystalline prose, profound wisdom, great humor, and hard-won humility, it merits becoming this generation's *The Road Less Traveled*. In my two-word summation, *The Myth of Normal* is Fiercely Tender."

—William M. Watson, SJ, DMin, president and founder, Sacred Story Institute

"*The Myth of Normal* is a detailed and wide-ranging look at what we all need to know—but all too often fail to live up to—when it comes to human health, sanity, maturation, and happiness. It's also a clear-eyed examination of the benefits, triumphs, limitations, and blind spots of our health and mental health care system."

—Resmaa Menakem, bestselling author of *My Grandmother's Hands*, *The Quaking of America*, and *Monsters in Love*

"*The Myth of Normal* is a tour de force journey into the dissonant experience of being human in our aberrant and toxic modern culture. The journey is both heartrending and exalted in its underlying purpose—to heal the rift from our authentic selves and the collective trauma that stifles our natural expression and joy. If you are ready to do the brave and life-shaking work of examining the truth of your life and the culture that we are literally in the death grips of—this is your read."

—Rachel Carlton Abrams, MD, MHS, ABoIM

"*The Myth of Normal* presents a unique perspective in viewing what we see as 'normal' and opens up a way to wake up to what is real and authentic in our lives. Gabor and Daniel Maté have written a compelling book that will challenge your views and help lift the veil of illusion to what is truly happening in your mind and in your body."

—Sharon Salzberg, author of *Lovingkindness* and *Real Happiness*

"With rigorous research and painstaking detail, this book by esteemed physician Gabor Maté is a tour de force manifesto of how trauma impacts not just our individual bodies and psyches but our whole society. *The Myth of Normal* plants seeds for revitalizing what we consider 'normal' and giving ourselves permission to say no to what is making us unnecessarily sick."

—Lissa Rankin, MD, *New York Times* bestselling author of *Mind Over Medicine* and *Sacred Medicine*

"This, Gabor Maté's magnum opus, is essential reading for us all. A genius writer, he gives it to us straight: From the mindbody to the body politic, we learn how loss of authenticity takes its toll psychologically, physically, spiritually, and socially."

—Julie Holland, MD, author of *Good Chemistry: The Science of Connection, from Soul to Psychedelics*

"Every once in a rare while a book comes along creating a new vision of the world, illuminating for us that which until now has been invisible, yet as vital to our health and well-being as water is to fish, oxygen is for our bodies, and love is for our souls. This work is such a tour de force, a humbling and brilliantly written exposition of what deeper healing requires."

—Jeffrey D. Rediger, MD, MDiv, assistant professor, Harvard Medical School, and author of *Cured: Strengthen Your Immune System and Heal Your Life*

"Gabor Mate is brilliant and passionate, tender and fierce, writing with an urgent honesty. His analysis is comprehensive and penetrating, combining deep scholarship, hard-earned clinical wisdom, personal trauma, and practical suggestions. This is a masterwork that reads like an intelligent thriller, highlighting our challenges with dramatic clarity while showing the way to their solutions. A must-have book for anyone interested in their own mind, in how our world got so crazy, and in the better future we can forge together."

—Rick Hanson, PhD, author of *Resilient: How to Grow an Unshakable Core of Calm, Strength, and Happiness*

the Myth of Normal

Trauma, Illness & Healing
in a Toxic Culture

Gabor Maté, MD,
with Daniel Maté

Alfred A. Knopf Canada

PUBLISHED BY ALFRED A. KNOPF CANADA

www.penguinrandomhouse.ca

Knopf Canada and colophon are registered trademarks.

Library and Archives Canada Cataloguing in Publication

Title: The myth of normal : trauma, illness and healing in a toxic culture / Gabor Maté with Daniel Maté.
Names: Maté, Gabor, author. | Maté, Daniel, author.
Identifiers: Canadiana (print) 20210260319 | Canadiana (ebook) 20210260408 | ISBN 9780735278363 (hardcover) | ISBN 9780735278370 (EPUB)
Subjects: LCSH: Health—Social aspects. | LCSH: Diseases—Social aspects. | LCSH: Social medicine. | LCSH: Civilization, Modern—21st century—Health aspects.
Classification: LCC RA418 .M38 2022 | DDC 306.4/61—dc23

Book design by Shannon Nicole Plunkett
Jacket design: Pete Garceau
Jacket image: PressureUA / iStock / Getty Images Plus

Printed in the United States of America

2nd Printing

Penguin
Random House
KNOPF CANADA

To dearest Rae, my life partner, who saw me before I could see myself and who loved all of me long before I could love myself at all. None of my work would exist without her. And to the children we brought forth together—Daniel, Aaron, and Hannah—who light up our world.

The best physician is also a philosopher.

—Aelius Galenus (Galen of Pergamon)

For if medicine is really to accomplish its great task,
it must intervene in political and social life. It must point
out the hindrances that impede the normal social functioning
of vital processes, and effect their removal.

—Rudolf Virchow, nineteenth-century German physician

When you're trying to survive, you turn malady into
a coping strategy, and loss into culture.

—Stephen Jenkinson

Author's Note

There are no composite or fictional characters in this book. Each story told is that of a real person whose words, from transcribed interviews, are reproduced accurately with occasional editing for purposes of clarity. When only a given name is used, it is a pseudonym to protect privacy, at the interviewee's request. In such cases, some biographical data may also be slightly altered. Where both names are given, the identity is real.

Unless otherwise stated, all italics are mine.

A word about authorship. This book was co-written with my son Daniel. Usually the word "with" in identifying authors is meant to denote a ghostwriter, one who actually renders the main author's ideas into written form. That wasn't the case here: on most chapters I was the primary author, with Daniel following up with a particular eye to style, tone, clarity of argument, and accessibility, and often contributing his own thoughts. Occasionally, when I found myself stuck on what to say or how to say it, he would take the writing reins for a while, crafting a particular section or chapter based on material I had collated and penned. In all cases, we would pass the chapters back and forth until we were both satisfied. The structure and flow of the book was also very much an ongoing collaboration between us, from the preparation of the book proposal through the final draft.

So while the book's *authorship* is unequally distributed, in that it reflects my work, research, analysis, and experience, it was very much *co-written*. I truly could not have accomplished the task without Daniel's brilliant partnership.

Gabor Maté
Vancouver, B.C.

Contents

Introduction   Why Normal Is a Myth (And Why That Matters) – 1

Part I: Our Interconnected Nature

Chapter 1   The Last Place You Want to Be: Facets of Trauma – 15

Chapter 2   Living in an Immaterial World:
Emotions, Health, and the Body-Mind Unity – 37

Chapter 3   You Rattle My Brain: Our Highly Interpersonal Biology – 52

Chapter 4   Everything I'm Surrounded By:
Dispatches from the New Science – 59

Chapter 5   Mutiny on the Body:
The Mystery of the Rebellious Immune System – 68

Chapter 6   It Ain't a Thing: Disease as Process – 85

Chapter 7   A Traumatic Tension: Attachment vs. Authenticity – 96

Part II: The Distortion of Human Development

Chapter 8   Who Are We Really? Human Nature, Human Needs – 115

Chapter 9   A Sturdy or Fragile Foundation: Children's Irreducible Needs – 123

Chapter 10   Trouble at the Threshold: Before We Come into the World – 136

Chapter 11   What Choice Do I Have? Childbirth in a Medicalized Culture – 146

Chapter 12   Horticulture on the Moon: Parenting, Undermined – 160

Chapter 13   Forcing the Brain in the Wrong Direction:
The Sabotage of Childhood – 179

Chapter 14   A Template for Distress: How Culture Builds Our Character – 197

Part III: Rethinking Abnormal: Afflictions as Adaptations

Chapter 15   Just Not to Be You: Debunking the Myths About Addiction – 211

Chapter 16   Show of Hands: A New View of Addiction – 224

Chapter 17   An Inaccurate Map of Our Pain:
               What We Get Wrong About Mental Illness – 235

Chapter 18   The Mind Can Do Some Amazing Things:
               From Madness to Meaning – 253

Part IV: The Toxicities of Our Culture

Chapter 19   From Society to Cell:
               Uncertainty, Conflict, and Loss of Control – 275

Chapter 20   Robbing the Human Spirit: Disconnection and Its Discontents – 286

Chapter 21   They Just Don't Care If It Kills You: Sociopathy as Strategy – 297

Chapter 22   The Assaulted Sense of Self: How Race and Class Get
               Under the Skin – 311

Chapter 23   Society's Shock Absorbers: Why Women Have It Worse – 329

Chapter 24   We Feel Their Pain: Our Trauma-Infused Politics – 343

Part V: Pathways to Wholeness

Chapter 25   Mind in the Lead: The Possibility of Healing – 361

Chapter 26   Four *A*'s and Five Compassions: Some Healing Principles – 374

Chapter 27   A Dreadful Gift: Disease as Teacher – 390

Chapter 28   Before the Body Says No: First Steps on the Return to Self – 408

Chapter 29   Seeing Is Disbelieving: Undoing Self-Limiting Beliefs – 422

Chapter 30   Foes to Friends: Working with the Obstacles to Healing – 430

Chapter 31   Jesus in the Tipi: Psychedelics and Healing – 447

Chapter 32   My Life as a Genuine Thing: Touching Spirit – 463

Chapter 33   Unmaking a Myth: Visioning a Saner Society – 481

Acknowledgments – 499

Notes – 503

Index – 546

Why Normal Is a Myth (And Why That Matters)

*The fact that millions of people share the same vices does not
make these vices virtues, the fact that they share so many errors
does not make the errors to be truths, and the fact that millions
of people share the same forms of mental pathology does not
make these people sane.*

—Erich Fromm, *The Sane Society*

In the most health-obsessed society ever, all is not well.

Health and wellness have become a modern fixation. Multibillion-dollar industries bank on people's ongoing investment—mental and emotional, not to mention financial—in endless quests to eat better, look younger, live longer, or feel livelier, or simply to suffer fewer symptoms. We encounter would-be bombshells of "breaking health news" on magazine covers, in TV news stories, omnipresent advertising, and the daily deluge of viral online content, all pushing this or that mode of self-betterment. We do our best to keep up: we take supplements, join yoga studios, serially switch diets, shell out for genetic testing, strategize to prevent cancer or dementia, and seek medical advice or alternative therapies for maladies of the body, psyche, and soul.

And yet our collective health is deteriorating.

What is happening? How are we to understand that in our modern world, at the pinnacle of medical ingenuity and sophistication, we are seeing more and more chronic physical disease as well as afflictions such as mental illness and addiction? Moreover, how is it that we're not more alarmed, if we notice at all? And how are we to find our way to preventing and healing the many ailments that assail us, even putting aside acute catastrophes such as the COVID-19 pandemic?

As a physician for over three decades, in work ranging from delivering infants to running a palliative care ward, I was always struck by the links between the individual and the social and emotional contexts in which our lives unfold and health or illness ensue. This curiosity, or should I say fascination, led me in time to look deeply into the cutting-edge science that has elegantly delineated such links. My previous books have explored some of these connections as they manifest in particular ailments such as attention deficit hyperactivity disorder (ADHD), cancer and autoimmune disease of all types, and addiction. I have also written about child development, the most decisively formative period of our lives.[1]

This book, *The Myth of Normal*, sets its sights on something far more encompassing. I have come to believe that behind the entire epidemic of chronic afflictions, mental and physical, that beset our current moment, something is amiss in our culture itself, generating both the rash of ailments we are suffering *and*, crucially, the ideological blind spots that keep us from seeing our predicament clearly, the better to do something about it. These blind spots—prevalent throughout the culture but endemic to a tragic extent in my own profession—keep us ignorant of the connections that bind our health to our social-emotional lives.

Another way of saying it: chronic illness—mental or physical—is to a large extent a *function* or *feature* of the way things are and not a *glitch*; a consequence of how we live, not a mysterious aberration.

The phrase "a toxic culture" in this book's subtitle may suggest things like environmental pollutants, so prevalent since the dawn of the industrial age and so antagonistic to human health. From asbestos particles to carbon dioxide run amok, there is indeed no shortage of real, physical toxins in our midst. We could also understand "toxic" in its more contemporary, pop-psychological sense, as in the spread of negativity, distrust, hostility, and polarization that, no question, typify the present sociopolitical moment.

We can certainly fold these two meanings into our discussion, but I am using "toxic culture" to characterize something even broader and more deeply rooted: *the entire context of social structures, belief systems, assumptions, and values that surround us and necessarily pervade every aspect of our lives.*

That social life bears upon health is not a new discovery, but the recognition of it has never been more urgent. I see it as the most important and consequential health concern of our time, driven by the effects of burgeoning stress, inequality, and climate catastrophe, to name a few salient factors. Our concept of well-being must move from the individual to the global in every sense of that word. That is particularly so in this era of globalized capitalism, which, in the words of the cultural historian Morris Berman, has become the "total commercial environment that circumscribes an entire mental world."[2] Given the mind-body unity to be highlighted in this book, I would add that it constitutes a total physiological environment as well.

It is my contention that by its very nature our social and economic culture generates chronic stressors that undermine well-being in the most serious of ways, as they have done with increasing force over the past several decades.

Here's an analogy I find helpful. In a laboratory, a culture is a biochemical broth custom-made to promote the development of this or that organism. Assuming the microbes in question start out with a clean bill of health and genetic fitness, a suitable and well-maintained culture should allow for their happy, healthy growth and proliferation. If the same organisms begin showing pathologies at unprecedented rates, or fail to thrive, it's either because the culture has become contaminated or because it was the wrong mixture in the first place. Whichever the case, we could rightly call this a *toxic culture*—unsuitable for the creatures it is meant to support. Or worse: dangerous to their existence. It is the same with human societies. As the broadcaster, activist, and author Thom Hartmann asserts, "Culture can be healthy or toxic, nurturing or murderous."[3]

From a wellness perspective, our current culture, viewed as a laboratory experiment, is an ever-more globalized demonstration of what can go awry. Amid spectacular economic, technological, and medical resources, it induces countless humans to suffer illness born of stress, ignorance, inequality, environmental degradation, climate change, poverty, and social isolation. It allows millions to die prematurely of diseases we know how to prevent or of deprivations we have more than enough resources to eliminate.

In the United States, the richest country in history and the epicenter of the globalized economic system, 60 percent of adults have a chronic disorder such as high blood pressure or diabetes, and over 40 percent have two or more such conditions.[4] Nearly 70 percent of Americans are on at least one prescription drug; more than half take two.[5] In my own country, Canada, up to half of all baby boomers are on track for hypertension within a few years if current trends continue.[6] Among women there is a disproportionate elevation in diagnoses of potentially disabling autoimmune conditions like multiple sclerosis (MS).[7] Among the young, non-smoking-related cancers seem to be on the rise. Rates of obesity, along with the multiple health risks it poses, are going up in many countries, including in Canada, Australia, and notably the United States, where over 30 percent of the adult population meet the criteria. Recently Mexico has surpassed its northern neighbor in that unenviable category, with the result that thirty-eight Mexicans are diagnosed with diabetes every hour. Thanks to globalization, Asia is catching up. "China has entered the era of obesity," Ji Chengye, a child health researcher in Beijing, reported. "The speed of growth is shocking."[8]

Throughout the Western world, mental health diagnoses are escalating among the young, in adults, and among the elderly. In Canada, depression and anxiety are the fastest-growing diagnoses; and in 2019 more than fifty million Americans, over 20 percent of U.S. adults, suffered an episode of mental illness.[9] In Europe, according to the authors of a recent international survey, mental disorders have become "the largest health challenge of the 21st century."[10] Millions of North American children and youths are being medicated with stimulants, antidepressants, and even antipsychotic drugs whose long-term effects on the developing brain are yet to be established—a perilous social experiment in the chemical control of young people's brains and behavior. A chilling 2019 headline on the online news site ScienceAlert speaks for itself: "Child Suicide Attempts Are Skyrocketing in the US, and Nobody Knows Why."[11] The picture is similarly stark in the U.K., where the *Guardian* recently reported, "British universities are experiencing a surge in student anxiety, mental breakdowns and depression."[12] As globalization envelops the world, conditions hitherto found in "developed" countries are finding their way into new venues. ADHD among children, for example, has become "an increasing public health concern" in China.[13]

The climate catastrophe already afflicting us has introduced an entirely new health hazard, a magnified version—if that is possible—of the existential threat that nuclear war has posed since Hiroshima. "Distress about climate change is associated with young people perceiving that they have no future, that humanity is doomed," found the authors of a 2021 survey of the attitudes of over ten thousand individuals in forty-two countries. Along with a sense of betrayal and abandonment by governments and adults, such despondence and hopelessness "are chronic stressors which will have significant, long-lasting and incremental negative implications on the mental health of children and young people."[14]

Casting ourselves as the organisms in the laboratory analogy, these and other metrics indicate unmistakably that ours is a toxic culture. Worse yet, we have become accustomed—or perhaps better to say *acculturated*—to so much of what plagues us. It has become, for lack of a better word, normal.

In medical practice, the word "normal" denotes, among other things, the state of affairs we doctors aim for, setting the boundaries delineating health from disease. "Normal levels" and "normal functioning" are our goal when we apply treatments or remedies. We also gauge success or failure against "statistical norms"; we reassure worried patients that this symptom or that side effect is completely normal, as in "to be expected." These are all specific and legitimate uses of the word, enabling us to assess situations realistically so that we can aim our efforts appropriately.

It is not in these senses that this book's title refers to "normal," but rather in a more insidious one that, far from helping us progress toward a healthier future, cuts such an endeavor off at the pass.

For better or worse, we humans have a genius for getting used to things, especially when the changes are incremental. The newfangled verb "to normalize" refers to the mechanism by which something previously aberrant becomes normal enough that it passes beneath our radar. On a societal level, then, "normal" often means "nothing to see here": all systems are functioning as they should, no further inquiry needed.

The truth as I see it is quite different.

The late David Foster Wallace, master wordsmith, author, and essayist, once opened a commencement speech with a droll parable that well illustrates the trouble with normality. The story concerns two fish crossing aquatic paths with an elder of their species, who greets them jovially: " 'Morning, boys. How's the water?' And the two young fish swim on for a bit, and then eventually one of them looks over at the other and goes, 'What the hell is water?' " The point Wallace wanted to leave his audience pondering was that "the most obvious, ubiquitous, important realities are often the ones hardest to see and talk about." On its surface, he allowed, that might sound like "a banal platitude" but "in the day-to-day trenches of adult existence, banal platitudes *can have a life-or-death importance.*"

He could have been articulating this book's thesis. Indeed, the lives, and the deaths, of individual human beings—their quality and in many cases their duration—are intimately bound up with the aspects of modern society that are "hardest to see and talk about"; phenomena that are, like water to fish, both too vast and too near to be appreciated. In other words, those features of daily life that appear to us now as normal are the ones crying out the loudest for our scrutiny. That is my central contention. My core intention, accordingly, is to offer a new way of seeing and talking about these phenomena, bringing them from the background to the foreground so we might more swiftly find their much-needed remedies.

I will make the case that much of what passes for normal in our society is neither healthy nor natural, and that to meet modern society's criteria for normality is, in many ways, to conform to requirements that are profoundly *abnormal* in regard to our

Nature-given needs—which is to say, unhealthy and harmful on the physiological, mental, and even spiritual levels.

If we could begin to see much illness itself not as a cruel twist of fate or some nefarious mystery but rather as an *expected and therefore normal consequence of abnormal, unnatural circumstances,* it would have revolutionary implications for how we approach everything health related. The ailing bodies and minds among us would no longer be regarded as expressions of individual pathology but as living alarms directing our attention toward where our society has gone askew, and where our prevailing certainties and assumptions around health are, in fact, fictions. Seen clearly, they might also give us clues as to what it would take to reverse course and build a healthier world.

Far more than a lack of technological acumen, sufficient funds, or new discoveries, our culture's skewed idea of normality is the single biggest impediment to fostering a healthier world, even keeping us from acting on what we already know. Its occluding effects are particularly dominant in the field where clear sight is most called for: medicine.

The current medical paradigm, owing to an ostensibly scientific bent that in some ways bears more resemblance to an ideology than to empirical knowledge, commits a double fault. It reduces complex events to their biology, and it separates mind from body, concerning itself almost exclusively with one or the other without appreciating their essential unity. This shortcoming does not invalidate medicine's indisputably miraculous achievements, nor sully the good intentions of so many people practicing it, but it does severely constrain the good that medical science could be doing.

One of the most persistent and calamitous failures handicapping our health systems is an ignorance—in the sense either of not knowing or of actual, active ignoring—of *what science has already established.* Case in point: the ample and growing evidence that living people cannot be dissected into separate organs and systems, not even into "minds" and "bodies." Overall, the medical world has been unwilling or unable to metabolize this evidence and to adjust its ways accordingly. The new science—much of which isn't all that conceptually new—has yet to have significant impact on medical school training, leaving well-meaning health providers to toil in the dark. Many end up having to connect the dots for themselves.

For me, the process of putting the pieces together began several decades ago when, on a hunch, I went beyond the standard repertoire of dry doctorly questions about symptom presentation and medical history to ask my patients about the larger context for their illnesses: their lives. I am grateful for what these men and women taught me through how they lived and died, suffered and recovered, and through the stories they shared with me. The core of it, which accords entirely with what the science shows, is this: health and illness are not random states in a particular body or body part. They are, in fact, an expression of an entire life lived, one that cannot, in turn, be understood in isolation: it is influenced by—or better yet, it arises from—a web of circumstances, relationships, events, and experiences.

Of course, we have cause to celebrate the past two centuries' astonishing medical advances and the tireless fortitude and intellectual brilliance of those whose work has led to giant strides in many different fields of human health. To take just one example, the incidence of polio—an awful illness that killed or maimed countless children only two or three generations back—has dropped by more than 99 percent since 1988, according to the U.S. Centers for Disease Control and Prevention; most kids today probably have never heard of the disease.[15] Even the more recent epidemic of HIV has been downgraded in a relatively short period of time from a death sentence to a manageable chronic condition—at least for those with access to the right kinds of treatment. And as destructive as the COVID-19 pandemic has been, the rapid development of vaccines may be counted among the triumphs of modern science and medicine.

The problem with good news stories like these—and they are very good news—is that they stoke the reassuring conviction that we are, overall, making advances toward a healthier standard of life, lulling us into a false passivity. The actual picture is quite different. Far from being on the verge of curbing the contemporary health challenges facing us, we are barely keeping pace with most of them. Often the best we can do is mitigate symptoms, whether surgically or pharmacologically, or both. As welcome as medical breakthroughs are, and as fruitful as research can be, the crux of the problem is not a dearth of facts, not a lack of technology or techniques, but an impoverished, out-of-date perspective that cannot account for what we are seeing. My aim here is to offer a fresh one that I believe brings with it enormous possibilities for a healthier paradigm: a new vision of normal that nurtures the best in who we are.

This book's arc follows the concentric circles of cause, connection, and consequence that influence how healthy or unhealthy we are. Beginning from the inside at the level of human biology, and then examining the close relationships within which our bodies, brains, and personalities develop, we will make our way outward to the most macro dimensions of our collective existence, namely the socioeconomic and the political. Along the path I will show how our physical and mental health is intricately interwoven with how we feel, what we perceive or believe about ourselves and the world, and the ways that life does or does not satisfy our nonnegotiable human needs. Because trauma is a foundational layer of experience in modern life, but one largely ignored or misapprehended, I will begin with a working definition to set up everything that follows.

At each stage, my task is to lift the veil of common knowledge and received wisdom, considering what science and watchful observation tell us, with the aim of unfastening the myths that keep the status quo locked in place. As in my previous books, the science and its health implications will be brought home via real-life stories and case studies of people who have generously shared something of their journeys through illness and health with me. These range from the mildly surprising to the truly incredible, the heartbreaking to the inspiring.

Yes, inspiring. For there is a heartening corollary to all the difficult news. When we can look soberly at what we as a culture have normalized about health and illness, and realize that it is not, in fact, the way things are meant or fated to be, there arises the possibility of returning to what Nature has always intended for us. Hence the "healing" in our subtitle: once we resolve to see clearly how things are, the process of healing—a word that, at its root, means "returning to wholeness"—can begin. That statement contains no promise of miracle cures but simply the recognition that each of us contains as-yet-unimagined possibilities for wellness, possibilities that reveal themselves only when we face and debunk the misleading myths† about normality to which we have become passively accustomed. If that is true for us as individuals, it must also be true for us as a species.

Healing is not guaranteed, but it is available. It is no exaggeration to say at this point in Earth's history that it is also required. Everything I have seen and learned over the years gives me confidence that we have it in us.

---

†   Although I'll mostly be using "myth" in its contemporary meaning of "fictional" or "misleading," I will have occasion much later in the book to acknowledge the healing power of genuine *mythic thinking*, in the ancient sense of the word.

Part I

Our Interconnected Nature

Because we think in a fragmentary way, we see fragments. And this way of seeing leads us to make actual fragments of the world.

—Susan Griffin, *A Chorus of Stones*

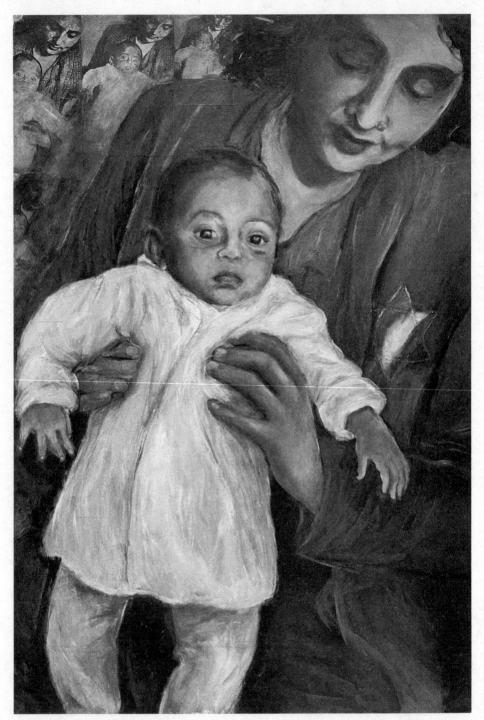

A painting by my wife, Rae, based on a 1944 photograph (seen in the upper left corner) of me at three months, held by my mother, Judith. The yellow star she wears is the badge of shame mandated for Hungarian Jews, as in other Nazi-occupied territories. Rae well captures the haunted look and fear in my infant eyes. Acrylic on canvas, 40 × 30 inches, 1997.

Chapter 1

The Last Place You Want to Be: Facets of Trauma

*It is hard to imagine the scope of an individual life without
envisioning some kind of trauma, and it is hard for
most people to know what to do about it.*
—Mark Epstein, *The Trauma of Everyday Life*[†]

Picture this: At the tender age of seventy-one, six years before this writing, your author arrives back in Vancouver from a
speaking jaunt to Philadelphia. The talk was successful, the audience enthusiastic, my message about addiction and trauma's
impact on people's lives warmly received. I have traveled in unexpected comfort, having been upgraded to the business-class
cabin, thanks to a courtesy from Air Canada. Descending over
Vancouver's pristine sea-to-sky panorama, I am a regular Little
Jack Horner in my corner of the plane, suffused with a "What a
good boy am I" glow. As we touch down and begin to taxi to the
gate, the text from my wife, Rae, lights up the tiny screen: "Sorry.
I haven't left home yet. Do you still want me to come?" I stiffen,
satisfaction displaced by rage. "Never mind," I dictate tersely
into the phone. Embittered, I disembark, clear customs, and take
a taxi home, all of a twenty-minute ride door-to-door. (I trust the
reader is already gripping the pages in empathetic outrage at the

†   Mark Epstein is a psychiatrist, Buddhist meditation teacher, and author.

indignity suffered by your author.) Seeing Rae, I growl a hello that is more accusation than greeting, and scarcely look at her. In fact, I barely make eye contact for the next twenty-four hours. When addressed, I utter little more than brief, monotone grunts. My gaze is averted, the upper part of my face tense and rigid, and my jaw in a perma-clench.

What is happening with me? Is this the response of a mature adult in his eighth decade? Only superficially. At times like this, there is very little grown-up Gabor in the mix. Most of me is in the grips of the distant past, near the beginnings of my life. This kind of physio-emotional time warp, preventing me from inhabiting the present moment, is one of the imprints of trauma, an underlying theme for many people in this culture. In fact, it is so deeply "underlying" that many of us don't know it's there.

The meaning of the word "trauma," in its Greek origin, is "wound." Whether we realize it or not, it is our woundedness, or how we cope with it, that dictates much of our behavior, shapes our social habits, and informs our ways of thinking about the world. It can even determine whether or not we are *capable* of rational thought at all in matters of the greatest importance to our lives. For many of us, it rears its head in our closest partnerships, causing all kinds of relational mischief.

It was in 1889 that the pioneering French psychologist Pierre Janet first depicted traumatic memory as being held in "automatic actions and reactions, sensations and attitudes . . . replayed and reenacted in visceral sensations."[1] In the present century, the leading trauma psychologist and healer Peter Levine has written that certain shocks to the organism "can alter a person's biological, psychological, and social equilibrium to such a degree that the memory of one particular event comes to taint, and dominate, all other experiences, spoiling an appreciation of the present moment."[2] Levine calls this "the tyranny of the past."

In my case, the template for my hostility to Rae's message is to be found in the diary my mother kept, in a nearly illegible scrawl and only intermittently, during my first years in wartime and post–World War II Budapest. The following, translated by me from the Hungarian, is her entry on April 8, 1945, when I was fourteen months old:

> My dear little man, only after many long months do I take in hand again the pen, so that I may briefly sketch for you the unspeakable horrors of those times, the details of which I do not wish you to know . . . It was on December 12 that the Crossed-Arrows[†] forced us into the fenced-in Budapest ghetto, from which, with extreme difficulty, we found refuge in a Swiss-protected house. From there, after two days, I sent you by a complete stranger to your Aunt Viola's because I saw that your little organism could not possibly endure the living conditions in that building. Now began the most dreadful five or six weeks of my life, when I couldn't see you.

I survived, thanks to the kindness and courage of the unknown Christian woman to whom my mother entrusted me in the street and who conveyed me to relatives living in hiding under relatively safer circumstances. Reunited with my mother after the Soviet army had put the Germans to flight, I did not so much as look at her for several days.

The great twentieth-century British psychiatrist and psychologist John Bowlby was familiar with such behavior: he called it detachment. At his clinic he observed ten small children who had to endure prolonged separation from their parents due to uncontrollable circumstances. "On meeting mother for the first time

---

† The viciously anti-Semitic fascist Hungarian political movement and paramilitary allied with the Nazi occupiers.

after days or weeks away every one of the children showed some degree of detachment," Bowlby observed. "Two seemed not to recognize mother. The other eight turned away or even walked away from her. Most of them either cried or came close to tears; a number alternated between a tearful and expressionless face."[3] It may seem counterintuitive, but this reflexive rejection of the loving mother is an adaptation: "I was so hurt when you abandoned me," says the young child's mind, "that I will not reconnect with you. I don't dare open myself to that pain again." In many children—and I was certainly one—early reactions like these become embedded in the nervous system, mind, and body, playing havoc with future relationships. They show up throughout the lifetime in response to any incident even vaguely resembling the original imprint—often without any recall of the inciting circumstances. My petulant and defensive reaction to Rae signaled that old, deep-brain emotional circuits, programmed in infancy, had taken over while the rational, calming, self-regulating parts of my brain went offline.

"All trauma is preverbal," the psychiatrist Bessel van der Kolk has written.[4] His statement is true in two senses. First, the psychic wounds we sustain are often inflicted upon us before our brain is capable of formulating any kind of a verbal narrative, as in my case. Second, even after we become language-endowed, some wounds are imprinted on regions of our nervous systems having nothing to do with language or concepts; this includes brain areas, of course, but the rest of the body, too. They are stored in parts of us that words and thoughts cannot directly access—we might even call this level of traumatic encoding "subverbal." As Peter Levine explains, "Conscious, *explicit* memory is only the proverbial tip of a very deep and mighty iceberg. It barely hints at the submerged strata of *primal implicit experience* that moves us in ways the conscious mind can only begin to imagine."[5]

To her credit, my wife will not allow me to get away with pinning the entire blame for my arrivals-gate hissy fit on Nazis and fascists and infant trauma. Yes, the backstory merits compassion and understanding—and she has given me an abundance of both—but there comes a point when "Hitler made me do it" won't fly. Responsibility can and must be taken. After twenty-four hours of the silent treatment, Rae had had enough. "Oh, knock it off already," she said. And so I did—a measure of progress and relative maturation on my part. In times past, it would have taken me days or longer to "knock it off": to drop my resentment, and for my core to unfreeze, my face to relax, my voice to soften, and my head to turn willingly and with love toward my life partner.

"My problem is that I am married to someone who understands me," I have often grumbled, only partly in jest. Really, of course, my great blessing is to be married to someone with healthy boundaries, who sees me as I am now and who will no longer bear the brunt of my prolonged and unplanned visits to the distant past.

What Trauma Is and What It Does

Trauma's imprint is more endemic than we realize. That may seem a puzzling statement, as "trauma" has become something of a catchword in our society. To boot, the word has taken on a number of colloquial valences that confuse and dilute its meaning. A clear and comprehensive reckoning is warranted, especially in the field of health—and, since everything is connected, in virtually all other societal domains as well.

The usual conception of trauma conjures up notions of catastrophic events: hurricanes, abuse, egregious neglect, and war. This has the unintended and misleading effect of relegating trauma to the realm of the abnormal, the unusual, the exceptional. If there exists a class of people we call "traumatized," that must mean that most of us are not. Here we miss the mark by a wide margin. Trauma pervades our culture, from personal functioning through social relationships, parenting, education, popular culture, economics, and politics. In fact, someone *without* the marks of trauma would be an outlier in our society. We are closer to the truth when we ask: Where do we each fit on the broad and surprisingly inclusive trauma spectrum? Which of its many marks has each of us carried all (or most) of our lives, and what have the impacts been? And what possibilities would open up were we to become more familiar, even intimate, with them?

A more basic question comes first: What is trauma? As I use the word, "trauma" is an inner injury, a lasting rupture or split within the self due to difficult or hurtful events. By this definition, trauma is primarily what happens within someone as a result of the difficult or hurtful events that befall them; it is not the events themselves. "Trauma is not what happens *to* you but what happens *inside* you" is how I formulate it. Think of a car accident where someone sustains a concussion: the accident is what happened; the injury is what lasts. Likewise, trauma is a psychic injury, lodged in our nervous system, mind, and body, lasting long past the originating incident(s), triggerable at any moment. It is a constellation of hardships, composed of the wound itself and the residual burdens that our woundedness imposes on our bodies and souls: the unresolved emotions they visit upon us; the coping dynamics they dictate; the tragic or melodramatic or neurotic scripts we unwittingly but inexorably live out; and, not least, the toll these take on our bodies.

When a wound doesn't mend on its own, one of two things will happen: it can either remain raw or, more commonly, be replaced by a thick layer of scar tissue. As an open sore, it is an ongoing source of pain and a place where we can be hurt over and over again by even the slightest stimulus. It compels us to be ever vigilant—always nursing our wounds, as it were—and leaves us limited in our capacity to move flexibly and act confidently lest we be harmed again. The scar is preferable, providing protection and holding tissues together, but it has its drawbacks: it is tight, hard, inflexible, unable to grow, a zone of numbness. The original healthy, alive flesh is not regenerated.

Raw wound or scar, unresolved trauma is a constriction of the self, both physical and psychological. It constrains our inborn capacities and generates an enduring distortion of our view of the world and of other people. Trauma, until we work it through, keeps us stuck in the past, robbing us of the present moment's riches, limiting who we can be. By impelling us to suppress hurt and unwanted parts of the psyche, it fragments the self. Until seen and acknowledged, it is also a barrier to growth. In many cases, as in mine, it blights a person's sense of worth, poisons relationships, and undermines appreciation for life itself. Early in childhood it may even interfere with healthy brain development. And, as we will witness, trauma is an antecedent and a contributor to illness of all kinds throughout the lifespan.

Taken together, these impacts constitute a major and foundational impediment to flourishing for many, many people. To quote Peter Levine once more, "Trauma is perhaps the most avoided, ignored, belittled, denied, misunderstood, and untreated cause of human suffering."[6]

Two Types of Trauma

Before we go on, let's distinguish two forms of trauma. The first—the sense in which clinicians and teachers like Levine and van der Kolk usually employ the word—involves automatic responses and mind-body adaptations to specific, identifiable hurtful and overwhelming events, whether in childhood or later. As my medical work taught me and as research has amply shown, painful things happen to many children, from outright abuse or severe neglect in the family of origin to the poverty or racism or oppression that are daily features of many societies. The consequences can be terrible. Far more common than usually acknowledged, such traumas give rise to multiple symptoms and syndromes and to conditions diagnosed as pathology, physical or mental—a linkage that remains almost invisible to the eyes of mainstream medicine and psychiatry, except in specific "diseases" like post-traumatic stress disorder. This kind of injury has been called by some "capital-*T* trauma." It underlies much of what gets labeled as mental illness. It also creates a predisposition to physical illness by driving inflammation, elevating physiological stress, and impairing the healthy functioning of genes, among many other mechanisms. To sum up, then, capital-*T* trauma occurs when things happen to vulnerable people that should *not* have happened, as, for example, a child being abused, or violence in the family, or a rancorous divorce, or the loss of a parent. All these are among the criteria for childhood affliction in the well-known adverse childhood experiences (ACE) studies. Once again, the traumatic events themselves are not identical to the trauma—the injury to self—that occurs in their immediate wake within the person.

There is another form of trauma—and this is the kind I am calling nearly universal in our culture—that has sometimes been termed "small-*t* trauma." I have often witnessed what long-lasting marks seemingly ordinary events—what a seminal researcher poignantly called the "less memorable but hurtful and far more prevalent misfortunes of childhood"—can leave on the psyches of children.[7] These might include bullying by peers, the casual but repeated harsh comments of a well-meaning parent, or even just a lack of sufficient emotional connection with the nurturing adults.

Children, especially highly sensitive children, can be wounded in multiple ways: by bad things happening, yes, but also by good things not happening, such as their emotional needs for attunement not being met, or the experience of not being seen and accepted, even by loving parents. Trauma of this kind does not require overt distress or misfortune of the sort mentioned above and can also lead to the pain of disconnection from the self, occurring as a result of core needs not being satisfied. Such non-events are what the British pediatrician D. W. Winnicott referred to as "nothing happening when something might profitably have happened"—a subject we will return to when we consider human development. "The traumas of everyday life can easily make us feel like a motherless child," writes the psychiatrist Mark Epstein.[8]

If, despite decades of evidence, "big-*T* trauma" has barely registered on the medical radar screen, small-*t* trauma does not even cause a blip.

Even as we make this distinction between big-*T* and small-*t* traumas, given the continuum and broad spectrum of human experience, let's keep in mind that in real life the lines are fluid, are not easily drawn, and should not be rigidly maintained. What the two types share is succinctly summarized by Bessel van der Kolk: "Trauma is when we are not seen and known."

Although there are dramatic differences in the way the two forms of trauma can affect people's lives and functioning— the big-*T* variety, in general, being far more distressing and disabling—there is also much overlap. They both represent a fracturing of the self and of one's relationship to the world. *That fracturing is the essence of trauma.* As Peter Levine writes, trauma "is about a loss of connection—to ourselves, our families, and the world around us. This loss is hard to recognize, because it happens slowly, over time. We adapt to these subtle changes;

sometimes without noticing them."[9] As the lost connection gets internalized, it forges our view of reality: we come to believe in the world we see through its cracked lens. It is sobering to realize that who we take ourselves to be and the ways we habitually act, including many of our seeming "strengths"—the least and the most functional aspects of our "normal" selves—are often, in part, the wages of traumatic loss. It may also be disconcerting for many of us to consider that, as happy and well adjusted as we think ourselves to be, we may fall somewhere on the trauma spectrum, even if far from the capital-T pole. Ultimately, comparisons fail. It doesn't matter whether we can point to other people who seem more traumatized than we are, for there is no comparing suffering. Nor is it appropriate to use our own trauma as a way of placing ourselves above others—"You haven't suffered like I have"—or as a cudgel to beat back others' legitimate grievances when we behave destructively. We each carry our wounds in our own way; there is neither sense nor value in gauging them against those of others.

What Trauma Is Not

Most of us have heard someone, perhaps ourselves, say something like "Oh my God, that movie last night was so disturbing, I left the theater traumatized." Or we've read a (typically dismissive) news story about university students agitating for "content warnings" lest they be "retraumatized" by what they hear. In all these cases, the usage is understandable but misplaced; what people are actually referring to in these cases is *stress*, physical and/or emotional. As Peter Levine aptly points out, "Certainly, all traumatic events are stressful, but not all stressful events are traumatic."[10]

An event is traumatizing, or retraumatizing, only if it renders one *diminished*, which is to say psychically (or physically) *more limited* than before in a way that *persists*. Much in life, including in art and/or social intercourse or politics, may be upsetting, distressing, even very painful without being newly traumatic. That is not to say that old traumatic reactions, having nothing to do with whatever's going on, cannot be triggered by present-day stresses—see, for example, a certain author arriving home from a speaking gig. That is not the same as being retraumatized, unless over time it leaves us even more constricted than before.

Here's a fairly reliable process-of-elimination checklist. It is *not* trauma if the following remain true over the long term:

- It does not limit you, constrict you, diminish your capacity to feel or think or to trust or assert yourself, to experience suffering without succumbing to despair or to witness it with compassion.
- It does not keep you from holding your pain and sorrow and fear without being overwhelmed and without having to escape habitually into work or compulsive self-soothing or self-stimulating by whatever means.
- You are not left compelled either to aggrandize yourself or to efface yourself for the sake of gaining acceptance or to justify your existence.
- It does not impair your capacity to experience gratitude for the beauty and wonder of life.

If, on the other hand, you *do* recognize these chronic constraints in yourself, they might well represent trauma's shadow on your psyche, the presence of an unhealed emotional wound, no matter the size of the *t*.

Trauma Separates Us from Our Bodies

"Once somebody has invaded you and entered you, your body is no longer yours," the writer V, formerly known as Eve Ensler, told me, recalling her sexual abuse by her father as a young girl.[†] "It's a landscape of dread and betrayal and sorrow and cruelty. The last place you want to be is in your body. And so, you begin to live in your head, you begin to live up here without any ability to protect your body, to know your body. Look, I had a tumor the size of an avocado inside me, and I didn't know it— that's how separated I was from myself." Although the details of my past diverge wildly from V's, I know whereof she speaks. For many years the most difficult question that could be put to me was "What are you feeling?" My customary response was an ir- ritated "How should I know?" I faced no such problem on being asked what my thoughts were: on those I am a tenured expert. Not knowing how or what one feels, on the other hand, is a sure sign of disconnect from the body.

What causes such a disconnect? In my case, the answer requires no speculation. As an infant in wartime Hungary, I en- dured chronic hunger and dysentery, states of acute discomfort threatening and distressing to adults, let alone to a one-year-old. I also absorbed the terrors and unrelenting emotional distress of my mother. In the absence of relief, a young person's natu- ral response—their only response, really—is to repress and dis- connect from the feeling-states associated with suffering. One no longer knows one's body. Oddly, this self-estrangement can show up later in life in the form of an apparent *strength*, such as my ability to perform at a high level when hungry or stressed or fatigued, pushing on without awareness of my need for pause, nutrition, or rest. Alternatively, some people's disconnection from their bodies manifests as not knowing when to stop eating or drinking—the "enough" signal doesn't get through.

In whatever form, disconnection is prominent in the life

---

† See chapter 6, first paragraph and footnote.

experience of traumatized people and is an essential aspect of the trauma constellation. As was the case for V, it begins as a natural coping mechanism on the organism's part, and a mandatory one. She could not have survived her childhood horrors had she stayed present in and aware of her moment-by-moment experience of physical and emotional torment, fully taking in what was happening. And so these coping mechanisms ride in on the wings of grace, as it were, to save our lives in the short term. Over time, though, if untended to, they become stamped on the psyche and soma, indelibly so, as conditioned responses harden into fixed mechanisms that no longer suit the situation. The result is chronic suffering and frequently, as we will proceed to explore, even disease.

"What was so remarkable about my encounter with cancer," V told me, "was that the whole journey from waking up after a nine-hour surgery and losing several organs and seventy nodes—I woke up with bags and tubes and everything coming out of me, but for the first time in my life, I was a body . . . It was painful, but it was also exhilarating. It was like, 'I'm a body. Oh my God, I'm here. *I'm inside this body.*'" Her account of a sudden at-home-ness in her physical self is emblematic of how healing works: when trauma's shackles begin to loosen, we gladly reunite with the severed parts of ourselves.

Trauma Splits Us Off from Gut Feelings

For the average person in V's early predicament, Nature's best recommendations would be to escape or to fight back against the misuse of her body and the assault on her soul. But therein lies the rub: neither option is available to a small child, for to attempt either would be to put herself in further jeopardy. Therefore, Nature defaults to plan C: both impulses are suppressed by tuning out the emotions that would propel such responses. This suppression would seem to be akin to the *freeze* response that creatures often display when *fight* and *flight* are both impossible. The crucial difference is this: once the hawk is gone, the possum is free to go about his business, his survival strategy having succeeded. A traumatized nervous system, on the other hand, never gets to *un*freeze.

"We have feelings because they tell us what supports our survival and what detracts from our survival," the late neuroscientist Jaak Panksepp once said. Emotions, he stressed, emerge not from the thinking brain but from ancient brain structures associated with survival. They are drivers and guarantors of life and development. Intense rage activates the fight response; intense fear mobilizes flight. Therefore, if the circumstances dictate that these natural, healthy impulses (to defend or run away) must be quelled, their gut-level cues—the feelings themselves—will have to be suppressed as well. No alarm, no mobilization. If this seems self-defeating, it is so only in a limited sense: on an existential level, it is the "least worst" option, being the only available one that reduces risk of further harm.

The result is a tamping down of one's feeling-world and often, for extra protection, the hardening of one's psychic shell. A vivid example is given by the writer Tara Westover in her bestselling memoir, *Educated*. Here she recalls the impact of abuse at the hands of a sibling, willfully ignored by her parents:

> I saw myself as unbreakable, tender as stone. At first I merely believed this, until one day it became the truth. Then I was able to tell myself, without lying, that it didn't affect me, that *he* didn't affect me, because nothing affected me. I didn't understand how morbidly right I was. How I had hollowed myself out. For all my obsessing over the consequences of that night, I had misunderstood the vital truth: that its not affecting me, that *was* its effect.[11] [Italics in original.]

Trauma Limits Response Flexibility

A flashback to our chapter's tragic opening scene, only this time set in a parallel universe where my trauma imprints don't rule the day: The plane lands and Rae's text pops up on my screen. "Hmm, that's not what I expected," I say to myself. "But I get it: she's probably immersed in her painting. Nothing new there, nor anything personal. Actually, I can empathize: How many times have *I* gotten so absorbed in work that the clock got away from me? Okay, taxi it is." I might well notice some disappointed feelings, in which case I allow myself to feel them until they pass; in effect, I choose vulnerability over victimhood. Arriving home, there is no upset, no emotional detaching, no sulking—maybe some gentle teasing, but all within the bounds of loving humor and with affinity intact.

I would have thus exhibited what is called *response flexibility*: the ability to choose how we address life's inevitable ups and downs, its disappointments, triumphs, and challenges. "Human freedom involves our capacity to pause between stimulus and response and, in that pause, to choose the one response toward which we wish to throw our weight," wrote the psychologist Rollo May.[12] Trauma robs us of that freedom.

Response flexibility is a function of the midfrontal portion of our cerebral cortex. No infant is born with any such capacity: babies' behavior is governed by instinct and reflex, not conscious selection. The freedom to choose develops as the brain develops. The more severe and the earlier the trauma, the less opportunity response flexibility has to become encoded in the appropriate brain circuits, and the faster it becomes disabled. One becomes stuck in predictable, automatic defensive reactions, especially to stressful stimuli. Emotionally and cognitively, our range of movement becomes well-nigh sclerotic—and the greater the trauma, the more stringent the constraints. The past hijacks and co-opts the present, again and again.

Trauma Fosters a Shame-Based View of the Self

One of the saddest letters I have ever received was from a Seattle man who had read my book on addiction, *In the Realm of Hungry Ghosts*, in which I show that addiction is an outcome—not the only one possible, but a prevalent one—of childhood trauma. Nine years sober, he was still struggling, had not worked for a decade, and was being treated for obsessive-compulsive disorder (OCD). Although he found the book fascinating, he wrote, "I resist the opportunity to blame my mother. I'm a piece of shit because of me." I could only sigh: self-assaulting shame so easily moonlights as personal responsibility. Moreover, he had missed the point: there is nothing in my book that blamed parents or advocated doing so—in fact, I explain over several pages why parent-blaming is inappropriate, inaccurate, and unscientific. This man's impulse to protect his mother was not a defense against anything I had said or implied but against his own unacknowledged anger. Stored away in deep-freeze and finding no healthy outlet, the emotion had turned against him in the form of self-hatred.

"Contained in the experience of shame," writes the psychologist Gershen Kaufman, "is a piercing awareness of ourselves as fundamentally deficient in some vital way as a human being."[13] People bearing trauma's scars almost uniformly develop a shame-based view of themselves at the core, a negative self-perception most of them are all too conscious of. Among the most poisonous consequences of shame is the loss of compassion for oneself. The more severe the trauma, the more total that loss.

The negative view of self may not always penetrate conscious awareness and may even masquerade as its opposite: high self-regard. Some people encase themselves in an armored coat of grandiosity and denial of any shortcomings so as not to feel that enervating shame. That self-puffery is as sure a manifestation of self-loathing as is abject self-deprecation, albeit a much more normalized one. It is a marker of our culture's insanity that certain individuals who flee from shame into a shameless narcissism may even achieve great social, economic, and political status and success. Our culture grinds many of the most traumatized into the mud but may also—depending on class background, economic resources, race, and other variables—raise a few to the highest positions of power.

The most common form shame assumes in this culture is the belief that "I am not enough." The writer Elizabeth Wurtzel, who died of breast cancer at age fifty-two in 2020, suffered depression from an early age. Her childhood was traumatic, beginning with a secret deliberately kept from her about who her actual father was. "I was intensely downcast," she chronicled in an autobiographical piece for *New York* magazine, "with a chronic depression that began when I was about 10, but instead of killing my will, it motivated me: I thought if I could be good enough at whatever task, great or small, that was before me, I might have a few minutes of happiness."[14] That conviction of one's inadequacy has fueled a great many glittering careers and instigated many instances of illness, often both in the same individual.

Trauma Distorts Our View of the World

"Everything has mind in the lead, has mind in the forefront, is made by the mind." Thus opens the *Dhammapada*, the Buddha's timeless collection of sayings.[15] Put another way, the world we believe in becomes the world we live in. If I see the world as a hostile place where only winners thrive, I may well become aggressive, selfish, and grandiose to survive in such a milieu. Later in life I will gravitate to competitive environments and endeavors that can only confirm that view and reinforce its validity. Our beliefs are not only self-fulfilling; they are world-building.

Here's what the Buddha left out, if I may be so bold: before the mind can create the world, the world creates our minds. Trauma, especially severe trauma, imposes a worldview tinged with pain, fear, and suspicion: a lens that both distorts and determines our view of how things are. Or it may, through the sheer force of denial, engender a naively rosy perspective that blinds us to real and present dangers—a veneer concealing fears we dare not acknowledge. One may also come to dismiss painful realities by habitually lying to oneself and others.

Trauma Alienates Us from the Present

I once shared a meal in an Oslo restaurant with the German psychologist Franz Ruppert. The noise was overwhelming: loud pop music pumping through several speakers and multiple TV channels blaring from bright screens mounted high on the walls. I have to think that when the great Norwegian playwright Henrik Ibsen used to hold court in that same establishment a little over a century before, the ambience was much more serene. "What's this all about?" I shouted to my companion over the cacophony, shaking my head in exasperation. "Trauma," he replied as he shrugged his shoulders. Ruppert meant, simply, that people were desperately seeking an escape from themselves.

If trauma entails a disconnection from the self, then it makes sense to say that we are being collectively flooded with influences that both exploit and reinforce trauma. Work pressures, multitasking, social media, news updates, multiplicities of entertainment sources—these all induce us to become lost in thoughts, frantic activities, gadgets, meaningless conversations. We are caught up in pursuits of all kinds that draw us on not because they are necessary or inspiring or uplifting, or because they enrich or add meaning to our lives, but simply because they obliterate the present. In an absurd twist, we save up to buy the latest "time-saving" devices, the better to "kill" time. Awareness of the moment has become something to fear. Late-stage capitalism is expert in catering to this sense of present-moment dread—in fact, much of its success depends on the chasm between us and the present, our greatest gift, getting ever wider, the false products and artificial distractions of consumer culture designed to fill in the gap.

What is lost is well described by the Polish-born writer[†] Eva Hoffman as *"nothing more or less than the experience of experience itself.* And what is that? Perhaps something like the capacity to enter into the textures or sensations of the moment; to relax enough so as to give oneself over to the rhythms of an episode or a personal encounter, to follow the thread of feeling or thought without knowing where it leads, or to pause long enough for reflection or contemplation."[16] Ultimately, what we are distracted from is living.

It Didn't Start with You

Helen Jennings, a sixty-seven-year-old resident of the B.C. Interior region, is caring for her two grandchildren, their father— her son—having died of an overdose. Her other son suffered the same fate. As I interviewed her, it occurred to me that Helen even being willing to speak with me was remarkable, knowing my view that addiction originates in childhood trauma, most often in the family of origin. "When I go back and look at my sons' lives, I understand that there was a lot of trauma," she explained. "I was living with them, so I was part of that. I was a single parent from the time they were two and three until I remarried, when they were six and seven. I understand that how I lived, what I was doing, what I knew and what I didn't know, affected them."

After the birth father abandoned the family early, a stepfather abused the boys both physically and emotionally. "I was very

---

† And fellow 1950s émigré to Vancouver, now a longtime London resident.

lonely and scared and feeling trapped," Helen recalled. That she would lack the gut-sense not to choose such men and that she would not assert herself and protect her sons in the face of abuse were themselves the marks of trauma sustained in Helen's own childhood. Apart from being physically hit on her bare bottom by her father up until age ten, Helen endured emotional torment. "I was ashamed a lot for my feelings as a child," she recalled. "I was very sensitive, and I cried a lot."

Trauma is in most cases multigenerational. The chain of transmission goes from parent to child, stretching from the past into the future. We pass on to our offspring what we haven't resolved in ourselves. The home becomes a place where we unwittingly re-create, as I did, scenarios reminiscent of those that wounded us when we were small. "Traumas affect mothers and mothering and fathers and fathering and husbanding and wifeing," the family constellations therapist Mark Wolynn told me. "The repeated traumas continue to proliferate from that—as a result, they never get healed." Wolynn is the author of the aptly titled *It Didn't Start with You: How Inherited Family Trauma Shapes Who We Are and How to End the Cycle.* Trauma may even affect gene activity across generations, as we will see.[†]

It is no surprise, then, that Helen's eldest grandchild has faced problems with substance use and behavior and learning difficulties. Because of all she has learned and despite her unfathomable losses, she is able to be present for him much more warmly and effectively than she ever could be for her own sons. Note, too, the absence of self-judgment in Helen's description of the situation: she speaks of "understanding" rather than castigating herself for what she didn't—nay, couldn't—understand way back when. The act of blaming herself, its gravitational center planted

---

†   Chapter 4.

permanently in the past, would only divert her from showing up for her loved one in the here and now.

Blame becomes a meaningless concept the moment one understands how suffering in a family system or even in a community extends back through the generations. "Recognition of this quickly dispels any disposition to see the parent as villain," wrote John Bowlby, the British psychiatrist who showed the decisive importance of adult-child relationships in shaping the psyche. No matter how far back we look in the chain of consequence—great-grandparents, pre-modern ancestors, Adam and Eve, the first single-celled amoeba—the accusing finger can find no fixed target. That should come as a relief.

The news gets better: seeing trauma as an internal dynamic grants us much-needed agency. If we treat trauma as an external event, something that happens *to* or around us, then it becomes a piece of history we can never dislodge. If, on the other hand, trauma is what took place *inside* us as a result of what happened, in the sense of wounding or disconnection, then healing and reconnection become tangible possibilities. Trying to keep awareness of trauma at bay hobbles our capacity to know ourselves. Conversely, fashioning from it a rock-hard identity— whether the attitude is defiance, cynicism, or self-pity—is to miss both the point and the opportunity of healing, since by definition trauma represents a distortion and limitation of who we were born to be. Facing it directly without either denial or over-identification becomes a doorway to health and balance.

"It's those adversities that open up your mind and your curiosity to see if there are new ways of doing things," Bessel van der Kolk told me. He then cited Socrates: "An unexamined life is not worth living. As long as one doesn't examine oneself, one is completely subject to whatever one is wired to do, but once you become aware that you have choices, you can exercise those choices." Notice that he didn't say "once you spend decades in therapy." As I will present later, we can access liberation via even modest self-examination: a willingness to question "many of the truths we cling to" and the "certain point of view" that makes them seem so real—as a famous Jedi master's Force ghost told his dispirited young apprentice at a pivotal moment in a galaxy far, far away.[†]

Although this chapter has focused on its personal dimensions, trauma exists in the collective sphere, too, affecting entire nations and peoples at different moments in history. To this day it is visited upon some groups with disproportionate force, as on Canada's Indigenous people. Their multigenerational deprivation and persecution at the hands of colonialism and especially the hundred-year agony of their children, abducted from their families and reared in church-run residential schools where physical, sexual, and emotional abuse were rampant, has left them with tragic legacies of addiction, mental and physical illness, suicide, and the ongoing transmission of trauma to new generations. The traumatic legacy of slavery and racism in the United States is another salient example. I will have more to say about this painful subject in Part IV.

[†]   Obi-Wan Kenobi to Luke Skywalker in 1983's *Return of the Jedi*.

Chapter 2

Living in an Immaterial World: Emotions, Health, and the Body-Mind Unity

Unless we can measure something, science won't concede
it exists, which is why science refuses to deal with such
"nonthings" as the emotions, the mind, the soul, or the spirit.
—Candace Pert, Ph.D., *Molecules of Emotion*

"I was thirty-six when they told me it was a very early breast cancer," said Caroline, a resident of the Pocono Mountains of Pennsylvania. That diagnosis occurred more than three decades ago, in 1988. The tumor was treated with surgery and radiation. A few years later, when a new malignancy showed up in her left hip and femur, Caroline required emergency joint replacement; the surgeons had to remove a large part of her thigh bone as well. "At that time, they gave me a timeline of one to two years," she recalled. "My boys were very young, only eight and nine. I've just turned fifty-six, so I've beaten all their records."

Caroline had multiple courses of chemotherapy over the intervening years. By the time of our conversation, the cancer had reached the palliative stage, having spread to her right hip and thigh. As we spoke, she could not expect to outpace her current prognosis by much;‡ still, this mother of two radiated deep satis-

---

‡   I was saddened to learn of her death, about a year after our interview.

faction with how things had gone. She had, after all, gained two unforeseen decades to raise her kids. "You know," she mused, "looking at my own mortality, and them telling me I had twelve to twenty-four months . . . I got extremely profane with the doctor and said, you know, sorry, I need ten years to raise them to be men. I will do anything in my power to raise them to be men."

" 'Profane,' " I repeated. "What exactly did you say?"

"I used the f-word. I said, 'Fuck your statistics.' "

"Good for you," I offered. "That probably helped extend your life."

"Well, that's what I said to him." Caroline laughed. "I said, 'Fuck your statistics. I need those years to raise them to be men.' He walked out of the room. He didn't appreciate my language. He thought I was a crazy, vulgar woman. I've often wanted to look for that doctor—he has since moved to California—and tell him that my boys are now twenty-four and twenty-five. One's in grad school at Princeton. The other one went through a difficult period, pulled himself up, and will be graduating with three degrees, on the dean's list."

Caroline's outburst at the unsuspecting physician was out of character. All her life she had fit the profile of the nice person who avoids confrontation. "My way was always being the caretaker, being needed, always coming to somebody's rescue, a lot of the time to my own detriment," she told me. "I never wanted to have conflict with anyone. And I always had to be in charge, making sure everything was okay." Caroline had exhibited what has been called "superautonomous self-sufficiency,"[†] which means exactly what it sounds like: an exaggerated and outsize aversion to asking anything of anyone.

A quick note: Nobody is born with such traits. They invariably stem from coping reactions to developmental trauma, beginning

---

†   A phrase coined in 1982 by researchers at Heidelberg University, Germany.

with self-abnegation in early childhood. Such suppression takes a lasting toll, a process we'll explore more fully in chapter 7.

"I've come to believe that virtually all illness, if not psychosomatic in foundation, has a definite psychosomatic component," the pioneering neuroscientist Candace Pert wrote in her 1997 book, *Molecules of Emotion*. By "psychosomatic," Pert did not imply the modern, often derisive dismissal of disease as a neurotic figment. Instead she meant the word's strict scientific connotation: having to do with the oneness of the human *psyche* (mind and spirit) and the *soma* (the body), a oneness she did much to measure and record in the laboratory. Her discoveries, as she justly claimed, would help fuel "a synthesis of behavior, psychology, and biology."[1]

There is nothing novel about the notion of the mind and body being intricately linked; if anything, what is new is the belief, tacitly held and overtly enacted by many well-meaning doctors, that they are separable. Traditional healing practices the world over, while lacking the wondrous technology and scientific know-how developed in the West, have long understood this unity implicitly. Despite Western medicine's artificial cleaving of the two, most people still know—if only on a gut level—that what they think and how they feel have everything to do with each other. It is run-of-the-mill, for instance, to speculate about which life stresses have contributed to one's ulcer, what mental strain is behind a headache, or what unprocessed fears lead one to experience panic attacks. The same principle applies when we look not just at individual symptoms but at most types of diseases. Emotional perturbances stemming from relationship troubles, financial worries, or any other source of chronic upset impose physiological burdens that can result in illness.

Pert coined the term "bodymind" to describe this oneness. The official website dedicated to her work and legacy takes care to note that this expression was "intentionally written without a hyphen *in order to emphasize unity of its component parts.*" Body and mind, while not identical, cannot be understood separately from each other. We can ignore or deny this paradox, but we cannot escape it. Since Pert's groundbreaking work, the biological impacts of emotions—those "nonthings" whose non-recognition she lamented—have been extensively researched and documented in many thousands upon thousands of ingenious studies. It's worth looking at a few of these, bearing in mind that each is only the tip of an iceberg of similarly compelling findings.

A 1982 German study presented at the fourth international Symposium on the Prevention and Detection of Cancer in London found certain personality traits to have a strong association with breast cancer. Fifty-six women admitted to hospital for biopsy were evaluated for characteristics such as emotional suppression, rationalization, altruistic behavior, the avoidance of conflict, and the superautonomous self-sufficiency we saw embodied by Caroline. Based on the interview results alone, both the interviewers and "blind" raters who had no direct contact with the women were able to predict the correct diagnosis in up to 94 percent of all cancer patients, and in about 70 percent of the benign cases.[2] In a previous British study at King's College Hospital in London, it had also been shown that women with cancerous breast lumps characteristically exhibited "extreme suppression of anger and of other feelings" in "a significantly higher proportion" than the control group, which was made up of women admitted for biopsy at the same time but found to have benign breast tumors.[3]

In 2000 the publication *Cancer Nursing* surveyed the relationship of anger repression and cancer, often noted by, among others, the cancer nurses themselves: "Somehow, nurses had an intuitive understanding that this 'niceness' was deleterious.

[This] view now is being supported by research."[4] The nurses' insight reminded me of a paper on amyotrophic lateral sclerosis (ALS)[†] presented by two Cleveland Clinic neurologists at an international congress in Bavaria in the 1990s.[5] Their staff, too, found that their ALS patients were extraordinarily nice—so much so, that the staff could in most cases accurately predict who would be diagnosed with the condition and who would not. "I'm afraid this person has ALS, she is too nice," they would jot on the patient's file. Or, "This person cannot have ALS, he is not nice enough." The neurologists were dumbfounded. "In spite of the briefness of [the staff's] contact with the patients, and the obvious unscientific method by which they form their opinions, almost invariably they prove to be correct," they remarked.

I interviewed Dr. Asa J. Wilbourn, senior author of the paper. "It's almost universal," he told me. "It becomes common knowledge in the laboratory where you evaluate a lot of patients with ALS—and we do an enormous number of cases. I think that anyone who deals with ALS knows that this is a definite phenomenon." Such anecdotal observations have since been reaffirmed by more formal research, as seen in the title of a recent paper from a neurological journal: " 'Patients with Amyotrophic Lateral Sclerosis (ALS) Are Usually Nice Persons'—How Physicians Experienced in ALS See the Personality Characteristics of Their Patients."[6]

In a study of men with prostate cancer, anger suppression was associated with a diminished effectiveness of natural killer (NK) cells—a frontline immune system defense against malignancy and foreign invaders. These cells play a key role in tumor resistance.[7] In previous research, NK cell activity was reduced in healthy young people in response to even relatively minor

---

[†]   A degenerative and nearly always fatal disease of the nervous system, it is known in Britain as motor neuron disease and in the United States also as Lou Gehrig's disease.

stresses—especially for those who were emotionally isolated, a significant source of chronic stress.

Grief, too, has a powerful physiological dimension. An illuminating study from the British journal *Lancet Oncology* described the impact of psychological factors on the intricate pathways linking the immune system, the hormones, and the nervous system in, for example, bereavement. Among parents who lost an adult son to an accident or military conflict, the authors reported increased occurrence of lymphatic and hematological malignancy—cancers of the blood, bone marrow, and lymph nodes—along with skin and lung cancer.[8] War kills, and so, it seems, can deep emotional loss. As for cancer, so with other illnesses. In a Danish nationwide study, grieving parents had double the risk of multiple sclerosis.[9]

(Despite such compelling evidence, I do not believe the loss of a loved one, howsoever tragic, by itself necessarily poses a health risk. I believe the latter depends on how people are able to process their loss, including what support they may reach out for and receive. It's not only events as such but also our emotional responses and how we process them that affect our physiology.)

One 2019 study alone in *Cancer Research* should set every clinician on a fast-track exploration of bodymind medicine. Women with severe post-traumatic stress disorder (PTSD) were found to have twice the risk of ovarian cancer as women with no known trauma exposure.[10] The *Daily Gazette,* published by Harvard University, where the study was done, reported, "The findings indicate that having higher levels of PTSD symptoms, such as being easily startled by ordinary noises or avoiding reminders of the traumatic experience, can be associated with increased risks of ovarian cancer even decades after women experience a traumatic event." The more severe the trauma symptoms, the more aggressive the cancer proved to be.

This Harvard research provided further striking evidence that emotional stresses are inseparable from the physical states of our bodies, in illness and health. Already in previous work, depression had been associated with elevated ovarian cancer risk. The impact of stress had also been studied: among lab mice with ovarian cancer cells injected into their abdominal cavities, those subjected to emotional aggravation such as being physically restrained or isolated had much greater incidence of tumor growth and spread than socially housed animals that were not restrained.[11] The Harvard scientists theorized that stress can "promote ovarian cancer development by inhibiting key defenses against unrestrained cell growth." In other words, stress may disable our immune systems' capacity to control and eliminate malignancy.

The implications extend far beyond PTSD, since, in our culture, stress and trauma affect many people who do not qualify for that diagnosis. Finnish researchers, writing in the *British Journal of Psychiatry* in 2005, found, quite remarkably, that people undergoing "life events"—relatively ordinary stresses and emotional losses such as relationship issues and work problems that would not qualify them for a formal diagnosis—suffered more PTSD-like symptoms such as bad dreams or emotional numbing than more obviously traumatized people who had endured war or disaster.[12]

The Harvard paper on ovarian cancer pointed to some promising possibilities for treatment, suggesting that women whose PTSD symptoms had abated, perhaps due to effective psychotherapy, had less risk for malignancy than women with active symptoms. It is exciting to contemplate the preventive and healing potentials, as well as the social implications, of a wellness perspective that treats emotions like the real and relevant "things" they are.

While all this is timely and the science freshly minted, the principles are not new. In a 1939 lecture to a graduating medical class, published in the *Journal of the American Medical Association* (*JAMA*), Dr. Soma Weiss informed his audience that "social and psychic factors play a role in every disease, *but in many conditions, they represent dominant influences.*"[13] The revered Hungarian-American clinician added that "mental factors represent as active a force in the treatment of patients as chemical and physical agents." He made these comments not as a psychoanalytic theoretician, but as a respected practitioner of pathophysiology and pharmacotherapy—the use of medications in treating illness. At Harvard Medical School, Weiss's memory is kept alive by a yearly research day in his honor, yet his integrative perspective, and the extensive scientific literature now supporting it, still elude conventional medical thinking. "The mind-body stuff is historically something that one pursues at great peril to their career at Harvard," a leading physician and academic at that hallowed institution told me recently. "That's starting to change, but it's a very difficult thing."[14]

Difficult indeed. When I give talks, I often ask audience members to raise their hands if, in the past five years, they have visited a neurologist, cardiologist, respirologist, rheumatologist, gastroenterologist, dermatologist, immunologist—"any kind of a medical ologist," I say. Many hands shoot up. "Now keep your hands up," I continue, "if these specialists asked you about your childhood stresses or traumas, your relationship with your parents, the quality of your current relationships, your degree of loneliness or companionship, your job satisfaction and how you relate to work, how you feel about your boss or how your boss treats you, your experience of joy or anger, any present stresses, or how you feel about yourself as a person." In rooms packed with hundreds of people, the number of hands remaining elevated can most often be counted on the fingers of one of them. "And yet," I add, "those unasked questions had everything to do with why most of you had reason to seek medical help."

For all that, a clear picture is emerging as modern research confirms traditional wisdom. A (relatively) new science, psychoneuroimmunology maps the myriad pathways of the body-mind unity; its field of study includes the connections between emotions and our nervous and immune systems, and how stress might instigate disease. Even "connection" is a misleading word: only entities distinct from each other can be connected, whereas reality knows only oneness. Sometimes referred to even more tongue-twistingly as psychoneuroimmunoendocrinology, this new discipline is predicated on the unity between *all* our constituent parts: mind, brain, nervous and immune systems, and the hormonal apparatus (that's the "endocrine" part). The pieces can be studied separately, but we cannot fully understand any of them without grasping the whole picture. From the cerebral cortex to the brain's emotional nuclei to the autonomic nervous system, from the solid or fluid aspects of the immune apparatus to the hormonal organs and secretions, from the stress-response system to the viscera . . . it's all one.

That evolution has furnished us with instincts, emotions, complex behaviors, and individuated organs and systems does not, in the slightest way, diminish this unity. No matter how sophisticated our minds may be, the fact remains that their basic contents—what we think, believe consciously or unconsciously, feel or are prevented from feeling—powerfully affect our bodies, for better or worse. Conversely, what our bodies experience from conception onward cannot but affect how we think, feel, perceive, and behave. This, in a nutshell, is psychoneuroimmunology's core lesson.

One fascinating example is the demonstrated link between

the brain's fear center, the amygdala, and cardiovascular disease. The more stress someone perceives or experiences, the higher the resting activity of the amygdala and the greater the risk of heart ailments. The pathway from amygdala overactivation to heart problems runs through increased bone-marrow activity and arterial inflammation.[15] Emotional stress affects the heart more generally as well. In 2012, a study from Harvard Medical School showed that women with high job strain are 67 percent more likely to experience a heart attack than women in less stressful jobs.[16] A Canadian study from the University of Toronto in the same year found that men sexually abused as children had a tripled rate of heart attacks.[17] The researchers' natural assumption was that abused men would be more prone to high-risk behavior, such as smoking and drinking, which would account for their higher rate of heart attacks. To the team's surprise, the impacts of abuse were more direct, quite independent of behavioral factors.

The Machinery of Stress

Understanding stress and its mechanics can give us a finer appreciation for how the bodymind unity plays itself out in real time and real tissue.

Like its cousin, the pain response, stress is a mandatory survival function for any living being. When activated, our stress apparatus immediately empowers us to confront or escape threats to our existence or to the existence or well-being of those we care for. It's an impressive whole-body event involving virtually every organ and system.

Stress can show up in two forms: as an immediate reaction to a threat or as a prolonged state induced by external pressures or internal emotional factors. While *acute* stress is a necessary reaction that helps maintain our physical and mental integrity, *chronic stress,* ongoing and unrelieved, undermines both. Situational anger, for example, is an instance of acute stress being marshaled for a positive purpose—think self-defense or setting interpersonal boundaries. It makes us more alert of mind, quicker, and stronger of limb. Chronic rage, by contrast, floods the system with stress hormones long past the allotted time. Over the long term, such a hormonal surplus, whatever may have instigated it, can

- make us anxious or depressed;
- suppress immunity;
- promote inflammation;
- narrow blood vessels, promoting vascular disease throughout the body;
- encourage cancer growth;
- thin the bones;
- make us resistant to our own insulin, inducing diabetes;
- contribute to abdominal obesity, elevating the risk of cardiovascular and metabolic problems;
- impair essential cognitive and emotional circuits in the brain; and
- elevate blood pressure and increase blood clotting, raising the risk of heart attacks or strokes.

The hub of our body's system for handling stress smoothly and economically is called the "HPA axis." This acronymic term describes the pathways and feedback loops linking the *hypothalamus*—the small, crucial area in the center of our brain whose role is to keep our body in a healthful, balanced state—with the *pituitary gland* at the top of our brain stem and the *adrenal gland* that sits atop our kidneys. Think of a busy transportation corridor connecting three major urban centers, replete with on-ramps, exits, and interchanges, and you start to get a picture.

Although our species can survive in a broad range of *external* environments—far more than almost any other animal—our *internal* milieu must stay within a relatively narrow range of physiological states. Our temperature, blood acidity or pressure, and heart rate, along with many other bodily metrics, are all obliged by Nature, on pain of death, to stay within definite and nonnegotiable limits.

The renowned American stress researcher Bruce McEwen[†] popularized the word "allostasis" to capture the body's attempt to maintain inner equilibrium in the face of changing circumstances. The term is a combination of the Greek words *allo,* for "variable," and *stasis*, for "standing" or "stoppage"; combined, we have something like "staying the same amid change." We cannot do without it, and so our bodies will go to great lengths to maintain it—even to the point of long-term wear and tear if stresses do not abate. Such strain on our body's regulatory mechanisms, which McEwen dubs "allostatic load," leads to an excessive and prolonged release of the stress hormones adrenaline and cortisol, nervous tension, immune dysfunction, and, in many cases, exhaustion of the stress apparatus itself.

We now know that the infrastructure of the HPA axis is set early in life, starting in utero and on through the young childhood years. Stress or abuse incurred during this delicate period can distort the stress-hormonal apparatus for a lifetime. Again and again, we see supposedly immaterial "nonthings" such as emotions having a material impact, decidedly and decisively.

Reducing stress where possible, attending to emotions, overt or repressed, and taking care of our psychic well-being can have profound effects on physical health—this is intuitively obvious to many people. Yet for all their dazzling physiological and technical

---

[†]   Longtime head of the Harold and Margaret Milliken Hatch Laboratory of Neuroendocrinology at Rockefeller University (d. 2020).

expertise, doctors by and large are not initiated by their training into the ancient wisdom and new science of the bodymind unity. Medical professionals often do little to encourage—and may even resist—people trusting their own hunches, which tend to synthesize signals from both mind and body.

Memories Aflame: Glenda's Story

Such was the case with Glenda, a Montreal woman, now fifty-eight, who thirty years ago underwent removal of parts of her intestine for severe Crohn's disease, an ulcerative, painful inflammatory disease of the bowel. In 2010 Glenda got some more bad news when she was diagnosed with stage 2 aggressive breast cancer. It was during the healing journey from the latter that she recovered repressed memories of being raped as a young girl. "Through the process of journaling and dreaming," she told me, "subconscious memories of my childhood began to emerge along with feelings of sheer panic and terror." Afraid to know the truth, she tried to keep the memories at bay, but they would not be deterred. "Every time the memories of the trauma surfaced," she continued, "they were accompanied with very visceral emotional feelings and physical digestive symptoms including indigestion, nausea, and gut aches."

The memories are harrowing enough to roil even an outside listener's guts. Eight-year-old Glenda and a younger friend were gang-raped by four teenage boys from the neighborhood. The first responder was her mother, who rushed Glenda into the house, she said, "and put me right into the bath. She told me that we were never going to tell anyone about this or ever speak of it again. My mom said it would always be 'our little secret,' and put me to bed."

When the memories returned at age fifty-three, they came as "this intense clear visual" of her young self in the bathtub, with her mother crouched on the floor beside her "trying to wash away the rape." I asked Glenda, gently, whether she had any independent evidence for these recovered memories. She nodded. "My older sister recalls that she actually came into the bathroom that day. Arriving home and hearing my mother bawling her eyes out, she came and opened the door. My back was to her; she said, 'What's wrong with Glenda?' My mother said, 'Nothing, she'll be fine. Get out.' [My sister] told me that I looked very disheveled—my mother never let us go out disheveled—and that my whole body was shaking."

As if that scene weren't intense enough, Glenda's intuitive understanding, now emerging into awareness after a lifetime of self-protective submersion, produced an additional visual layer. "As soon as I recovered the memory of being in the bathroom," she said, "I saw my body, I was transparent . . . I saw my entire digestive system from mouth to rectum. There were red blistering ulcers throughout my entire digestive system. There was a flaming, flowing hot lava, adding fuel to the fire. It was just raging, and that to me was a guide telling me that these two things are connected, the rape and my Crohn's." It doesn't take a psychoanalyst or a poetry professor to see the image of the "raging" fire as a powerful analogue for the rage and pain Glenda had to bury away in the deepest parts of herself, given her mother's utter inability to be there for her emotionally.

Glenda's "visual" is apt not only metaphorically but scientifically as well. To quote just one survey of research among an ever-growing trove, there is "strong evidence that childhood traumatic events significantly impact the inflammatory immune system . . . offering a potential molecular pathway by which early trauma confers vulnerability to developing psychiatric and physical disorders later in life."[18] None of Glenda's many physicians, nor even her psychiatrist—in her depiction, "very science-and-medicine"—ever once asked her about the possible childhood antecedents of her psychic turmoil.

Candace Pert envisioned the mind as involving the unconscious flow of information "among the cells, organs and systems of the body... occurring below the level of awareness." Thus, she asserted, "the mind as we experience it is immaterial, yet it has a physical substrate, which is both the body and the brain." By "immaterial" she did not mean the word's usual connotation of insignificant or irrelevant but—on the contrary—that the mind, unlike the brain, is not a material thing: we cannot get a hold of it, put it in a test tube or petri dish, or even "see" it directly. Its impacts and consequences, however, are material indeed.

The opportunity we have today is to create a multivalent health care approach that appreciates the impact of "nonthings" on the "thinglike" bodies we've come to be so marvelously expert in. The "immaterial" mind and its "physical substrate," the brain and body, are in a constant dance, as intimate as it is intricate.

On closer examination, we see that this choreography of psyche and soma involves far more than two "partners" contained within one person: there is also a vital and underappreciated *interpersonal* component. After all, the mind and body exist inescapably in the context of relationships, social circumstances, history, and culture. If we want a clear and accurate view of human health, we will have to broaden our understanding of "bodymind" to include the myriad roles that *other* minds and *other* bodies play in shaping our well-being, indeed our very sense of self. Unity, it turns out, extends well beyond the unitary individual.

Chapter 3

You Rattle My Brain:
Our Highly Interpersonal Biology

For every atom belonging to me as good belongs to you.
—Walt Whitman, "Song of Myself," in *Leaves of Grass*

"All my relations." I have often heard this greeting when visiting Native communities in Canada. These are the places where my country, to its shame, sees the highest levels of physical and mental illness, addictions, and early death—a tragic situation analogous with that of similarly colonized aboriginal populations in the United States and Australia. The phrase, as I understand it, refers to the individual's multidimensional bond with the entire world, including people—from close relatives to strangers, from the living to ancestors who lived long before—and also the rocks, the plants, the earth, the sky, and all creatures. Ancient cultures have long understood that we exist in relationship to all, are affected by all, and affect all.

In the Hindu scripture the Bhagavad Gita, the divine avatar Krishna declares, "They live in wisdom who see themselves in all and all in them." And the early seventeenth-century cleric and poet John Donne famously mused, "No man is an island, entire of itself." He composed this line, perhaps not coincidentally, during a period of illness and convalescence. Walt Whitman, writing in mid-nineteenth-century America, could have cribbed the verse cited in the above epigraph from today's quantum physics.

Then we have the man born 2,500 years ago as Gautama. "Contemplate the nature of interdependent co-arising during every moment," the Buddha said. "When you look at a leaf or a raindrop, meditate on the conditions, near and distant, that contributed to the presence of that leaf or raindrop. Know that the world is woven of interconnected threads. This is because that is. This is not because that is not. This is born because that is born. This dies because that dies." The leaf, as the Buddha implied, is both a discrete entity—a thing—*and* a process that derives from sun, sky, and earth: light, photosynthesis, rain, organic matter, and minerals and perhaps even the activity of humans and animals. "The one contains the many and the many contains the one. Without the one, there cannot be the many. Without the many, there cannot be the one." These are not merely esoteric wisdom teachings; they accurately describe the physical and organic universe, including health and pathology. Indeed, Friedrich Nietzsche once called the Buddha "that profoundest physiologist."

The pioneering U.S. internist and psychiatrist George Engel argued nearly half a century ago that the "crippling flaw" of modern medicine "is that it does not include the patient and his attributes as a person. Yet in the everyday work of the physician the prime object of study is a person." We must make provision for the whole person in their full "psychological and social nature,"[1] he said, calling for a *biopsychosocial* approach: one that recognizes the unity of emotions and physiology, knowing both to be dynamic processes unfolding in a context of relationships, from the personal to the cultural.[2]

The great traumatologist Dr. Bessel van der Kolk has noted that "our culture teaches us to focus on our personal uniqueness, but at a deeper level we barely exist as individual organisms."[3] This will certainly be news to the average ego. The word "ego," as I use it here, refers not to the trait of arrogance or conceit in

certain "egotistical" people but to the internally perceived separate self with which we each identify: the "me," "myself," and
"I" we mean when we use these personal pronouns, as we do
hundreds of times a day. Even a healthy ego is convinced of its
separateness, an entirely reasonable perception: the capacity
to experience individual selfhood in all its facets (physical, psychological, biographical, etc.) is part and parcel of being human.
Our difficulties begin when we lose sight of the other side of the
equation, which is just as real, if less apparent.

The interrelatedness of seemingly isolated organisms has
now been discovered even in the lives of trees that form living
networks, communicating through electrical impulses akin to
animal and human nervous systems, hormones, chemical signals, and scents. As an article in *Smithsonian* magazine reports,
"Trees of the same species are communal, and will often form
alliances with trees of other species." Peter Wohlleben, the German forester who has become well known for popularizing such
information, wittily calls it "the wood-wide web."[4]

That our own individual minds and bodies are intimately
linked is fairly simple to grasp. Less obvious but no less true is
the fact that those same bodyminds are in many ways shaped, in
the first place and throughout our lives, by factors *external* to us.
Although modern medicine's focus on the individual organism
and its internal processes isn't wrong as such, it misses something vital: the pivotal influence of the mental, emotional, social,
and natural environments in which we live. Our biology itself is
interpersonal.

The concept of *interpersonal neurobiology* was introduced
some years ago by Dr. Daniel Siegel,[†] a psychiatrist, researcher,
and prolific author. Like myself and many of our colleagues, Dr.

---

†   Clinical professor at the University of California, Los Angeles (UCLA), School of
Medicine and executive director of the Mindsight Institute.

Siegel had become uncomfortable with the limitations of his education. "When I was in medical school," he writes, "many of the fine teachers we had approached their patients, and their students, as if they had no center of inner experience—no subjective internal core we might call our mental life. It was as if we were just bags of chemicals and bodily organs without a self, without a mind."[5] He sensed that both research and practice lacked a consensus definition of "health" and, startlingly, in the mental health field lacked even a shared agreement of what "mind" is, let alone a shared view of the relationship of mind and brain. Recruiting co-workers in medicine, neurology, psychiatry, psychology, anthropology, sociology, history, physiology, biology, physics, and related disciplines that study the human experience, he set out to explore what such a consensus might look like. The team's findings confirmed that our brains and minds are not independent operators, functioning in isolation from other brains and minds. In fact, nothing about us, mental or physical, can be comprehended apart from the many-faceted milieu in which we exist. We can perhaps treat human biology as strictly self-contained in an artificial setting like a medical laboratory or pathology theater, but not in real life. "Interpersonal neurobiology is both a way of understanding the world through many disciplines and it is also the reality of our interconnected nature," Dan told me in an interview. My amendment is to remove the "neuro-" prefix—leaving us with the broader "interpersonal biology," which places not only the brain and nervous system under the interpersonal banner but our entire mental-physical makeup.

The brain itself is the central organ of a supersystem that extends throughout the body and influences every aspect of physiological functioning, from the caliber of blood vessels to the contractions of our intestines, the beating of our heart, the manufacture of immune cells in our bone marrow, the secretions of hormones from our sex glands, and the functioning of our kidneys. Again, it's all one: emotions affect nerves and vice versa; nerves act on hormones; hormones on the immune system; the immune system on the brain; the brain on the gut; the gut on the brain; and all of these act on the heart, and vice versa. In turn, our bodies influence our brains and minds and, necessarily, the brains, minds, and bodies of others.

We all know the power of interpersonal biology from a lifetime of personal experience. Think of the effect that other people can have on you: it can be quite literally visceral. Poets and songwriters tell of being weak in the knees, shot through the heart, or even, in Bruce Springsteen's vivid image, stabbed in the brain by a dull, serrated blade.[†] Jerry Lee Lewis was right: we really do shake each other's nerves and rattle each other's brains.[‡]

Unsurprisingly, the closer we are to someone, the more our physiology interacts with theirs. Accordingly, the phenomenon of interpersonal biology has been well studied in the case of intimate relationships. Married people have lower rates of mortality than their age-matched single contemporaries, whether the latter were separated, divorced, widowed, or had never married.[6] Single people showed an elevated risk for heart disease and cancer, for infectious diseases such as pneumonia and influenza, and for such life-habit-related conditions as cirrhosis of the liver and lung disease. Tellingly, the degree of protection offered by married status was five times as great for men as for women, a finding that speaks to the relative roles of the genders in this culture, with profound implications for health—a topic I will circle back to in chapter 23. Interestingly, "unhappily married persons are worse off in well-being than unmarried persons."[7]

---

† "I'm on Fire" (1984), third verse.

‡ As in his rock-and-roll classic "Great Balls of Fire."

In other studies, perfectly healthy married couples' stress hormone levels were elevated in those exhibiting higher degrees of hostility during conflict, and their immune functioning was diminished. The results were the same for newlyweds as for septuagenarians.[8]

Given their vulnerability and dependence, children's physiology is especially susceptible to the emotional states of their caregivers. Young kids' stress hormone levels, for example, are heavily influenced by the emotional atmosphere in the home, whether outright conflict or bristling tension.[9] Asthma is a well-studied example: the inflammation of the child's lungs is directly affected by the mother's or father's emotions.[10] In the words of a recent review: "It has been consistently shown that parents in an unfavorable mental health state such as 'depression,' 'anxiety,' 'stress,' or 'chronic irritation' may predict a poorer status for the child's asthma."[11]

Racism is another risk factor for asthma. In a large cohort of Black American women, experiences of racial discrimination were associated with the adult onset of the disease.[12] And that raises an inescapable question we should all ponder: Is the inflammation and airway constriction of these women a case of individual pathology or the manifestation of a social malaise?

The more we learn, the more we realize that our health is a complex consequence of "all our relations," and not just the ones close at hand (family, friends, intimate others, etc.). Leading U.S. stress researchers Teresa Seeman and Bruce McEwen noted in 1996 that human biology "seem[s] to be highly sensitive" also to factors like one's social status relative to others, and even how stable or precarious the social order happens to be at a given time.[13] In a British study, unemployed people had higher markers of inflammation in their bodies, and hence were at higher risk for illness; the longer the unemployment, the greater the risk. The most severe inflammation levels were recorded in Scotland, the part of the U.K. where unemployment was most endemic and chronic.[14] Even the gainfully employed can experience physiological blowback. In a study of the British civil service, a lower ranking on the ladder of authority was a greater predictor of death from heart disease than commonly listed risk factors such as smoking, cholesterol, or hypertension. Along similar lines, Australian researchers found that a bad job is worse for mental health than being out of work.[15] So the next time a co-worker complains to you, "This job is killing me," you can tell them they may be right.

Interpersonal biology also accounts for why loneliness can kill, especially in older people separated from pleasures, social connections, or support. A vast review of multiple studies encompassing more than three hundred thousand participants concluded that the lethal effect of deficient interpersonal relationships is comparable to such risk factors as smoking and alcohol, and even exceeds the dangers posed by physical inactivity and obesity.[16]

The recently deceased Buddhist monk and renowned spiritual leader Thich Nhat Hanh long taught the concept of "inter-being." It's not merely that we are, he said: we "inter-are." "There are no separate entities," he wrote, "only manifestations that rely on each other to be possible."[17] Again, we would be quite mistaken to relegate these observations to the realm of mystical belief. A scientist lacking a spiritual bone in his body, yet conversant with the growing body of evidence, would nod in agreement: "Yup, that about covers it."

Chapter 4

Everything I'm Surrounded By:
Dispatches from the New Science

So much of what makes people either well or not is not coming
from within themselves, it's coming from their circumstances.
It makes me think much more about social justice and the
bigger issues that go beyond individuals.

—Elizabeth Blackburn, Ph.D.[†]

In 2009 Dr. Elizabeth Blackburn shared the Nobel Prize in Physiology or Medicine for her work on telomeres—minuscule DNA structures at the end of chromosomes. Not unlike the plastic aglets placed at the end of shoelaces to keep them from fraying, these tiny sheaths help protect chromosomal integrity. Good thing, too, since as chromosomes unravel, so do we. Tracking the length and stability of telomeres throughout the lifespan, it turns out, can tell us a great deal about health and longevity.

You wouldn't think it to look at them, but what has been discovered about these tiny biological structures also has huge social implications. One of Dr. Blackburn's discoveries was that telomeres bear the actual marks—or rather, the markers—of the circumstances in which we live our lives. Amazingly, she found that factors such as poverty, racism, and urban blight can directly impact our genetic and molecular functioning. As the psychologist

---

† Professor emerita, Department of Biochemistry and Biophysics, University of California San Francisco.

Elissa Epel, who is Dr. Blackburn's research collaborator and co-author of the bestselling volume *The Telomere Effect: A Revolutionary Approach to Living Younger, Healthier, Longer*, told me in an interview, "These effects are not small."

The neuroscientist Candace Lewis, whose own research is in epigenetics, the growing field that investigates the impact of life experience on the activity of our genes, sees things the same way. "More and more the science is demonstrating this holistic model of who we are," she told me. "It's more than just what's enclosed in my skin—it's everything I'm surrounded by. Not to see that is to remove healing from medicine." As Dr. Lewis has peered at molecules and strands of DNA, she, too, has found herself lifting her gaze to the whole person and from the individual to broader social issues. "As a specialist in the complexity of brain and behavior, I know it's not just brain and behavior," said the former Fulbright scholar. "One of the biggest take-home messages from my work is how malleable we are as an organism, how responsive to environmental cues throughout the lifespan."

The dominant assumption in our culture is that genetic inheritance determines the better part of our destiny, who we are, what we suffer from, and what we are capable of. In 2000, at a White House briefing, Bill Clinton proclaimed the findings of the Human Genome Project "the most wondrous map ever produced by humankind," adding that "today we are learning the language in which God created life." The new science, the soon-to-be ex-president predicted, "will revolutionize the diagnosis, prevention and treatment of most, if not all, human disease," leading to cures for conditions like Alzheimer's, Parkinson's, and cancer "by attacking their genetic roots."[†]

---

†   There are a few diseases that are determined purely by genes, such as Huntington's and one that runs in my family, muscular dystrophy. If one has the gene, one is almost 100 percent certain to get the disease. Such conditions are exceedingly rare. There is, for example, a gene for breast cancer, but only about 7 percent of women with the disease have the gene. And far from all the ones with the gene will necessarily get the disease, though their risk, to be sure, is significantly elevated.

Two decades later, we know that little of the sort has happened.[1] And for good reason: genes are not, in fact, life's language, any more than a scrambled alphabet or a randomly arranged dictionary is a Shakespeare play, or a musical scale is equivalent to a John Coltrane solo. For letters or words to become language, they must be arranged, enunciated, inflected, punctuated with pauses, EMPHASIZED or softened. Like all building blocks, genes help make up the language of existence, but it is through the workings of epigenetics that they are activated, accented, or quieted. The mechanisms of epigenetics include, among myriad others, adding certain molecules to DNA sequences so as to change gene function, modifying the numbers of receptors for certain messenger chemicals, and influencing the interactions between genes.‡

Experience, in other words, determines how our genetic potential expresses itself in the end. This is what the field of epigenetics—meaning "on top of" genes—is all about. Epigenetic processes act on chromosomes, delivering and translating messages from the environment that "tell" the genes what to do. All this takes place without in any way altering the genes themselves. As the BBC's Martha Henriques explains, epigenetics offers "a way of adapting to changing conditions without inflicting a more permanent shift in our genomes."[2]

It isn't that genes don't matter—they certainly do—only that they cannot dictate even the simplest behaviors, let alone account for most illnesses or address possible cures for them. Far from being the autonomous arbiters of our destinies, genes answer to their environment; without environmental signals, they could not function. In fact, life for us would be impossible if not

---

‡ Receptor molecules embedded in the membranes of cells receive and bind with chemical messengers such as opiates and hormones. Their interaction with these messenger substances induces the DNA in the cell's nucleus to manufacture proteins that instigate life processes. By such mechanisms, the environment instructs the cell what to do and when.

for the epigenetic mechanisms that "turn" genes "on" or "off" in response to signals from within and from outside the body.[†]

Epigenetics revamps our understanding of human development from embryo to adult, and even how our species got to be here. I spoke with one of the foremost researchers in the field, Dr. Moshe Szyf, at McGill University's storied medical school. "Evolutionary theory is a difficult one to change because it became almost religion, a religion of science," he said. "And any questioning of it seems to be a heretical question of the whole system, which obviously it isn't. Epigenetics doesn't deny evolution. Epigenetics is part of evolution, but it demands a new look at how evolution works." The new biology improves upon the standard Darwinian view of spontaneous mutations and random selection as the motors of species adaptations; it demonstrates that circumstances themselves can shape how genes adjust to the environment.

Said another way, our lives are what happens when life acts upon life.

Dr. Szyf and his team in Montreal performed one of the most cited epigenetic studies, with major implications for how we view development, behavior, and health. Working with laboratory rats, they examined the effect of the mother's interactions with the infant in the first days after birth on how the offspring, for the rest of their lives, respond to stress—whether appropriately and confidently or with anxiety and over-reactivity. The focus was the HPA axis, the stress-regulating feedback loop between the hypothalamus and the pituitary and adrenal glands.[‡] In particular, the researchers looked at receptor molecules in the

---

[†]   How a gene acts—that is, what protein messengers it will produce, if any—is called *gene expression*. Gene expression is determined by inputs from the environment that reach the DNA by means of receptors on the cell membrane, and also by complex intracellular mechanisms programmed by experience.

[‡]   The hypothalamic-pituitary-adrenal axis is discussed in chapter 2.

brain whose task it is to modulate stress, which is to say, to ensure the appropriate behavior when stress is present. Creatures
with poorly self-regulated stress reactions will be more anxious,
less capable of confronting ordinary environmental challenges,
and overstressed even under normal circumstances.

The study showed the quality of early maternal care to have a
causal impact on the offspring's brains' biochemical capacity to
respond to stress in a healthy way into adulthood. Key epigenetic
markers—the ways certain genes expressed themselves—were
different in the brains of rats who had received either more, or less,
nurturing contact from their mothers.[3] Strikingly, the offspring
in turn passed on to their *own* infants the type of mothering they
had been given. Szyf and his colleagues have also shown that the
quality of maternal care affects the receptor activity for estrogen—a
key female hormone—in daughters, with ramifications for mothering patterns down the generations.[4] Through ingenious manipulation of the rat population studied—inconceivable in human
research—both the physiological and behavioral effects of early
nurturing patterns were found to be *nongenetic*: that is, not transmitted through the so-called genetic code, which remained unchanged. Rather, they were *epigenetic*—in other words, determined
by how the various kinds of maternal nurturing influenced gene
activity in the offspring's brain. (The specific maternal behavior tracked by these researchers was how "lovingly" the moms
"groomed," or licked, their infants.)

"Okay, but these are rodents in a lab," you might find yourself saying. "What do these findings mean for people in the real
world?" A reasonable question, to which Nature provided an
eloquent answer in the form of a devastating ice storm in January 1998—in the same province, no less, where Dr. Szyf and his
team did their work.[5] Considered one of Canada's worst-ever
natural disasters, the storm left many Quebecers without heat or

electricity. The more "objective stress" that pregnant women had to live through during those trying days—as in concrete, measurable factors like darkness, cold, and home damage[†]—the more their kids' physiology was marked by that adversity even near puberty. (The participants were of a similar socioeconomic, cultural, and ethnic background, and lived in the same suburban area.) "Over the years [of tracking the children]," Suzanne King, a professor of psychiatry at McGill University said, "we found that that objective stress explained how kids varied one from another in a whole host of things: language, BMI [body mass index] and obesity, insulin secretion, their immune system."[6] Even IQ was affected. "We also saw increased asthma," Dr. Szyf added, "as well as increased inflammatory genes and immune genes that are connected with autoimmunity."

I should emphasize that mothers aren't alone in transmitting chronic disturbances of the body's stress apparatus to their young. In one experiment, healthy male mice were vexed by a series of stressors: frequent cage changes, constant light or white noise, exposure to fox odor, being restrained in a small tube, and so on. They were then mated with non-stressed females who provided their pups with perfectly good mothering. Their young showed impaired stress-response behaviors and blunted stress hormone patterns. In other words, despite the mothers' best efforts, the fathers had transmitted the disturbing effects through their sperm.[7] In humans, paternal stress early in a child's life can also have long-term effects, into adolescence at the least. Adversity among *both* mothers and fathers bear "reliable linkages" to the epigenetic profiles of the children, a group of researchers concluded.[8]

Socioeconomic circumstances, too, can alter the epigenome— the web of epigenetic influences on genes. The indefatigable

---

† The impact of "subjective" stress—fear, loss, emotional pain, etc.—is no less physiologically impactful.

Dr. Szyf teamed with scientists from Canada and the U.K. to study the epigenetic workings of a broad range of genes in blood samples of middle-aged British males. The study subjects had begun life at opposite ends of the wealth-to-poverty spectrum, some poor and others rich. Gene expression in those who were born well-off was markedly different from that observed in their counterparts who grew up disadvantaged.[9]

Another study observed higher rates of inflammation in African Americans than in Caucasians, an epigenetic effect that remained even when comparing those of the same socioeconomic level.[10] "We found that experiences with racism and discrimination accounted for more than 50% of the black/white difference in the activity of genes that increase inflammation," wrote the lead author, Dr. April Thames, in an article titled "Racism Shortens Lives and Hurts Health of Blacks by Promoting Genes That Lead to Inflammation and Illness."[11]

Much like gene expression, telomeres manifest the vagaries of fate and history, class and race, stress and trauma. How? At birth, telomeres have many "units"—the DNA base pairs of which they are constituted—and by old age, far fewer. "We start out with about ten thousand when we're a baby, and we get down to four thousand when we die," Elissa Epel told me. Every time a cell in our body divides, telomeres shorten; when they get too short, their host cell dies or may deteriorate and become dysfunctional. As they shrink, immune function is impaired, inflammation rises, and we fall more prone to illness.

Telomeres have been called "cellular clocks," in that they are a measure of biological rather than chronological age. Two people, even identical twins, could be the same age as computed in years, months, weeks, and days, yet one may be biologically older than the other, depending on how much stress, adversity, or trauma they have endured. That's because stress shortens telomeres.

(Doctors should take special heed: the telomeres of medical residents suffer greater attrition than those of other young adults in their age group.)[12] One of Dr. Epel's studies found that caregiving mothers of chronically ill children had shorter telomeres than their counterparts of the same age. This biological age differential was proportionate to both the number of years of caregiving *and* the degree of stress as perceived by the moms.[13] Similar results were seen in caregivers of people with dementia: shortened telomeres and impaired immunity, reinforcing the idea that "chronic psychological stress has a negative impact on immune cell function and may accelerate their aging."[14] In other words, stress ages our chromosomes, and therefore ages us.

Just as poverty and racism affect epigenetic functioning, so do these factors also shorten telomeres, and therefore lives. This sobering linkage was brought home vividly by a study of Black American men in 2014. "Our findings literally suggest that racism makes people old," the lead author commented.[15] The same holds true for women. As part of the U.S.-based Study of Women's Health Across the Nation (SWAN), the telomeres of Black and white middle-aged women were compared. The results were shocking: Black women were found, on average, to be over seven years more biologically aged than their white counterparts, consistent with higher rates of poverty, stress, hypertension, obesity, and related health conditions.[16]

As Dr. Epel told me, the effects of our socioeconomic environment are visible within our cells, if one knows what to look for. "The neighborhood deprivation, the crime, the income of the zip code," she said, "all of that is associated with aging of the cells. That is to me one of the biggest demonstrations that our health is outside of our body." Dr. Szyf spoke in similar tones: "For a century we've been obsessed with chemical changes, thinking anything that is chemical is true and anything that is not chemical is not true. What epigenetics taught us is that social changes are really not different than chemical changes." The one is manifested in the other.

Fortunately, the door of environmental effects swings both ways: it turns out that experiences that build stress resilience can *lengthen* our telomeres, even in the face of illness or adversity. This has been shown by the work of Dr. Epel and colleagues with meditators, by Dr. Gene Brody's work with deprived Black American teenagers, and in other research on men with prostate cancer.[7] This will be a recurring theme as we proceed: the seemingly bad news giving way to something empowering, if we approach it wisely. By learning about the impacts of adversity, we can also find pathways toward healing.

Chapter 5

Mutiny on the Body: The Mystery of the Rebellious Immune System

A lot of times I've had to pretend I felt good when I felt terrible.

—Venus Williams

"I kind of injured myself," Mee Ok[†] told me recently, "because I was doing very well and then I tripped, running up a flight of stairs. So I stubbed my toe." Her warm, impish humor radiates in the telling, as does a certain sense of pride. For most of us that would be an odd reaction to a painful mishap like that. But to the Mee Ok of seven years ago, such an injury, incurred while moving vigorously against gravity, would have seemed like an impossible dream. Diagnosed at age twenty-seven with scleroderma, she had become completely disabled in a short time despite all that mainstream medicine had to offer. She lives in the Boston area and was assessed and treated at one of Western medical science's most hallowed venues.

From the Greek for "hard skin," scleroderma is an autoimmune disorder that manifests in debilitating joint inflammation and painful tightening of the connective tissues. A more inclusive

---

† Her Korean given name, pronounced "Mee Oak." For much of her life, growing up in the United States, she went by "Mandy." Her full name now is Mee Ok Icaro, for reasons I'll explain when we return to her remarkable story in chapter 31 (see footnote, p. 458).

name for the condition is systemic sclerosis, as the buildup of hardened tissue can occur in many organs, including the esophagus, blood vessels, and lungs. In Mee Ok's case, it showed up in agonizing swelling of her hands, shoulders, and knees. "The pain was everywhere," she recalls. "It flooded my whole body." She soon had to leave her job at Harvard as an assistant to a prominent academic. Formerly a 120-word-per-minute typist, she now found her hands becoming rigid and clawlike, stiffening into near paralysis. Merely touching the keyboard was agony. When I first interviewed her in 2014, her physiognomy was grim, her face a rigid mask, her taut lips barely able to cover her teeth. She was unrecognizable to herself—and wholly incongruous with the person one encounters now, her smile quick and responsive.

Within a few years of the onset of her disease, still in her early thirties, Mee Ok wanted only to end her life. Facing a death-sentence diagnosis, needing a wheelchair to mobilize, unable even to get out of bed without assistance, and anticipating that her torments would only intensify the longer she lived, she investigated the possibility of medically assisted suicide. "If I had been in a country where euthanasia was legalized, I would have fit all the criteria. The pain was unbelievable," she told me. "There was no prognosis that really gave me a reason to stick around. I was losing my body so quickly, I knew that if I waited much longer, I was going to be trapped and I wouldn't have even been able to push a button."

Today, in defiance of all conventional medical logic, Mee Ok—completely off all medications—walks, travels, and hikes independently. She is currently writing her memoir, albeit at the speed of fifty words per minute: relative to the shape she was in not long ago, a true victory.

Scleroderma is among eighty or more related conditions dubbed autoimmune, each representing a virtual civil war inside the body. In effect, autoimmunity amounts to an assault by one's immune system against the body it ought to defend. The particular form of the disease depends on which tissues or organs become the targets of this ruinous internal rebellion. If the nervous system is under fire, the result may show up as multiple sclerosis; if the gut, celiac disease or inflammatory bowel disease (IBD) such as Crohn's or ulcerative colitis; if the joints and connective tissues, systemic lupus erythematosus (SLE) or rheumatoid arthritis (RA) or scleroderma; if the skin, psoriasis or autoimmune eczema; if the pancreas, type 1 diabetes; if the lungs, pulmonary fibrosis; if the brain, perhaps Alzheimer's. In many of these conditions, several regions of the body are affected at once. Chronic fatigue syndrome—also known as myalgic encephalomyelitis (ME)—which affects millions worldwide, is among the best known of the recent additions to this roster.

Virtually all autoimmune diseases are characterized by inflammation of the afflicted tissues, organs, and body parts—which explains why frontline medical measures often begin with anti-inflammatory drugs. When nonsteroidal anti-inflammatories like ibuprofen or heavier artillery such as steroids themselves prove inadequate, physicians may prescribe medications to suppress the body's immune activity.

Because the disease had first affected Mee Ok's joints, the doctors believed it was rheumatoid arthritis. Their prescription was steroids: lab-made analogues of the natural stress hormone cortisol, a secretion of the adrenal gland in response to a threat. Ultimately it was the failure of both steroids and immunosuppressants that drove Mee Ok to suicidal despair. Her doctors had nothing left to prescribe. (I should add that Mee Ok's illness was so extreme that her recovery is entirely unexpected, indeed unexplainable, according to standard medical thinking. I contacted her family physician in Boston, who verified the details.)

Although often disruptive and highly distressing, autoimmune symptoms can be nebulous and hard to pinpoint at first— not so much to the patient suffering them and seeking validation and support as to the physician in search of precise findings. Hence, it is not unusual for such diseases, which not infrequently overlap with each other, to fly under the diagnostic radar. Such was the experience of the tennis star Venus Williams, whose illness expressed itself in swollen hands, persistent fatigue, and misshapen joints: symptoms that would be alarming for anyone, even more so for an elite athlete. "I'd go to doctors, but never get any answers, so there was nothing I could do but keep going," she told a newspaper reporter. "You almost get used to having all these symptoms," she said. "You tell yourself to shake it off. Just keep going. Over time, you do start to wonder what's happening and if you're going crazy."[1] She was eventually found to have Sjögren's syndrome, a condition that primarily affects moisture-producing glands so that people suffer dry mouth and dry eyes, but which can also cause dysfunction in many organs such as the lungs, kidneys, pancreas, and blood vessels. Like many others, Williams was relieved to finally learn there was some objective reason, and even a name, for her physical tribulations.

In Mee Ok's case it fell to the patient herself to make the diagnosis: a not-unusual role reversal in the internet age, particularly in cases where doctors have already thrown up their hands. "My body just continued to stiffen," she recalled. "It was like it was undergoing mummification, like a self-mummification over time. It kept spreading and spreading throughout my body, and the pain was just unbelievable . . . They were giving me steroids and telling me that it was something that I would have to maintain, that the arthritis would never be cured—it wasn't curable. I insisted on being tested for scleroderma, and that was when I found out my diagnosis: six months after the symptoms started."

Autoimmune diseases are among the great unsolved mysteries of the medical profession. Most are considered "idiopathic" in nature, which simply means "of unknown origin." Naturally, if we cannot identify the *cause* of a condition, we will be stymied in our efforts to cure or reverse it. In many cases symptom suppression or, sometimes, surgical repair or removal of damaged tissue is the most modern medicine can offer. Such measures do afford welcome relief to many, but they cannot reverse the course of disease and, as with Mee Ok, leave a great number of people consigned to prolonged deterioration and disability.

Troubling as this lack of clarity is for doctors and patients alike, these illnesses also present a number of other headscratchers, scientifically speaking.

The first mystery is why they are becoming more frequent. Across many Western countries, rates of everything from celiac disease to IBD, from lupus to type 1 diabetes, and even allergies, are steadily rising, stymieing researchers.[2] "In the last half-century, the prevalence of autoimmune disease . . . has increased sharply in the developed world," a 2016 *New York Times* article noted. "An estimated one in 13 Americans has one of these often debilitating, generally lifelong conditions."[3] In the U.K., the diagnosis of Crohn's disease increased more than threefold between 1994 and 2014,[4] while in Canada the rate of IBD in children grew by over 7 percent a year between 1999 and 2010, giving my country among the highest rates of this disease in the world.[5]

Such trends immediately rule out that go-to of medical explanations, genetic causes. Whatever effect genetics may exert—and no doubt they figure in some cases—logically they cannot account for the rise in prevalence of autoimmune disorders. "Genes do not change in such a short period of time," Virginia Ladd, chief executive of the American Autoimmune Related Diseases Association, told

Medical News Today in 2012. "The rapid increase in autoimmune diseases . . . clearly suggests that environmental factors are at play."[6] In other words, something in our environment—or a combination of somethings—is inflaming our bodies.

For most of us, when we hear "environmental factors" in conjunction with disease, our minds tend to go to well-publicized, material factors such as air pollution, lead paint, and cell phone radiation. One interesting but unproven theory has it that the rise in junk food consumption is responsible for the globally increasing prevalence of autoimmunity.[7] Studies have not yet identified such a link.[8] Either way, a complete understanding of health and disease requires a far more encompassing view of the word "environment": a biopsychosocial one.

The second mystery is the highly skewed gender distribution of autoimmune diseases. About 70 to 80 percent of sufferers are women, among whom such conditions are a leading cause of disability and death. Rheumatoid arthritis, for example, is three times more likely to strike women than men; lupus affects women by a disproportionate factor of nine. Mee Ok's condition, systemic sclerosis, is three times more common among females.[9] Even more of a puzzle is why the gender imbalance is *increasing* in, for example, multiple sclerosis, a chronic, highly debilitating, potentially lifelong disease of the nervous system.

In 1930s Canada, the gender ratio was about equal; nowadays more than three women are diagnosed with MS for every man.[10] The trend is reflected internationally. "There is an increasing incidence of multiple sclerosis in women in Denmark. Danish women's risk of developing MS has more than doubled in twenty-five years, while it has remained virtually unchanged for men," noted a recent article in the *Danish Medical Journal*. Then, right in line with Dr. Ladd's observations: "The explanation for these epidemiological changes *should be sought in the environment*, as genetics only explain a small part of the MS risk. The changes are too rapid to be explained by gene alterations."[11]

None of the specialists who looked after Mee Ok inquired about the conditions—physical and emotional—that preceded her life-blighting illness. This, despite the voluminous research that links stress, trauma, and inflammation, and despite the multiple studies that over many decades have explored such connections in rheumatoid arthritis, in MS, and in other autoimmune conditions. Not only are such possible lines of inquiry not pursued, but they seem to be verboten in mainstream circles. "I've come to feel a little bit off the wall when talking about these issues," a specialist in rheumatic diseases at one of the best-known U.S. teaching hospitals told me. "Since my graduation I have markedly changed the way I practice, because I started observing in my patients the relation between stress and the onset of their disease, and how great a role trauma, psychological and physical, plays in their disease." This doctor, who requested anonymity for fear of alienating her colleagues (!), has observed firsthand what she calls "remarkable results" among her patients, both in terms of recovery and even, in some cases, getting off medications altogether. Yet she feels like a renegade in her own profession. "I'm surrounded by all my, you know, esteemed colleagues at the university who are investigators, and nobody is looking at these things." Hearing this, I recalled the Harvard physician who told me that doctors follow these sorts of threads "at their own peril"—though he did think it was changing.

If even doctors who stray beyond medical orthodoxy can feel intimidated and misunderstood, what do patients experience? Another lamentable feature of Western medical practice—not universal, but all too often seen—is a power hierarchy that casts physicians as the exalted experts and patients as the passive recipients of care. For all doctors' dedication and goodwill, the imbalance compromises patients' agency over their own health and healing process. Essential questions about their lives go un-asked, while patients in turn lack the confidence to insist that their intuitions and insights about themselves contribute to the process, much less guide it.

Had Mee Ok's doctors inquired along these lines when she presented her distressing symptoms, they would have learned that she had sustained two major abandonments by the end of her first year. She was born in Korea to a single mom who placed her in an orphanage when Mee Ok was six months old. At one year of age, she was adopted and brought to the United States by an evangelical couple who reared her according to the strictest fundamentalist principles. Before Mee Ok was ten, her adoptive mother suffered a nervous breakdown. Sometime in her teenage years, her father, in a fit of religious remorse, confessed to her that he had sexually abused her for much of her early childhood, from age two onward. She had completely repressed these mem-ories, secreted them and all associated feelings—pain, terror, rage—deep beneath the surface of her awareness. As we will see later when we discuss healing, Mee Ok's improbable recovery, veritably a deathbed resurrection, owed everything to her con-fronting this long-buried trove of hurt.

Upon the emotional graveyard of what she could not afford to feel, Mee Ok erected an impressive edifice: a positive, can-do persona that not only kept her from experiencing her despair and impelled her to ignore her own needs, but also helped her achieve success beyond what she really believed was her due. In her job as assistant to the world-renowned professor, the grown-up Mee Ok found her work stressful and would habitually bear the tensions and pressures of everyone around her. "I was re-ally not myself while I was there," she said. "I was always hav-ing to operate as a more highly functioning person than I really was." Such hyperfunctioning on top of hidden inner distress is a recurring theme among the many autoimmune patients I've encountered in my years of practice and teaching.

Just prior to the onset of her agonizing joint inflammation, Mee Ok was in a complicated romantic partnership whose many ups and downs took a psychic toll and culminated in a wrenching breakup. All the lifelong hurt she could not allow herself to experience, all her terror of abandonment, showed up in her reactions to the loss of the relationship. It was a full-body grief response. Once more, none of her history, from childhood to the present day, was considered as admissible evidence by the highly trained experts who treated her scleroderma. "My body was really like a battleground, and I was losing," Mee Ok told me. Her language resonated with me: I've long pictured autoimmune disease as resembling a powerful army invading its own motherland, a violent mutiny against the body. In effect, with no conscious outlet and lacking resolution, Mee Ok's inflamed emotions rebelled, manifesting in the inflammation of her tissues.

Microbiologists these days speak of "neurogenic inflammation," stress-induced inflammation triggered by discharges of the nervous system—a system we now understand to be powerfully influenced by emotions.[12] And there is elegant research connecting early adversity, such as the traumas Mee Ok endured in childhood, to inflammation in adult life. A recent American study found that emotional and physical abuse in childhood more than doubles the risk of systemic lupus erythematosus, with inflammation being one of the likely pathways.[13] Yet more connections between stress and compromised autoimmunity have been found in other studies.[14] In 2007, British scientists found that adults who had been maltreated in childhood had higher blood levels of certain inflammation-signaling substances† produced in the liver,

---

†   For example, the C-reactive protein (CRP).

independent of personal behaviors and lifestyle considerations. "Childhood maltreatment is a previously undescribed, independent, and preventable risk factor for inflammation in adulthood," wrote the researchers.[15] "Inflammation *may be* an important developmental mediator linking adverse experiences in early life to poor adult health," they added cautiously. Many studies since attest that there is no "may be" about it.

Some clinicians have noted a relationship between rheumatoid arthritis and certain types or features of personality. We will have much more to say about personality in chapter 7, but, to avoid misunderstanding, a quick clarification is in order here. What we call the personality traits, in addition to reflecting genuine inborn temperaments and qualities, also express the ways that people, as children, had to accommodate their emotional environment. They reflect much that is neither inherent nor immutable about a person, no matter how closely identified he or she is with them. Nor are they character faults; though they may cause us difficulty now, they began as modes of survival.

As far as back as 1892 the great Canadian-born Johns Hopkins physician William Osler—later knighted by Queen Victoria for his contributions to British medicine—had already noted "the association of the disease with shock, worry, and grief." Many years later, a 1965 survey reported the prevalence in rheumatoid arthritis–prone individuals of an array of self-abnegating traits: a "compulsive and self-sacrificing doing for others, suppression of anger, and excessive concern about social acceptability."[16] An unusually perceptive Canadian specialist in autoimmune disease, Dr. C. E. G. Robinson, wrote in 1957 that his patients with RA "usually tried very hard to please both in professional and personal contacts, and either concealed hostility or expressed it indirectly. Many of them were perfectionistic." The onset of disease was often preceded by stress. He added, sagely, "Frequently as much time is needed for dealing with the emotional problems of the patient with chronic rheumatoid arthritis as with the joint or systemic disorders . . . I think the emotional and psychological aspect of many rheumatoid patients is of first importance."[17] Four decades after Dr. Robinson published his comments, American researchers likewise found that the degree of interpersonal stress was correlated with disease severity among a group of women with rheumatoid arthritis.[18]

A case in point is forty-two-year-old Julia, from one of Canada's prairie provinces, diagnosed with rheumatoid arthritis at age twenty-nine. She had been rear-ended in a motor vehicle accident and the next day felt some pain in her left shoulder, which quickly resolved—only to flare up again and again in various joints throughout her body, migrating with bewildering unpredictability. "It would show up in a joint and then leave," she told me. "Then all at once I ended up with twenty-six joints that were all inflamed simultaneously." Blood tests found one of the indicators of rheumatoid arthritis highly elevated, clinching the diagnosis. Her emotional profile aligned with the hyper-responsible, anger-suppressing personae described in the literature, traits she developed in a family of origin with an alcoholic father and an emotionally dependent mother to whom she could not divulge her sexual abuse at the hands of a family friend who also victimized the younger sister Julia tried to protect.

None of Julia's treating physicians ever asked about her inner life. Why does that matter? Because such personality patterns as Dr. Robinson and others have observed are reversible and, with them, so may be the disease. Despite having been told the illness would inevitably progress, Julia is now symptom-free and medication-free. "I have beautiful conversations with my rheumatoid arthritis these days—it makes me want to cry telling you," she said to me. "I'm great." What could such a statement mean, and why so deeply felt in Julia's case? We will return to these "beautiful conversations" later, when we look at healing.†

Grief and Vexation: Miray, Bianca, and Multiple Sclerosis

Miray is a fifty-one-year-old physician from Turkey, now working as a clinical trial coordinator at a Canadian hospital. She first experienced diplopia—double vision—at age eighteen, but without the advanced imaging techniques now available, she remained at first undiagnosed. "I saw an ophthalmologist, and he said, oh, this is just a temporary thing," she recalled. "So I went on corticosteroids for six weeks, and it went away. At twenty-two I had multiple attacks. *Whenever I would see my mom, I would see double.* I studied in another city and was perfectly okay, but when I would go back to Istanbul, I would have another attack every time I saw my mom." At age twenty-four, Miray had an MRI that confirmed the diagnosis of multiple sclerosis. After she immigrated to Canada, she was symptom-free for years. But during her pregnancy, her husband, in the midst of some business woes, became abusive. "He had this rage and hatred toward women," she said, "and he would project it on me." One stress begat another. "He wasn't making enough money to hire people, so I would work in the hospital from morning to afternoon, then I had to go and mind the store from four until midnight. When I gave birth, things got worse. He was shouting, extremely angry. He was always demeaning me, mocking me, ridiculing me." Finally, Miray left the marriage and, after many years, saw her parents again. When she did, she was soon unable to walk—a pattern that has persisted ever since. The emotional triggers of suppressed fear and anger instilled in her in childhood were activated around her family, and that, in turn, would inflame her nervous system.

---

† See chapter 27.

Multiple sclerosis is another autoimmune condition for which personal histories, childhood adversity, and the decisive influence of stress have been extensively studied. The first to describe this illness, the French physician Jean-Martin Charcot, sometimes called the father of modern neurology, proposed in 1872 that MS resulted from "long-continued grief and vexation." As with his younger contemporary and fellow medical giant William Osler's insights about rheumatoid arthritis, much information has since accrued to support Charcot's pioneering formulation. "A majority of the MS patients had grown up against an unhappy family background," found a 1958 study at two Montreal hospitals. "Marital discord, broken homes, alcoholism, and lack of parental love and affection were given as reasons for unhappiness." The vast majority had suffered prolonged emotional stress prior to the onset of their disease. Also salient in triggering relapses were such stresses as "worry over financial matters, unhappy home life, increased responsibility, either alone or in combination with such other factors as fatigue, overexertion, overwork, accidents, injuries, and childbirth."[19] A decade later, another study (in which Dr. George Engel, of the "biopsychosocial" coinage, participated) also concluded that "the majority of patients . . . reported psychologically stressful experiences to have preceded the onset of the symptoms that ultimately led to the diagnosis of multiple sclerosis, findings corroborated by family members when available."[20]

The evidence just keeps coming. MS patients experiencing significant life stresses were seen to have a nearly quadrupled incidence of disease flare-ups.[21] Finally, a major review of the literature presented at an international conference in Portugal in 2013 found a host of patterns among MS patients, including

- more unwanted stress or traumatic events occurring between six months to two years before onset;

- a cumulative correlation between stress and relapse: after one stressful life event, the relapse risk doubles or triples; after three or more, the risk increases by five- to nearly sevenfold;
- histories of childhood trauma, which are double or triple those of the general population;
- physical and sexual abuse histories correlated with higher relapse rates;
- being less in touch with their emotions, in general, and therefore less able to protect themselves from stress; and
- social support mitigating the effect of life stresses.[22]

Over the years I have interviewed dozens of people with MS, many of them long before I was aware of such studies. I have yet to find an exception to these general findings. The "long-continued grief and vexation" of which Jean-Martin Charcot spoke a century and a half ago factor mightily in the presence and severity of the illness. As in the other autoimmune conditions, in virtually every case the childhood patterning that led people to be overconscientious, hyper-responsible, and emotionally stoic about their own needs was evident—as were stresses preceding the illness, such as interpersonal conflict, family crisis, loss of a relationship, or added duties at work.

Bianca—like Miray, a physician—also had double vision (diplopia) as her first symptom of MS. Now thirty-seven, she first experienced it in her twenties while she was stressing herself over her school examinations. "Through the years," she told me as we spoke online, she from her home in Bucharest and I in Vancouver, "all the time that I had the symptom of double vision I was preparing for exams or a lot of stress in work—professional stress. The other symptoms, I make the connection, like numbness and tingling or pins-and-needles sensations or paralysis, happen usually when I have personal problems and emotional problems." Contrary to medical expectation, Bianca has made the disease work for her. She has learned to make friends with and allow herself to be instructed by a condition most of us would naturally regard as pure misfortune. "I was overcompensating all my life, and working hard, and trying to please people," she told me. "With MS, I finally had a reason to relax and focus on myself."

Why the Rise of Autoimmune Diseases?

Genetic explanations missing the mark, the hunt for elusive "environmental factors" continues; in the modern world, there are bound to be many.[23] I believe, however, that one such factor is salient, ubiquitous, and, for the most part, woefully overlooked. Here the very treatment of inflammatory conditions offers an essential, even obvious clue about their origins, a hint that may help resolve the mystery of where in the world these illnesses come from. We physicians frequently dole out large doses of synthesized stress hormones for inflammations of the skin, joints, brain, intestines, lungs, kidneys, and so on. We do so for a good reason: hormones often alleviate or ameliorate symptoms, albeit with many potentially hazardous side effects. Yet we rarely think to ask ourselves—or our patients—whether stress itself may, just may, have something to do with the condition we are treating.

There is plenty of evidence for such a view. A recent Swedish study in the *Journal of the American Medical Association* showed that people with stress-related disorders had significantly greater risk of autoimmune disease.[24] Tellingly, those who had been treated for their stress-related mental conditions with SSRI-type medication—the most widely prescribed class of antidepressants,[†] of which Prozac is probably the most famous—

---

†   SSRI stands for "selective serotonin uptake inhibitor," meaning that these medications block the uptake of the neural messenger chemical serotonin into nerve cells.

had lower risk for autoimmunity: a clear indication of the *body-mind*, to use Dr. Candace Pert's phrasing for the interflow of psychology and physiology in humans, and of the role of emotions in illness.

Not only in humans, either. Laboratory mice in a 2013 study were subjected to three weeks' stress, meant to mimic "the diversity of stressful events in daily human life." That meant immersing the creatures in cold water, wafting predator odors in their direction, making them endure bright lights or restraint or isolation—unpredictable stresses of variable duration they could not easily adapt to. The researchers called this "chronic variable stress." Mice so exposed were found to be at an elevated risk for pathogenic autoimmunity—in other words, for immune activity directed against the physical self.[25]

Life in our current culture, I believe, makes many of us experimental mice subject to "chronic variable stress" beyond our control.‡

A necessary caveat: in foregrounding the role of biographical factors in disease, we must be mindful to avoid blame or guilt. "Some people see lupus as an external attacker," a British woman with lupus has written. "But I prefer to think I did it to myself . . . Too much striving, too much living on the edge, too much stress. Yet despite the consequences, I wouldn't change how I lived my life. It is who I am, so this disease is who I am too."[26]

There is wisdom in that view, but I also hear an unwarranted self-accusation and an all-too-characteristic lack of self-compassion. No person *is* their disease, and no one *did* it to themselves—not in any conscious, deliberate, or culpable sense. Disease is an outcome of generations of suffering, of social conditions, of cultural conditioning, of childhood trauma, of physiology bearing the brunt of

---

‡ The striking gender differences in autoimmune disease as well as the racial disparities are addressed in chapters 22 and 23.

people's stresses and emotional histories, all interacting with the physical and psychological environment. It is often a manifestation of ingrained personality traits, yes—but that personality is not who we are any more than are the illnesses to which it may predispose us.

Yet if our British writer errs in identifying entirely with her disease, she is still skillfully directing us to a profound and fruitful set of questions. Could it be that illness as "external attacker" does not even exist when it comes to such chronic, auto-mutinous conditions as we have looked at in this chapter?† What if disease is not, in fact, a fixed entity but a *dynamic process* expressive of real lives in concrete situations? What new (or old) pathways to healing, unthinkable within the prevailing medical view, might follow from such a paradigmatic shift in perspective?

---

† Obviously, with an external agent such as the novel coronavirus, we are facing an entirely different challenge. But even there, internal factors and social conditions play a major role in people's vulnerability to the infection.

Chapter 6

It Ain't a Thing:
Disease as Process

Cancer is no more a disease of cells than a traffic jam is a
disease of cars. A lifetime study of the internal-combustion
engine would not help anyone to understand our traffic
problems . . . A traffic jam is due to a failure of the normal
relationship between driven cars and their environment and can
occur whether they themselves are running normally or not.

—Sir David Smithers, *Lancet*, 1962

V, formerly known as Eve Ensler,‡ rose to fame in the 1990s as
the author of the *Vagina Monologues*, the play the *New York Times*
called "probably the most important piece of political theater of
the last decade." Her blockbuster stage success has given rise to a
life of activism. A fearless advocate for and defender of women's
rights, she has traveled worldwide, witnessing the bloody aftermath of mass rape and misogynist brutality in Bosnia and the
war-torn Democratic Republic of the Congo.

The political is personal for V. In her heartrending yet triumphant memoir of surviving life-threatening stage IV uterine cancer, *In the Body of the World*, she poses a question of stunning
frankness and insight: "Do I have rape cancer?" From an early

‡   Since our original interview, the writer and activist has changed her name to V, eschewing
the names—personal and familial—given to her by her rapist father, by whose legacy
she does not wish to be defined. Throughout this book, we honor that self-affirming
designation.

age and over many years, her father sexually violated her—a chronic assault on which was superimposed severe emotional abuse and, later, terrifying physical violence. All the while, her mother, hobbled by the legacy of her own childhood suffering, remained oblivious and/or silent. The child Eve felt she was "betraying" her mom by having an affair with her own father. "As a child when your father incests you, you feel you were the betrayer," she told me in an online interview. "And my mother hated me for it. She hated me for how much he adored me." Toxic self-blame is one of the torments imposed on the traumatized child. For much of her life V loathed herself, as so many victims of early abuse end up doing.

"How did I get it?" she writes about the onset of her cancer. "Was it worry every day for fifty-seven years that I wasn't good enough? . . . Was it the pressure to fill Madison Square Garden with eighteen thousand or the Superdome with forty thousand? . . . Was it the line of two hundred women repeated in hundreds of small towns for many years after each performance, after each speech, women lined up to show me their scars, wounds, warrior tattoos? Was it suburban lawn pesticides? . . . Was it my first husband sleeping with my close friend? . . . Was it sleeping with men who were married? . . . Was it not enough boundaries? Was it too many walls?"

When I asked her what she thinks now, V prefaced her answer with a laugh, perhaps sardonic. "I think it's a combination of all of the above," she said. "But I think that if there were one underlying reason why I got sick, it was unreckoned—I hadn't gone deep enough in processing my trauma." She then made a profound observation about the nature of illness itself: "A disease *is not like a thing*. It is energy flow, it's a current; it is evolution or devolution that occurs when you're not awake and connected, and trauma is essentially ruling your life. I think it's such a mistake to identify it as a thing, because that makes it hard matter when it's in fact a much more psychological, spiritual, emotional condition."

This hard-won perspective raises some unfamiliar, potentially fruitful questions. What if, she writes, "when you got sick, you weren't a stage [of a disease] *but in a process*? And cancer, just like having your heart broken, or getting a new job, or going to school, were a teacher? What if, rather than being cast out and defined by some terminal category, you were identified as someone in the middle of a transformation that could deepen your soul, open your heart?"

V's survival of a near-terminal diagnosis owed much to the heroic efforts and skills of modern medicine, including multiple complex surgeries and chemotherapy. But that's not all that saved her, as she sees it. V herself generated a powerful complement to these interventions in the way she approached healing: a willingness to experience disease not as a "thing," an external enemy, but as a process that encompasses all of her life—present, past, and future—and, ultimately, even as a teacher.

Beyond the War Metaphor

We are used to seeing disease as a thing to get rid of or a foe to battle against—as, for example, in the "war on cancer." (Which "war," for the record, has been far from victorious.)[1] Someday, we tell ourselves, with enough research, we as a society will "beat" cancer and wipe it out; in the meantime, we maintain a tenaciously defiant attitude, as expressed in the viral hashtag #FuckCancer. Our everyday language gives voice to our combative stance: we hear of a friend or a family member courageously "battling MS" or some other illness; they will either prevail in the struggle or else "succumb."

It may be that these martial metaphors are so appealing because their force matches our feelings of anger and despair; that does not, however, make them helpful. In a previous work I quoted the Canadian oncologist Karen Gelman, a leading breast cancer specialist, who looks askance at the military depiction of cancer care and research. "What happens in the body is a matter of flow—there is input and there is output," she said, "and you can't control every aspect of it. We need to understand that flow, know there are things you can influence and things you can't. It's not a battle, it's a push-pull phenomenon of finding balance and harmony, of kneading the conflicting forces into one dough."[2] I noticed how closely her use of "flow" mirrors V's language—one woman speaking from medical expertise, the other from hard-earned, subjectively sourced insight.

Beyond the declarations of war, there is another, even more popular class of misapprehensions that cloud our view of disease: "I *have* cancer." "She *has* MS." "My nephew *has* ADD." Embedded in each phrase is the unexamined assumption that there is an *I* (or a *someone*) distinct and independent from the *thing* called disease, which the "I" *has*—as in the statement "I have a flat-screen TV." Here is my life, and over there is the disease that has encroached upon it. Seen this way, disease is something external with its own nature, existing independently of the person in whom it shows up. Given where that perspective has gotten us, it is time to consider a new one.

We have already glimpsed the countless hormonal, immunological, neurological, molecular, intracellular, and epigenetic pathways that make our physiology inseparable from our emotional, psychological, spiritual, and social lives. V's understanding of trauma and stress as major founts of the process that ultimately came close to killing her is completely aligned with modern science. In a five-decades-long British study that followed nearly ten thousand people from birth until the age of fifty, it was found that early-life adversity—abuse, socioeconomic disadvantage, family strife, for example—greatly increased the risk of cancer before the mid-century mark. Women who experienced two or more such adversities had a doubled risk by midlife.[3]

"These findings suggest that cancer risk may be influenced by exposure to stressful conditions and events early on in life," wrote the researchers, once more employing the carefully reticent language of "suggest" and "may." To my clinical sensibilities, concerned as I am with how people fall ill and/or find healing, such results, mirrored over and over in multiple other studies, do not *suggest*: they scream for attention. The disorganizing impact of stress hormones on the immune system as a risk for cancer is far from a scientific secret. We have also seen how stress and trauma are prime drivers of inflammation, another central gear in the cancer-causing apparatus. Along parallel lines, girls who are sexually and physically abused have far greater risk in adulthood of endometriosis, a painful and often disabling condition that heightens the risk of ovarian cancer and whose origins perplex conventional medical thinking.[4] Considered from the mind-body psychoneuroimmunological perspective, the puzzle becomes rather less puzzling.†

To restate a question essential to our theme: What if we saw illness as an imbalance in the entire organism, not just as a manifestation of molecules, cells, or organs invaded or denatured by pathology? What if we applied the findings of Western research and medical science in a systems framework, seeking all the connections and conditions that contribute to illness and health?

Such a reframing would revolutionize how we practice medicine. Rather than treating disease as a solid entity that imposes its ill will on the body, we would be dealing with a *process*, one that can't be extricated from our personal histories and the context and culture in which we live. This change in approach has much

---

†   Recall, too, the connection between PTSD symptoms and ovarian cancer (chapter 2).

to recommend it, and not only because it takes interpersonal biology into account. When we cease to view illness as a concrete, autonomous thing with a predetermined trajectory—and when we have the proper help and a willingness to look both within and without—we can start to exercise agency in the matter. After all, if disease is a manifestation of something in our lives rather than merely their cruel disruptor, we have options: we can pursue new understandings, ask new questions, perhaps make new choices. We can take our rightful place as *active participants in the process,* rather than remain its victims, helpless but for our reliance on medical miracle workers.

Disease itself is both a culmination of what came before and a pointer to how things might unfold in the future. Our emotional dynamics, including our relationship to ourselves, can be among the powerful determinants of that future. An attitude of helplessness and hopelessness at the time of diagnosis, for example, has been shown to exert a marked adverse effect on survival in women with breast cancer even ten years later.[5] Conversely, a decrease in depressive symptoms is associated with longer survival.[6] Even in a study of women requiring biopsies for cervical abnormalities identified on routine Pap smears, those with a dejected view of life *before* diagnosis were much more likely to find that they received a diagnosis of cancer.[7] In men, the immune system's capacity to react to prostate cancer was diminished in those with a tendency to suppress anger.[8] Another prostate study found that social support reduced the risk.[9]

Dr. Steven Cole[†] is a prolific researcher whose work has cast bright light on the disease process. "We now know that *disease is a long-term process,*" he told me, "a physiological process taking place in our bodies, and how we live influences how quickly

---

[†]   Professor of medicine and psychiatry and biobehavioral sciences at the UCLA School of Medicine.

that's going to get us at a clinical level . . . The more we understand about disease, the less clear it becomes when you have it and when you don't." Within the myth of normal, of course, this kind of nuance is barely comprehensible: you're either "sick" or you're "well," and it should be obvious which camp you're in. But really, there are no clear dividing lines between illness and health. Nobody all of a sudden "gets" an autoimmune disease, or "gets" cancer—though it may, perhaps, make itself known suddenly and with tremendous impact.

A few years ago, the *New Yorker* featured an article titled "What's Wrong with Me?," a poignant first-person account of yet another "idiopathic" autoimmune condition.[10] The piece was also a perfect depiction of disease as a long-term process rather than a distinct entity. "I got sick," the author writes with a pained humor, "the way Hemingway says you go broke: 'gradually and then suddenly.' One way to tell the story is to say that I was ill for a long time—at least half a dozen years—before any doctor I saw believed I had a disease. Another is to say that it took hold in 2009, the stressful year after my mother died, when a debilitating fatigue overcame me, my lymph nodes ached for months, and a test suggested that I had recently had Epstein-Barr virus."

The telltale hallmarks of the disease process are there: the prolonged course; the professional befuddlement at the lack of specific markers on physical examination, blood tests, or imaging studies; and the sudden interpersonal stress that finally brings on the full-blown manifestations of illness. Toward the end of the article the writer reports a revealing clue as to the source of her devitalizing malady, one that should have been a signal to her treating physicians: "In May, my endocrinologist speculated, after various M.R.I.s, that I had an 'idiopathic' disorder in the hypothalamus which is probably untreatable."

The clue? We've seen it already: the hypothalamus is the hub of the body's and brain's stress apparatus, a key modulator of immune activity, and the apex of the autonomic nervous system. It is the transducer into physiological data of our emotional functioning and, therefore, of our interpersonal relationships and of our relationship to ourselves. It translates fear, loss, grief, and stress into responses in our bloodstream, organs, cells, nerves, lymph nodes, messenger chemicals, and molecules throughout the entire organism. Thus, from a broader interpersonal biology point of view, her illness may not be so idiopathic after all, but the understandable outcome of chronic and acute stress. Even if untreatable by present-day medical techniques, it need not be beyond healing, especially if we bring in a wiser, science-based appreciation of the interconnected complexity of the disease process and the bodymind unity.

Returning to cancer, the work of Dr. Cole and colleagues has shown that activation of the body's stress response can promote tumor growth and spread. It is important to note, as they warned, "that stress *per se* does not cause cancer; however, clinical and experimental data indicate that stress and other factors such as mood, coping mechanisms, and social support can significantly influence the underlying cellular and molecular processes that facilitate malignant cell growth."[11]

This raises a key point. Stress cannot "cause" cancer, for the simple reason that our bodies naturally harbor potentially malignant cells at all times. The body contains over thirty-seven trillion cells, in all various stages of development, maturity, and decay. Malignant transformation happens regularly, as an accidental by-product of natural cell division. Under normal conditions the organism's defenses can eliminate such threats to well-being. We know from autopsies, for example, that many women have breast cancer cells, just as many men have prostate cancer cells, without ever developing the disease of cancer. The question is, What drives the progression of these cells into clinical illness? What keeps the immune system from successfully confronting the internal menace? This is where stress plays its incendiary role: for example, through the release of inflammatory proteins into the circulation—proteins that can instigate damage to DNA and impede DNA repair in the face of malignant transformation. These proteins, called cytokines, can also inactivate genes that would normally suppress tumor growth, enable chemical messengers that support the growth and survival of tumor cells, stimulate the branching of blood vessels that bring nutrients to feed the tumor, and undermine the immune system. Even at the cellular and molecular levels, the generation of ill health is a multifaceted, multistep process.

In 1962 the leading British cancer physician David Smithers published a paper of prophetic force. He explored cancer as process: not a disease of individual cells gone rogue but a manifestation of an imbalanced environment, "merely the terminal [event] in a much longer progressive chain of circumstances with no distinctive starting-point." Doctors and researchers, he wrote, do not experience cancer's "essential dynamic quality; they see its static effects, not the process in action."[12] The activity of cells, Smithers pointed out, "is possible only in relation to their environment, and none of their actions can be explained by laws governing intracellularly initiated events alone." That prescient assertion has been more than validated by the half century of research since.

"I now have a much more complex view of causation," Steve Cole told me. "If you get a disease, a whole series of things had to have gone wrong. Some of that may be related to your genes; some of that may be related to pathogen exposure. Some of it is related to hard lives—the way that can wreak wear and tear on the body and on what would otherwise be resilient tissues. It's better to think of it as a multistep causation . . . One of the things many diseases have in common is inflammation, acting as kind of a fertilizer for the development of illness. We've discovered that when people feel threatened, insecure—especially over an extended period of time—our bodies are programmed to turn on inflammatory genes."

A Physician Heals Herself

Threatened and insecure over an extended period of time is precisely how the obstetrician-gynecologist Lissa Rankin felt since childhood, an emotional state her medical training only exacerbated. Her book *The Anatomy of a Calling* begins with a nightmarish recounting of how she, as a medical resident, had to rush all night from one delivery room to another, dealing with one difficult delivery in the wake of another, supporting parents after the death of four babies, and all the while being berated by her superiors to suppress her own grief, even in the privacy of the women's changing room. "Doctors," she writes, "become masters at stuffing their emotions. We can't cry when we're grieving or when someone has hurt our feelings, or when we are sad." I recently spoke with the California-based physician. "In medical school," she told me, "I was being sexually harassed by my surgery professors all the time. All the time. I just had to tolerate it . . . I never went to the medical school director, I never told anybody, or asked for protection, because that was part of my wounding: I wasn't allowed to ask for help, to be 'needy,' to complain."

When she was twenty-seven, Dr. Rankin was admitted to the coronary care unit at her hospital for an episode of distressingly rapid heartbeat that did not respond to the usual noninvasive measures. After receiving electrical shock treatment to restore her normal heart rate, she was sent directly back to work. By age thirty-three, she was taking multiple medications for a number of conditions, including three drugs for high blood pressure and palpitations, antihistamines, and a steroid—which, again, is a stress hormone—and weekly injections for allergies, which, she was told, she'd have to stay on for the rest of her life. She was also treated for a cervical abnormality, a precancerous state that reappeared soon after the procedure. All the while—and this will sound familiar—no physician asked her what stresses might be weighing on her, promoting immune problems, and potentiating malignancy.

Today Dr. Rankin is fully healthy and taking no drugs at all. In her case, healing owed nothing to conventional medical treatment and everything to the personal transformation she was guided to undertake—a journey she began when, at age thirty-five, she was nearly suicidal. "Within six months of quitting my job I was off all my medications," she reports. She is now a mother, a healer, a seminar leader, and the author of several books. Her key insight was to recognize her entire life as the ground for her several illnesses, physical and mental; not separate entities but dynamic processes expressing her interactions with her world. "I had been a stereotypical good girl, overachiever, top of my class, always pushing to develop my talent and intellect, not to satisfy me but to be accepted by others," she told me. That relentless pressure, she learned, manifested in her medical conditions. She had to let it go.

As Lissa Rankin realized, much good can come from an open-minded engagement with the process that disease represents. It may not be the guest we ever desire to see, but a modicum of hospitality—welcoming the unwelcome, so to speak—costs us nothing. It may even lead to an opportunity to find out why this particular visitor has come to call, and what it might tell us about our lives.

Chapter 7

A Traumatic Tension: Attachment vs. Authenticity

Most of our tensions and frustrations stem from compulsive needs to act the role of someone we are not.

—János (Hans) Selye, M.D., *The Stress of Life*

To hear Anita Moorjani tell it, the disease that nearly killed her was no random misfortune. "The person I was before I got cancer," the bestselling author told me, "was afraid of disappointing other people. I was a pleaser. I completely lost myself in satisfying other people, I became so drained. I was someone who could not say no; I was a rescuer, and I would be the one who was there for everyone. I didn't even learn that it's okay to be me when I had cancer. It took being in a coma to learn that." Now a vibrant sixty-year-old, Moorjani is convinced that chronic stress induced by the compulsive suppression of her own needs was one of the roots of her metastatic lymphoma, thought to be terminal when she was diagnosed at age forty-three. "My personality was such that I needed something as drastic as cancer to give me reason to take care of myself."

Many of us have heard such sentiments: the notion of "finding the gold" in catastrophe is not at all unfamiliar, nor limited to the sphere of health crises. But the idea that features of our personality may contribute to the onset of pathology is anathema to many. In her still-influential 1978 essay "Illness as Metaphor," the late filmmaker, activist, and brilliant woman of letters Susan Sontag—then a forty-five-year-old cancer survivor—flatly and forcefully rejected the possibility that ill health might signify anything beyond bodily calamity. "Theories that diseases are caused by mental states . . . are always an index of how much is not understood about the physical terrain of a disease," she wrote.[1] To assert that emotions contribute to disease was, for her, to promote "punitive or sentimental fantasies," to traffic in "lurid metaphors" and their "trappings." She found this view especially distasteful because she perceived it as a way of blaming the patient. "I decided that I was not going to be culpabilized."[2]

Sontag's acerbic rejection of the mind-body connection resonated not only in intellectual circles but also in some of the most hallowed centers of medical thinking. A few years later, the *New England Journal of Medicine*'s future first woman editor, Dr. Marcia Angell, cited it approvingly, deriding as "folklore" the idea that "mental state is a factor in the causing and curing of specific diseases," a "myth" for which the evidence is at best "anecdotal." Like Sontag, Dr. Angell espied in this line of thinking an insidious patient-blaming tendency: "At a time when patients are already burdened by disease, they should not be further burdened by having to accept responsibility for the outcome."[3]

I agree wholeheartedly that no one, ever, ought to be made to feel guilty for whatever transpires with or within their body, whether that guilt arises from the self or is imposed from without. As I stated earlier, blame is inappropriate, unmerited, and cruel; it is also unscientific. But we have to take care not to fall into an easy fallacy. Asserting that features of the personality contribute to the onset of illness, and more generally perceiving connections between traits, emotions, developmental histories, and disease *is not* to lay blame. It is to understand the bigger picture for the purposes of prevention and healing—and ultimately for the sake of self-acceptance and self-forgiveness.

My intent in reframing Sontag's perspective, then, is to offer a more helpful view. I empathize with her apprehension about being blamed for becoming ill, even as I see her refutation of the mind-body confluence as misguided and scientifically untenable. A clear and honest look at the biographical factors that can disrupt our biological well-being helps us respond intelligently and effectively to illness—or preferably, to mitigate the risks in the first place. This is as true for individuals as for society.

There is nothing radical about the idea that certain personality traits can pose risks for illness; in fact, it is a restatement in modern scientific terms of insights that date far back. The physiological pathways connecting an irascible temper and heart disease, for instance, have long been well understood: they include increased blood pressure and heart rate, intensified clotting, and tightening of blood vessels, among others.[4, 5, 6] Already in ancient times Hippocrates spoke of the "choleric" temperament, believed to result from an excess of choler (yellow bile). In English we still speak of people who are habitually grumpy as "bilious." And in traditional Chinese medicine, the liver—the source of bile—is associated with anger, bitterness, and resentment. In 1896, the renowned internist and medical teacher Sir William Osler, often called the father of modern medicine, asserted to graduate students at Baltimore's Johns Hopkins Hospital that "it is not the delicate, neurotic person who is prone to angina [a cardinal symptom of coronary artery disease], but the robust, the vigorous in mind and body, the keen and ambitious man . . . whose engine is always at full speed ahead." He was foreshadowing the modern concept of the driven, compulsively preoccupied, impatient, readily upset, and heart-disease-prone type

A personality—a biopsychosocial dynamic, which, both scientifically and "anecdotally," is easy to grasp.

In 1987 the psychologist Dr. Lydia Temoshok[†] proposed what became known as the "type C personality," referring to traits strongly associated with the onset of malignancy.[‡] These couldn't have been further from the type A traits on the temperamental spectrum; they included being "cooperative and appeasing, unassertive, patient, unexpressive of negative emotions (particularly anger) and compliant with external authorities." She had interviewed 150 people with melanoma and found these patients to be "excessively nice, pleasant to a fault, uncomplaining and unassertive." They were identified "pleasers": while anxious about their disease progression, their worries were focused in a specifically outward direction, away from themselves and toward the effect that their illness was having on their families. Such self-abnegation was too well typified in an article I once read in the *Globe and Mail*, written by a woman just diagnosed with breast cancer. "I'm worried about my husband," she immediately told her physician. "I won't have the strength to support him."[7]

Around the same time, about ten years into my medical practice, I was beginning to notice similar patterns in the lives of many of my patients, folks with all manner of illnesses. This, despite my lack of familiarity at the time with the voluminous research that in the past half century has shed light on how stress, including the stress of self-suppression, may disturb our physiology, including the immune system. Not knowing then of Dr. Temoshok's work, I came to alike conclusions because they virtually urged themselves upon me: I couldn't help seeing what I saw. Time after time it was

---

†   At that time, director of the Behavioral Medicine Program at the University of Maryland Medical School.

‡   In fact, Temoshok was describing character traits, not a complete "personality"—more below on this misperception of her ideas.

the "nice" people, the ones who compulsively put other's expectations and needs ahead of their own and who repressed their so-called negative emotions, who showed up with chronic illness in my family practice, or who came under my care at the hospital palliative ward I directed. It struck me that these patients had a higher likelihood of cancer and poorer prognoses.

The reason, I believe, is straightforward: repression disarms one's ability to protect oneself from stress. In one study, the physiological stress responses of participants were measured by how their skin reacted electrically to unpleasant emotional stimuli, while the patients reported how much these stimuli bothered them. Flashed on a screen were insulting or demeaning statements, such as "You deserve to suffer," "You are ugly," "No one loves you," and "You have only yourself to blame." Three groups of participants were assessed in this way: people with melanoma, people with heart disease, and a healthy control group. Among the melanoma group there was a consistently large gap between what they reported—that is, to what degree they *consciously* felt upset by these scornful and disparaging messages—and the level of bodily stress their skin reactions betrayed. In other words, they had pushed their emotions below conscious awareness. This cannot help affecting the body: after all, if you go through life being stressed *while not knowing you are stressed*, there is little you can do to protect yourself from the long-term physiological consequences. Accordingly, the scientists concluded that repressiveness ought to be seen "as a mind-body, rather than as just a mental, construct."[8]

Some years later, psychologists at the University of California, Berkeley, investigated the physiological effects not of repression, a largely unconscious process, but of *suppression*, defined as "the *conscious* inhibition of one's own emotional expressive behavior while emotionally aroused." If I know I'm afraid but choose to conceal that from a rabid dog who can "smell fear," I am suppressing my feelings—as opposed to repressing them, as in compulsively pretending to agree with opinions one finds repellent and not realizing it until later. In the Berkeley study, participants were shown films normally expected to elicit disgust, such as burn patients being treated or an arm being surgically amputated. Some participants were specifically instructed not to reveal emotions when watching, while the control group was free to express emotion by means of facial or body movements. On a number of physiological measurements, the suppression group showed heightened activation of their sympathetic, or fight-or-flight, nervous system: in other words, a stress response.[9] There may be certain situations where a person, for perfectly valid reasons, deliberately chooses not to express how he feels; if one does it habitually or under compulsion, the impact is more than likely to be toxic.

I have distilled my own list of the personality features most often present in people with chronic illness, as observed by myself and many others. They may remind you of some of the personal stories I've included thus far. Whether a person exhibits one, a few, or every one of these features, they all, each in their own way, speak to self-suppression and/or repression. I have found them not only present but *prominent* among people with all manner of chronic illnesses, from cancer to autoimmune disease to persistent skin conditions, through a gamut of maladies including migraine headaches, fibromyalgia, endometriosis, myalgic encephalomyelitis (ME), also known as chronic fatigue syndrome, and many others.

In no particular order, these traits are

– an automatic and compulsive concern for the emotional needs of others, while ignoring one's own;

- rigid identification with social role, duty, and responsibility (which is closely related to the next point);
- overdriven, externally focused multitasking hyper-responsibility, based on the conviction that one must justify one's existence by doing and giving;
- repression of healthy, self-protective aggression and anger; and
- harboring and compulsively acting out two beliefs: "I am responsible for how other people feel" and "I must never disappoint anyone."

These characteristics have nothing to do with will or conscious choice. No one wakes up in the morning and decides, "Today I'll put the needs of the whole world foremost, disregarding my own," or "I can't wait to stuff down my anger and frustration and put on a happy face instead." Nor is anyone born with such traits: if you've ever met a newborn infant, you know they have zero compunction about expressing their feelings, nor do they think twice before crying lest they inconvenience someone else. The reasons these habits of personality, as we might call them, develop and grow to prominence in some people are both fascinating and sobering. At root they are coping patterns, adaptations originally formed to preserve something essential and nonnegotiable.

Why these features and their striking prevalence in the personalities of chronically ill people are so often overlooked—or missed entirely—goes to the heart of our theme: they are among the most *normalized* ways of being in this culture. Normalized how? Largely by being regarded as admirable strengths rather than potential liabilities. These dangerously self-denying traits tend to fly under our radar because they are easily conflated with their healthy analogues: compassion, honor, diligence, loving kindness, generosity, temperance, conscience, and so forth. Note that the qualities on the latter list, while perhaps superficially resembling those of the first, do *not* imply or require that a person overstep, ignore, or suppress who they are and what they feel and need. True compassion, for example, is an equal-opportunity offering, granted to others precisely because we know and honor what we ourselves feel. We might well admire someone who puts another's needs before their own in a crisis, or the leader of a struggle for the rights of many, but such sacrifices are undertaken in a conscious and time-bound manner, appropriate to the situation at hand and with full awareness of the risks.

I have a rather unusual habit when it comes to reading the newspaper: I've long been taken with reading obituaries in which friends and relatives pay homage to deceased loved ones. I frequently note in these a certain poignant paradox. Composed with affection and sorrow, these moving tributes often reveal and unwittingly celebrate their dearly departed's self-abnegating traits, without recognizing that these may have played a central role in the illness that ended the life being remembered. Consider, for instance, the case of an Ontario physician—we'll call him Stanley—who died of cancer. Stanley's closeness with his mother was approvingly lauded in his obituary in Canada's national newspaper, the *Globe and Mail*, in its daily "Lives Lived" section:† "Stanley and his mother had an incredibly special relationship, a bond that was apparent in all aspects of their lives until her death. As a married man with young children, Stanley made a point to have dinner with his parents every day, as his wife Lisa and their four kids waited for him at home. He would walk in, greeted by yet another dinner to eat and to enjoy. Never wanting to disappoint either woman in his life, Stanley kept having

---

†   I used to write the *Globe and Mail's* medical column and often contributed to the op-ed pages.

two dinners a day for years, until gradual weight gain began to raise suspicions."†

Another column memorializes a woman who, despite her metastatic cancer, "did not give up any of her roles," including "several hockey practices, school board, orchestra and other extracurricular activities," and even took on new ones—all directed toward helping others—as the disease spread throughout her body. I am all for enthusiastic engagement with one's community. But there is such a thing as a lust for life, and then there is being driven to derive one's sense of self from constant activity, even to the point of not being able to pause for self-care when disaster strikes.

As a final example, we have a widower remembering his wife (dead of breast cancer at age fifty-five) in these terms: "In her entire life she never got into a fight with anyone . . . She had no ego, she just blended in with the environment in an unassuming manner." The phrase "no ego" should give us pause. Intended to lovingly convey an admirable lack of arrogance or conceit, those two little words reveal, to me, a deeper story. A healthy ego—not in the sense of superiority, but as in a stable identity, the ground of self-respect, self-regulation, capacity for good decision making, a working memory, and more—is a vital asset of a thriving human being. Unbeknownst to the grieving spouse, what he was describing was the same lifelong repression of one's feelings— particularly healthy anger—which undermines the immune system and poses a risk for malignancy and other illness.

Where does such forsaking of the self come from? "Type C," Lydia Temoshok pointed out, "is not a personality, but rather a behavior pattern that can be modified."[10] I completely agree with her view. Precisely because no one is born with such traits ingrained,

---

† The original names appeared in the column; I've changed them here to further protect privacy. Otherwise, the obituary is cited verbatim.

we can unlearn them. That's a pathway toward healing—not an easy road by any means, and one we will take up later in detail. But first, let's see if we can trace the origins of these patterns.

A recurring theme—maybe the core theme—in every talk or workshop I give is the inescapable tension, and for most of us an eventual clash, between two essential needs: *attachment* and *authenticity*. This clash is ground zero for the most widespread form of trauma in our society: namely, the "small-*t*" trauma expressed in a disconnection from the self even in the absence of abuse or overwhelming threat.

Attachment, as defined by my colleague and previous co-author, the psychologist Dr. Gordon Neufeld, is the drive for closeness—proximity to others, in not only the physical but the emotional sense as well. Its primary purpose is to facilitate either caretaking or being taken care of. For mammals and even birds, it is indispensable for life. For the human infant especially—at birth among the most immature, dependent, and helpless animals, and remaining that way for by far the longest period of time—the need for attachment is mandatory. Without reliable adults moved to take care of us, and without our impulse to be close to these caregivers, we simply could not survive—not for a day. As we'll see in the next chapter, we each arrive in the world "expecting" attachment, just as our lungs expect oxygen. Hardwired into our brains, our drive for attachment is mediated by vast and complex neural circuits governing and promoting behaviors designed to keep us close to those without whom we cannot live. For many people, these attachment circuits powerfully override the ones that grant us rationality, objective decision-making, or conscious will—a fact that explains much about our behavior across multiple realms.

In infancy our dependence is an obligatory and long-haul proposition. Everything from crying to cuteness—two unignorable cues babies transmit—is an inbuilt behavior tailored by Nature to keep our caregivers giving and caring. But the need for attachment does not expire once we're out of diapers: it continues to motivate us throughout our lifespan. As we saw in chapter 3, unsatisfactory attachments can wreak havoc even with adult physiology. What distinguishes our earliest attachment relationships—and, crucially, the coping styles we develop to maintain them—is that they form the template for how we approach *all* our significant relationships, long after we have grown out of the do-or-die phase. We carry them into interactions with spouses, partners, employers, friends, colleagues: into all aspects of our personal, professional, social, and even political lives. It follows that attachment is a major concern of the culture—as we see, in a trivial form, in popular media gossip about who loves, leaves, or lies to whom. Attachment—along with attachment frustration, as in the "satisfaction" that we, along with Mick Jagger, can't get none of—is never far from our minds.

Our other core need is *authenticity*. Definitions vary, but here's one that I think applies best to this discussion: the quality of being true to oneself, and the capacity to shape one's own life from a deep knowledge of that self. What may not be apparent is that authenticity is not some abstract aspiration, no mere luxury for New Agers dabbling in self-improvement. Like attachment, it is a drive rooted in survival instincts. At its most concrete and pragmatic, it means simply this: knowing our gut feelings when they arise and honoring them. Imagine our African ancestor on the savanna, sensing the presence of some natural predator: Just how long will she survive if her gut feelings warning of danger are suppressed?

The elemental root of "authenticity" is the Greek *autos*, or "self," closely related to "author" and "authority." To be authentic is to be true to a sense of self arising from one's own unique and genuine essence, to be plugged into this inner GPS and to navigate from it. A healthy sense of self does not preclude caring for others, or being affected or influenced by them. It is not rigid but expansive and inclusive. Authenticity's only dictate is that we, not externally imposed expectations, be the true author of and authority on our own life.

The seed of woe does not lie in our having these two needs, but in the fact that life too often orchestrates a face-off between them. The dilemma is this: *What happens if our needs for attachment are imperiled by our authenticity, our connection to what we truly feel?* What happens, in other words, when one nonnegotiable need is pitted by circumstance against the other? These circumstances might include parental addiction, mental illness, family violence and poverty, overt conflict, or profound unhappiness—the stresses imposed by society, on children as well as adults. Even without these, the tragic tension between attachment and authenticity can arise. Not being seen and accepted for who we are is sufficient.

Children often receive the message that certain parts of them are acceptable while others are not—a dichotomy that, if internalized, leads ineluctably to a split in one's sense of self. The statement "Good children don't yell," spoken with annoyance, carries an unintended but most effective threat: "Angry children don't get loved." Being "nice" (read: burying one's anger) and working to be acceptable to the parent may become a child's way of survival. Or a child may internalize the idea that "I'm lovable only when I'm doing things well," setting herself up for a life of perfectionism and rigid role identification, cut off from the vulnerable part of herself that needs to know there is room to fail—or even to just be unspectacularly ordinary—and still get the love she needs.

Although both needs are essential, there is a pecking order: in the first phase of life, attachment unfailingly tops the bill. So when the two come into conflict in a child's life, the outcome is well-nigh predetermined. If the choice is between "hiding my feelings, even from myself, and getting the basic care I need" and "being myself and going without," I'm going to pick that first option every single time. Thus our real selves are leveraged bit by bit in a tragic transaction where we secure our physical or emotional survival by relinquishing who we are and how we feel.

The fact that we don't consciously choose such coping mechanisms makes them all the more tenacious. We cannot will them away when they no longer serve us precisely because we have no memory of them *not* being there, no notion of ourselves without them. Like wallpaper, they blend into the background; they are our "new normal," our literal *second* nature, as distinct from our original or authentic nature. As these patterns get wired into our nervous system, the perceived need to be what the world demands becomes entangled with our sense of who we are and how to seek love. Inauthenticity is thereafter misidentified with survival because the two were synonymous during the formative years—or, at least, seemed so to our young selves.

Here we see the perilous downside of our much-vaunted and wondrous capacity to adapt to diverse and challenging circumstances. After all, most adaptations are meant for specific situations, not as eternally applicable responses in every possible case. Here's an analogy plucked from the headlines: At the time of this writing, freezing weather has enveloped Texas.[†] People are adapting by wearing extra clothing, heating their homes when power is available, wrapping themselves in warm blankets—all necessary strategies for surviving inclement winter conditions. Those same adaptations, meant to be temporary, would jeopardize health and life if not discarded by the time of summer's

---

† February 2021.

blazing heat. The internal adaptations we make to our own personalities in order to survive adversity early in life carry the same risks as conditions shift, but we are far less wise to the danger. No matter how the weather changes, the protective gear, welded as it is onto the personality, never comes off.

It is sobering to realize that many of the personality traits we have come to believe *are us,* and perhaps even take pride in, actually bear the scars of where we lost connection to ourselves, way back when. The sources of these scars are most often evident in their shape, so to speak: in many cases, specific traits can be traced to particular kinds of wounding. For example, if we don't receive the agenda-free, unconditional attention we all require, one way to guard against that deprivation is to become concerned with physical attractiveness or other attention-getting attributes or accomplishments. A child who does not experience himself as consistently and unconditionally *lovable* may well grow to be preternaturally likable or charming, as with many a politician or media personality. Someone who is not *valued* or *recognized* for who she is early in life may develop an outsize appetite for status or wealth. If we are not made to feel important for just who we are, we may seek significance by becoming compulsive helpers—a syndrome I know intimately.

And here's the final part of the disappearing act: as mentioned, in our culture, many of these compensations for what we lost are seen as not only normal but even admirable. Valued as "strong suits," they too often encase and wall off the authentic self by assuming its guise.

These traits and the behaviors that follow are "runaway addictive," in Gordon Neufeld's phrasing. Funny enough, this tractor-beam pull exists precisely because they do *not* work—or to be more accurate, they work only temporarily. I am fond of the physician and trauma researcher Vincent Felitti's astute remark about addiction that "it's hard to get enough of something that almost works." Much like the rush an addict experiences immediately after using, the relief we buy with our compensatory pseudo-strengths does not last: we crave more and more, again and again and again. In fact, the analogy is entirely appropriate physiologically, since among the brain chemicals released when we have moments of feeling loved or valued or accepted are our own internal opiates, or endorphins. And just as an opiate like heroin does not satiate, so the temporary endorphin hit of valuation or appreciation or approval or success cannot possibly resolve the ache in the soul. We are compelled to persevere in seeking those external sources of fleeting relief, only to have to replenish them once the thrill is gone. Hence the seeming sturdiness of the personality: we keep experiencing the same emotions and associated body states, and we persist in performing the same behaviors. But it is closer to the truth to think of the personality as a *recurring* phenomenon than a *fixed* or *permanent* one, much like the way individual movie frames projected at rapid speed create the optical illusion of a single, continuous narrative.

For most of us it may require a crisis of some kind before we question the veracity and solidity of the self-concept we act from, before it even occurs to us that it might conceal something truer about us. Such crises might take the form of some relational catastrophe such as a divorce or near divorce; a debilitating addiction that disrupts our functioning, such that we can no longer ignore or tolerate it; the midlife bewilderment that may befog our forties or fifties; a sudden depression that ensnares us as we go along what we thought was our merry way; or a medical affliction, such as Anita Moorjani endured. All these can—and often seem uncannily as if they were designed to—point toward the need for a fundamental reassessment of who we think we are.

Strikingly, in her private musings Susan Sontag unwittingly pinpointed the emotional dynamics for which her cancer stood as a perfect metaphor. "I'm being wasted by self-pity and self-contempt," she wrote in her journal.¹¹ Cancer, of course, is a wasting disease—it devastates the body from the inside. She also located the source of her self-loathing in her anguished childhood. "Everyone who has had a bad childhood is angry. I must have felt angry at first (early). Then I 'did' something with it. Turned it into—what? Self-hatred." Eerily, Sontag touched upon the forbidden link just after her original diagnosis with breast cancer in 1971—some eight years before she wrote "Illness as Metaphor." "The first thing I thought was: What did I do to deserve this? I've led the wrong life, I've been too repressed." The word "wrong" there is a delicate thing, of course, resting very much on the spirit in which it is used. Sontag did not lead an *incorrect* life—that would be a harsh and blaming view—but neither, the word implies, did she get to live the life she might have wanted for herself.

Rereading "Illness as Metaphor" now, knowing what I know, I am saddened. Sontag spurned the connection between emotion, personality, and illness more forcefully and articulately than anyone—and, too, with bitter and unintended irony. The life and death of this powerful thinker, etched with tragedy, has much to tell us.

Abandoned as an infant by her mother and deserted again a few years later after a brief reunion, Sontag learned early to repress her rage: "I've always made excuses for her. I've never allowed my anger, my outrage." As an adult she reported herself "seething with resentment. But I dare not show it." "Profoundly neglected, ignored, unperceived as a child," she compensated by developing character features that promoted her success in the world. "One of the healthiest things about me—my capacity to 'take it,' to survive, to bounce back, to do, to prosper—is intimately connected with my biggest neurotic liability: *my facility in disconnecting from my feelings* . . . When a small child, I felt abandoned and unloved. My response to this was to want to be very good."

"Guilt is awful," Sontag said, poignantly—and yes, it is. But there *is* no culpability where there is no choice. No conceivable condition exists under which a human being has less agency or fewer options than in infancy and early childhood. The imperative to survive overrides everything, and that survival depends on the maintenance of attachment, at whatever cost to authenticity. This is why so many childhoods, particularly in a culture that both breeds stress and feeds on it, are marked by a tense standoff between the two, where the outcome is predictable and the consequences are lifelong.

Here's something else I've come to know, which I hope will be heartening for you as it is for me: it is not only necessary to leave blame and guilt behind on the road to healing, to move from self-accusation to curiosity, from shame to "response ability"—it is also and always possible. "What changed for me is that I realized that I had a choice," Anita Moorjani says. "When you are conditioned to do something, you're not even aware you're doing it. Not even aware that you're suppressing yourself, because you're in survival mode."

The onset of inauthenticity may not be a choice, but with awareness and self-compassion, authenticity can be.

Part II

The Distortion of Human Development

If our society were truly to appreciate the significance of children's
emotional ties throughout the first years of life,
it would no longer tolerate children growing up, or
parents having to struggle, in situations that cannot
possibly nourish healthy growth.

—Stanley Greenspan, M.D., *The Growth of the Mind*†

---

†   Stanley Greenspan (1941–2010), former director of the Clinical Infant Development
Program, U.S. National Institute of Mental Health.

Chapter 8

Who Are We Really?
Human Nature, Human Needs

There is always some conception of human nature, implicit or explicit, underlying a doctrine of social order or social change.
—Noam Chomsky, *The Chomsky-Foucault Debate:
On Human Nature*

What is our nature? The query is age-old, in part because it is so hard to get a handle on. Taking in the vast horizon of deeds and accomplishments, from the life-affirming to the murderous, it certainly seems as if "being human" is a rather plastic, malleable thing.

Though it may not be obvious why a book about health in the twenty-first century should concern itself with so broad and elusive a topic, I believe the question is central, with far-ranging implications. The relative health of any life-form is a function of its essential needs being met, or not met. Thus, to know what kind of beings we are is to know what we need in order to *be* those beings to the fullest. Who we take ourselves to be dictates how we set up our lives, individually and as a collective, and determines the extent to which a culture does or doesn't meet the requirements for optimal health and functioning.

Every society makes assumptions about human nature, and ours is no exception. "It's human nature," we say, shrugging our shoulders at someone's—often our own—manipulative, self-serving behavior. "Interestingly," notes the educator Alfie Kohn, "the characteristics we explain away in this fashion are almost always unsavory; an act of generosity is rarely dismissed on the grounds that it is 'just human nature.' "[1] There is a tendency in this culture, whether with approval or dismay, to see people as inherently aggressive, acquisitive, and ruggedly individualistic. We might cherish kindness, charity, and community-mindedness—our "better natures," so to speak—but these are often spoken of wistfully, as exceptions to a hardwired rule.

Not every culture accepts this as the quintessence of humanness. The anthropologist Marshall Sahlins, who studied societies across the Pacific basin, wrote: "For the greater part of humanity, self-interest as we know it is unnatural . . . it is considered madness . . . Rather than expressing human nature, such avarice is taken for a loss of humanity."[2] Some peoples even give such madness a name. The Cree word *wétiko* (with variants in other Native languages such as Ojibwa and Powhatan) refers to a creature, spirit, or mindset of greed and domination that cannibalizes people and drives them to exploit and terrorize others. (Strikingly, in the Quechua language of the Peruvian Andes, a similar entity—associated with the gold-craving and ruthless Spanish colonizers—is called *pishtako*.) Far from embodying our nature, such a relentless pursuit of narrowly defined self-interest is seen as its opposite: "a very contagious and rapidly spreading disease," according to the Native American scholar Jack Forbes.[3]

I find discussions of a fixed human nature unhelpful and even misleading. A cursory look at our history confirms that we are not one way: Jesus was a human being and so was Hitler. We can be noble and narcissistic, generous and genocidal, brilliant in our ingenuity and buffoonish in our stupidity. We are, it seems, all of the above. So where to begin?

Rather than trying to adjudicate between the many competing visions of what a human being is, we could instead see our nature as a range of possible outcomes. I very much like this formulation by Robert Sapolsky, professor of neurology and biology at Stanford University:† "The nature of our nature is *not to be particularly constrained by our nature*." If we're constrained by anything, maybe it's that very open-endedness; strange as it may sound, our miraculous talent for adaptation could also be a liability. Because our nature is so influenceable, different conditions evoke different versions of us, from benign to disastrous. When we reify—set in stone, mentally speaking—the particular way human behavior shows up in a certain place and time, we commit the fallacy of conflating how we're being with who we are. This error can keep us from considering other possibilities, even if our current way of operating isn't good for us. We then replicate conditions that are unfit for our well-being, and the sad saga continues. This is why, in seeking a vision of a healthier world, we had best disabuse ourselves of any fixed, limiting beliefs about what we're all about, and instead ask, What circumstances evoke which sorts of outcomes?

Encoded in our biology are some basic needs and potentials. How our nature unfolds depends on how well these needs are met, how these potentials are encouraged or frustrated. This is true throughout the lifespan, but at no time is it more consequential than during the process of development. Chronologically we can trace development's arc from conception through adolescence, although of course in many ways we never stop growing, changing, adapting, and developing—if we're lucky, for the healthier and wiser.

More than any other factor, it is the environment—the *conditions* under which development takes place, which either do or don't meet our multiple needs—that determines which

† And author, most recently, of *Behave: The Biology of Humans at Our Best and Our Worst.*

potentials will or will not manifest. This is as true for us as for any other life-form. Consider the acorn. It is in the nature of an acorn, we might say, to become an oak tree—but only if the climate and soil are right, and provided no enterprising squirrel squirrels it away for winter sustenance. Even if it roots and sprouts successfully, the size and healthy branching of the oak tree born of that acorn would depend on what nourishment the ground can provide, climatic conditions, sunlight and irrigation, its spacing from or proximity to its fellow flora, and so on.

We, too, have needs the environment must satisfy if we are to flourish. Before exploring this dynamic, we need to once again dispense with the prevalent myth that genetic traits account for human behavior. They do not. While we have a certain biological makeup, we are not genetically programmed to feel or believe or act in any particular manner. As Robert Sapolsky put it when we spoke, "We are freer from genetics than any other species on earth." Owing to our adaptability and capacity for invention, we can inhabit a much broader range of environments, for example, than any other large mammal. Further, as we have seen in our discussion of epigenetics, the expression of genes, in themselves inert, depends on the environment. Experience, therefore, is the decisive influence on how our biology manifests in our lives. "When all is said and done, the individual [is] genetically determined *not to be genetically determined*," in the apt phrase of two French scientists, restating Sapolsky's bon mot about "the nature of our nature" in biological terms.[4]

While it is in our nature to adjust to and survive in an almost infinite array of environments—certainly many more than oak trees can—we are not necessarily at our best or our healthiest in all of them. Some of these, whether physical, emotional, or social, will make wellness an uphill battle or a luxury for the lucky, rather than a widely available norm.

The needs that set the table for human health are far from arbitrary. They emerged over millions of years with the hominid and hominin[†] progenitors that preceded our own relatively late advent as a species, at most two hundred thousand years ago. Insofar as it is possible to speak coherently about human needs, we have to consider how they developed for eons before oral or written history. What we call civilization encompasses little more than 5 percent of our existence as a species; for the entire span of the human genus, it represents less than 1 percent. The evolutionary crucible that formed who we are and what we need was subject to very different conditions than our own. Thus, while civilization expresses aspects of our potential, it cannot by itself be used as a reliable gauge.

In *The Continuum Concept: In Search of Happiness Lost*, Jean Liedloff proposed that all life develops as "an *expectation* for its environment." Lungs can be seen as an expectation for oxygen, our cells for water and nutrients, ears for the vibration of sound waves. This is the essence of evolution: the long-term programming of creatures and all their constituent parts to arrive at life road-ready for a certain kind of setting. The same is true for all life, from organs to organisms to species. *"If one wants to know what is correct for any species, one must know the inherent expectations of that species,"* Liedloff added (italics in the original).[5] An inherent expectation is a wired-in need, something that if denied interferes with our physical and psychological equilibrium, leading to poorer health outcomes—physically, mentally, and socially.

Here's an inherent expectation in action: You walk into a corner store and select a candy bar. You smile as you greet the person behind the counter and say hello. The cashier is having a bad

---

† "Hominid": all the great apes, including humans, along with gorillas, bonobos, and chimpanzees; "hominin": species considered to be human or directly ancestral to humans.

day—perhaps nursing a toothache, a family crisis, or a crushing last-minute playoff loss by his favorite team. He looks at you sullenly (if he looks at you at all), takes your money with a monosyllabic grunt, and brusquely hands you the change. Your physiology alters: you feel tension as your body tightens, your heart rate goes up, and your breathing becomes shallower. You are irritated. Depending on your own state of mind, you might feel angry, perhaps even imagining bad things happening to the fellow.

Why? According to the neuroscientist and seminal researcher Stephen Porges, one of our inherent needs is reciprocity, to be attuned with—"well met," as the archaic greeting goes. It is what he calls a neural expectancy. Our brain may process the lack of welcoming response as an assault, a threat to safety.

Our nervous system's inherent expectation for reciprocity and connection makes sense when we consider how we developed as a species. For most of our evolutionary past, until about ten thousand to fifteen thousand years ago, human beings lived in small-band hunter-gatherer groups.[6] Indeed, if human existence were measured in the time span of one hour on a clock, we have inhabited newer environments only for the past six minutes or so. Liedloff described these forebears of ours as "people whose good relations are more important than their bargains." Her direct observations of Aboriginal people in their jungle habitat conform with the vast body of research on hunter-gatherers as collated, for example, by the psychologist Darcia Narvaez, professor emerita at Notre Dame. We have learned that such groups held values emphasizing hospitality, sharing, generosity, and reciprocal exchange for the purpose not of personal enrichment but of connection. These values were intelligent, time-tested guidelines for mutual survival. And the traditions they generated, passed down from parent to child, generation to generation, characterized human life throughout most of our existence. Yes, there was violence and bad behavior and all the rest; we have never been "perfect." But we knew something about setting the collective context for our humanness to flourish fruitfully; arguably, we knew nothing else.

Such guidelines, and the traditions that inscribed them into cultural behavior, survived for a long time even as societies became settled (i.e., not nomadic), as Westerners in contact with Indigenous peoples have found for many hundreds of years. "The community is there for them, and they are there for the community," wrote Frans de Waal about the Bushmen of the Kalahari, also known as the San people, a group widely thought to represent ways of life reaching back far into prehistory. "Bushmen devote much time and attention to the exchange of small gifts that cover many miles and multiple generations."[7]

No hominin species could have survived long enough to evolve had its members seen themselves as atomized individuals, pitted by Nature against their fellow beings. Contrary to our present ways of operating, a traditional view of self-interest would be *enhancing one's connection and membership in the community, to everyone's benefit.* Authentic self-interest need not be conflated with a suspicious and competitive stance toward others.

Hence my working assumption that our nature, all else being equal, *expects* or even *prefers* as its baseline state a condition of caring, relative harmony, and equilibrium, of the kind that obtains when interconnectedness rules the day. It is not that our nature *is* to be those ways, but that it *wants* them to be present. When they are, we thrive; when denied, we suffer.

What to make, then, of the modern received wisdom that we are fundamentally aggressive, selfish? Where does such an idea come from?

Under a capitalist system notions and expressions of human nature will both mirror the individualized, competitive ideal and justify it as being the inevitable status quo. It makes sense: if what's normal is assumed to be natural, the norm will endure; on the other hand, when suspicions emerge that the way things are may not be how they're meant to be . . . well, the quo may not be status for long. Thus do materialistic cultures generate notions—myths, in effect—of selfish, aggressive striving and dominance as behavioral baselines, encouraging characteristics that place a lesser value on connectedness to others and to Nature itself. In our present capitalist society, Darcia Narvaez suggested to me, we have become "species-atypical," a sobering idea when you think about it: no other species has ever had the ability to be untrue to itself, to forsake its own needs, never mind to convince itself that such is the way things ought to be.

As the following chapters will explore, today's culture hastens human development along unhealthy lines from conception onward, leading to a "normal" that, from the perspective of the needs and evolutionary history of our species, is utterly aberrant. And that, to state the obvious, is a life-size health hazard.

Chapter 9

A Sturdy or Fragile Foundation: Children's Irreducible Needs

We are born not knowing who we are, we don't know how to think. We only know how to feel. It is through our feelings that how we are raised creates the trajectory for our future lives.

—Natasha Khazanov[†]

Raffi Cavoukian woke suddenly at six o'clock one morning in 1997. "I bolted upright in bed," he tells me, "jaw dropped, eyes wide open, and the words 'child honoring' were playing right in front of my eyes, as a phrase and as the name of a philosophy." For the next decade, the internationally cherished children's troubadour took time away from the concert stage and recording studio to dedicate himself to envisioning, networking, and advocating for a world that honors children. He has maintained that commitment.[1] As he speaks of it, he sparkles with the playful enthusiasm and deep respect for young people that infuse his music—the same qualities that inspired my son Aaron as a toddler to dress up as his musical hero for Halloween, complete with ukulele and face-painted beard. "At its core, child honoring is respect for personhood," Raffi says. "Children are here to learn their own song."

The question of children's developmental needs is neither

[†] Personal communication. Dr. Khazanov is a neuropsychologist based in San Francisco.

abstract nor sentimental; it is of urgent practical importance. Although we often refer to childhood as "the formative years," our societal norms speak dismally to our appreciation of how formative these years really are, of just how much is being "formed." The individual and collective stakes are far higher than we tend to imagine.

"We discover who we are from the inside," Raffi says. "What's forming is no less than how it feels to be human. And I'm using my words carefully here: how it *feels* to be human." Our culture too often subordinates felt knowledge to the intellect. This inverted ranking system upends how we raise our children—which, in turn, serves to reinforce the error culturewide. Above all, the singer asserts, "we are feeling creatures."

He has science on his side. The neuroscientist Antonio Damasio explores the primacy of feeling in his authoritative volume *Descartes' Error: Emotion, Reason and the Human Brain.* "Nature seems to have built the apparatus of rationality not just on top of the apparatus of biological regulation, but also *from* it and *with* it," he wrote (italics his).[2] *Biological regulation* means the workings of the homeostatic[†] and emotional structures of our brains and bodies, which, before and after birth, are many months ahead of the thinking cortex in the developmental queue—as, in the bigger picture, they long preceded it over the course of our species' evolution.

These areas of the nervous system form the unconscious scaffolding for our thoughts and conscious feelings and, therefore, for our actions. "The earliest established components of an infant's psychobiological makeup are those most formative of his lifelong outlook," notes Jean Liedloff. "What he feels before

---

† *Homeostasis* refers to the processes by which the body maintains the stability and constancy needed for all its subsystems to function properly, including temperature regulation, pH levels, and so much more.

he can think is *a powerful determinant of what kind of things he thinks when thought becomes possible.*"[3] In fact, the impacts go well beyond the content of thoughts: research has shown beyond any doubt that early experience molds behaviors, emotional patterns, unconscious beliefs, learning styles, relational dynamics, and the ability to handle stress and regulate ourselves.

The new knowledge is summed up nicely in two brief paragraphs from an article published in *Pediatrics*, the official journal of the American Academy of Pediatrics; the authors are affiliated with perhaps the world's leading institute on childhood, Harvard University's Center on the Developing Child:

> The architecture of the brain is constructed through an ongoing process that *begins before birth,* continues into adulthood, and establishes either a sturdy or a fragile foundation for *all* the health, learning, and behavior that follow.
>
> The interaction of genes and experiences literally shapes the circuitry of the developing brain, and is critically influenced by the *mutual responsiveness of adult-child relationships,* particularly in the early childhood years.[4]

In other words, early development sets the ground—whether strong or shaky—for all the learning, behavior, and health (or lack of it) that will come later. The researchers' words, if taken to heart, would call our attention to much in our current culture that cries out for immediate renovation.

If emotion is the ground of cognition, then relationships are the tectonic plates that shape that ground. Of these, a child's early emotional interactions with their nurturing caregiver(s) exert the primary influence on how the brain is programmed—again, the unconscious comes first, followed later by things like intellect.[5] In the words of the renowned developmental psychiatrist

Stanley Greenspan and colleagues, "Emotional rather than intellectual interaction serves as the mind's primary architect."[6]

Given this order of operations, children's sense of security, trust in the world, interrelationships with others, and, above all, connection to their authentic emotions hinge on the consistent availability of *attuned, non-stressed,* and *emotionally reliable* caregivers. The more stressed or distracted the latter, the shakier the emotional architecture of the child's mind will be.

If that sounds like an indictment of parents, that's the farthest from my intention. At the risk of being overly repetitious, let me state again that parent-blaming isn't only cruel and unfair; it's nonsensical. Suffice it for now to say that the quality of early caregiving is heavily, even decisively, determined by the societal context in which it takes place. As we will see, children are increasingly set upon by an accumulation of potent influences—social, economic, and cultural—that overwhelm and, in many ways, subjugate their internal emotional apparatus to imperatives that have nothing to do with well-being; that are, in fact, inimical to the healthy growth of the mind. "Such growth is becoming seriously endangered by modern institutions and social patterns," according to Dr. Greenspan. "There exists a growing disregard for the importance of mind-building emotional experiences in almost every aspect of daily life including childcare, education, and family life." We see the result in the growing numbers of children, adolescents, and youths suffering so-called mental illnesses[†] such as ADHD, depression, and anxiety, or engaging in aggressive or self-harming behaviors in person or on social media.

As Dr. Gordon Neufeld told a session of the European Parliament in Brussels, "The unfolding of human potential is

---

†   My reasons for using the "so-called" qualifier will be taken up in chapters 17 and 18.

spontaneous but not inevitable . . . We all grow older, but we don't all grow up. *To truly 'raise' a child, then, would be to bring that child to his or her full potential as a human being.*"[7] So why, in our modern culture, do we chronically miss that goal? The problem begins with the failure to grasp the needs of the developing child.

Neufeld sums up eloquently what all young ones, whatever their temperament, need first and foremost: "Children must feel an invitation to exist in our presence, exactly the way they are." With that need in mind, the parents' primary task, beyond providing for the child's survival requirements, is to emanate a simple message to the child in word, deed, and (most of all) energetic presence, that he or she is precisely the person they love, welcome, and want. The child doesn't have to do anything, or be any different, to win that love—in fact, *cannot* do anything, because this abiding embrace cannot be earned, nor can it be revoked. It doesn't depend on the child's behavior or personality; it is just there, whether the child is showing up as "good" or "bad," "naughty" or "nice."

Do we then ignore dangerous or unacceptable behavior? No, that wouldn't be the loving thing to do either, since children's needs also include guidance and orientation, which include setting boundaries. Rather, we do our best to monitor and curtail undesirable actions *from an unconditionally loving place*: a way of being wherein children understand that nothing they might do can threaten the relationship, even if it elicits momentary anger or requires correction. Operating from this attitude may even allow us to see the child's "misbehavior" in a broader, more forgiving frame—perhaps it expresses a need frustrated, a communication unheard, an emotion unprocessed. We understand and respond to the needs and emotions the child is "acting out," rather than simply punishing the behavior and banishing the feeling.

Neufeld's point about maturation being "spontaneous but not inevitable" is crucial here. The same evolution that has over many millennia honed us to be social and empathic creatures also assumes—or, to hearken back to chapter 8, "expects"—a particular kind of developmental environment. "We are indeed born for love," assert the science writer Maia Szalavitz and the child psychiatrist and neuroscientist Bruce Perry, "[but] the gifts of our biology are a potential, not a guarantee."[8] Certain kinds of experiences water the seeds of love and empathy that Nature has planted in us; absent that consistent nourishment, growth is compromised.

The essence of those experiences can be expressed in one word: security.

My eldest son, Daniel, co-writer of this book, pinpoints the lack of security as a central feature of his own early memories. "I didn't know up from down," he says, "because up could become down at any moment, depending on what mood the two of you were in, or the state of your relationship on a particular day. I had recurring nightmares as a kid where the ground kept opening up under me, and I'd fall through into another dimension, only for it to happen again. The dreams aren't hard to decipher: in the world of my childhood, *the floor was not the floor.*" Indeed, without a "floor" of secure attachment, a young person is hard-pressed to feel any stable ground on which life can be experienced.

Despite all our love for our three children, Rae and I did not know how to provide the stable milieu they required, having lacked some essential aspects of nurturing in our own early years. Nor did the setup of our late-twentieth-century lives help us create the needed environment, what with our relationship tensions and my driven, workaholic tendencies, entrenched and amplified by the exigencies of medical training and practice. We were far from unique in these limitations.

Where does a sense of security come from? Once again, warm, attuned interactions with caregivers are the key ingredient. A 2010 study from Duke University reported that "early nurturing and warmth have long-lasting positive effects on mental health well into adulthood." The scientists examined nearly five hundred mother-infant pairs, noting how affectionate the moms were with their eight-month-old babies and assigning them categories such as "warm" or "occasionally negative" or "caressing" or "extravagant" in doting and tenderness. Most moms were rated as "warm," and about 1.5 percent as "extravagant." Over three decades later the grown children underwent a battery of mental health tests assessing their level of emotional distress and anxiety. Adults who had received the highest levels of maternal affection in infancy were shown to have the lowest levels of distress.[9] The lead researcher ventured that "maybe you can't be too affectionate . . . From the policy perspective, it definitely adds to that body of research that we should be able to protect time for mothers and fathers to be affectionate to kids." I consider it a sign of cultural lunacy that something so elemental, so essential, should be under such threat that we even have to exhort policymakers to "protect" it.

For a long time, it was assumed that infants are impelled to bond with caregivers only out of their helpless dependency on food, warmth, and shelter. We now know that social and emotional needs are just as much encoded in our neural circuitry by evolution, and that our optimal development requires that they be met. The neuroscientist Jaak Panksepp termed the cerebral apparatus governing these needs the "PANIC/GRIEF" system because, like a car alarm, these are the emotions that become activated in the *absence* of secure attachment. The message: we are wired to attach, to connect with one another, which we are able to do by dint of our early bonding with our caregivers. Not only that, but the wiring goes both ways: infants are "born to cry," in

Dr. Panksepp's words, precisely to activate the nurturing brain structures and affectionate behaviors of the parents—what he called the CARE system.[†]

Pondering this information sent me back to my mother's diary. Nothing to do with war or Nazis this time—just a woman of twenty-four trying to love her baby within the constraints of cultural norms, including medical advice that ran counter to her parenting instincts. According to accepted practice of the time, the doctor prescribed that I be fed on a strict schedule. Being a physician's dutiful daughter, my mom feared to disobey. Still in the hospital, with me a couple of weeks old, my mother writes:

> Now you are really giving me what for. For a change, you howled from half past midnight until 2:00 A.M. when the nurse came in and suggested I suckle you at least a little, so you finally slept. My greedy son, I definitely must warn you that we cannot make this a habit. In fact, soon we'll have to give up the 7:00 A.M. feeding. Believe me, my precious little son, my heart is rent in two as I hear you whimper your bitter complaints, but you are old enough of a fellow by now to realize that, pardon me, nighttime is for sleeping, not for eating.

There was my mom, following doctor's orders and so, for ninety long minutes, enduring my desperate vocalizations and her own emotional distress, coping as best she could via the dry wit that would be her signature until her death in 2001.

Revisiting this material now, versed in the neurobiology of parent-child attachment, I see a young woman in whose brain

---

[†] The world-renowned Dr. Panksepp distinguished seven such major brain systems responsible for our core emotional patterns. He rendered the names of each in capital letters. Along with CARE and PANIC/GRIEF, FEAR, RAGE, SEEKING, LUST, and PLAY are the others.

the instinctual CARE system described by Panksepp is at odds with the cultural mindset. Succumbing to the unnatural dictates of medical authority, her mother's heart aches.

And what of the infant in these now yellowed pages? What does he experience? Some three decades later, in 1975, Jean Liedloff warned her readers in *The Continuum Concept* about "the current fashion to let the baby cry until its heart is broken and it gives up, goes numb, and becomes a 'good baby.'" And indeed, I became a very good baby. Even as a four- or five-year-old I would lie in my bed before dawn, stoically enduring the stabbing pain of a middle-ear infection, whimpering quietly to myself so as not to disturb my sleeping parents.

Though it no doubt runs diametrically counter to most parents' intentions, a child whose cries are not responded to, who is not fed, not held close to a parent's warm body when in distress, learns a clear if wordless lesson: that his needs will not be met, that he must constantly strive to find rest and peace, that he is not lovable as he is. By taxing my brain's PANIC/GRIEF system, my poor mother's non-responsiveness also helped wire my brain for those chronic tendencies of mine that express the overactivation of that system: anxiety and depression. "When our brains are undercared for," writes Darcia Narvaez, "they become more stress-reactive and subject to dominance by our survival systems—fear, panic, rage." Don't I know it.

"The question," Gordon Neufeld said to me, "becomes, What are the irreducible needs of the child?" By "irreducible" he means a need that the child cannot do without if she is to reach her Nature-endowed potential; one that, if not met, will incur negative consequences. As he told the European Parliament, "It is true maturation, *not* schooling, learning or genetics that is key to becoming fully human and humane." We cannot *teach* maturity; nor can we cajole, entice, or coerce a child into it. What is required of us is to ensure the developmental conditions that satisfy the child's nonnegotiable needs; from there, Nature more or less takes care of the rest. There are four irreducible needs for human maturation, in Dr. Neufeld's astute formulation. These four needs are both simultaneous and build one on the other, in pyramidal fashion. I invite you, the reader, to consider how well our culture satisfies them for our children, or fails to.[†]

1. The attachment relationship: children's deep sense of contact and connection with those responsible for them.
Observe how my own neural expectation for such contact, instilled in infant me by eons of evolution, was frustrated within the first days and weeks of my life. Keep in mind that what matters is the child's *sense* of attachment; it has nothing to do with whether or how much the parents love the child or feel connected to her. Many young and well-meaning parents, myself and my wife included, have made the error of gauging the relationship by how *they* are feeling, how much attachment *they* are experiencing. Yet what makes the biggest difference is not what is *sent* so much as what is *received* by the child. It takes relatively mature and/or well-supported parents to be able to tune into the child's emotional needs as distinct from their own.

2. A sense of attachment security that allows the child to rest from the work of earning his right to be who he is and as he is.
Once foundational security is established, the young one can relax comfortably. This is the condition Dr. Neufeld identifies as "rest," one in which the child does not have to strive for attachment with the parent nor work to maintain the right equilibrium of contact. This state is the soil in which the roots of healthy

---

†   Dr. Neufeld's formulation happens to mirror precisely the basic requirements offered by the parenting practices of small-band hunter-gatherer groups, according to the research gathered by Dr. Darcia Narvaez. See chapter 12.

development can firmly take hold. From there we can reliably expect emotional, social, and intellectual growth to follow.

Despite my mother's love for me, I was essentially put to work from the moment I was born—no rest for the innocent. Contrary to her anxious half-joke that, before I was three weeks of age, I ought to be "old enough of a fellow by now to realize that . . . nighttime is for sleeping, not for eating," I was *years* away from being physiologically able to "realize" anything—much less that my needs were up for barter.

3. **Permission to feel one's emotions, especially grief, anger, sadness, and pain—in other words, the safety to remain vulnerable.** "Since emotion is the engine of maturation, when children lose their tender feelings, they become stuck in their immaturity," Neufeld explains. For the emotions to remain accessible, the environment must allow them to be safely experienced—meaning the child's expression of feelings *cannot threaten the attachment relationship* with the parents.

For reasons we have already begun to glimpse, many children in our culture are shut off from their authentic feelings.‡ And how would they not be, given the conformist expectations of society, amplified through parenting advice liberally dispensed by behaviorist "experts"? Consider the prescription of psychologist and mega-bestselling author Jordan Peterson: "An angry child should sit by himself until he calms down. Then he should be allowed to return to normal life. That means the child wins—instead of his anger. The rule is 'Come be with us as soon as you can behave properly.' This is a very good deal for child, parent and society."[10]

Is it, though? Notice the assumption: anger in a young child is neither normal nor acceptable. Contra her inborn need for unconditional warmth, any positive response to the child is to

---

‡   Chapter 7.

be distinctly *conditional*. She is not to be accepted for who she is, only for *how* she is. Here's the problem: even if the parent wins the behavior-modification game, the child loses. We have instilled in her the anxiety of being rejected if her emotional self were to surface. This exacts a heavy toll on both physical and mental health. While the expression of an emotion can be inhibited, or even its conscious experience blocked, the emotion itself is energy that cannot be obliterated. By banishing feelings from awareness, we merely send them underground, a locked cellar of emotions that will continue to haunt many lives.

I know for myself that the early hardening of my heart to my own pain shielded me not only from grief but also from joy. Rediscovering joy—or better yet, discovering it newly—remains part of my life's journey to this day.

4. The experience of free play in order to mature.
Rather than a frivolous activity to "grow out of," play is a requirement for the healthy development of all mammalian species. Jaak Panksepp coined a name for the neural system governing true recreation, to go with PANIC/GRIEF and CARE. "The PLAY system," he wrote, "may be especially important in the epigenetic development and maturation of the neocortex." A lack of secure infant bonding and a lack of early play, he asserted, can be contributory factors in the genesis of conditions such as ADHD, as well as of adult irritability and aggression.[11] Authentic play— agenda-free, interactive, engaging joy and imagination, and, rarer than ever these days, person-to-person—is easily compromised when children are under conditions of stress or deprivation. (Nor is it compatible with being distracted and mesmerized by digital technology, a vexing issue we will revisit in chapter 13.)

If the overall goal of development is to foster in children a felt sense of being alive in a nurturing world—"how it feels to be human," in Raffi's wonderful phrase—then we have utterly lost the plot. It takes a culture in good running order, with societal structures that take their cue from Nature's dictates, to support parents in ensuring the child's irreducible needs. How and why so many of our children's needs are going unmet will be the subject of our next chapters.

Chapter 10

Trouble at the Threshold: Before We Come into the World

My Tristram's misfortunes began nine months before
he ever came into the world.

—Walter Shandy, in *The Life and Opinions of Tristram Shandy,*
Gentleman (1759), by Laurence Sterne

Dear little son/daughter, I feel you kicking inside me. I am terribly sad and discouraged and frightened now but I love you and will protect and nourish you with all the love in the world. This adrenaline you feel is not meant for you nor flows because of you. One day I'll tell you about your gestation and I hope that if you carry with you ambivalent or painful memories, when I tell you the truth you will be able to heal. Dear little child: your Daddy will love you, too, when he gets to know you. He can't feel you moving inside him as I do inside me.

So wrote my wife when we were expecting our unexpected third child. It was a difficult period for us, and especially for Rae. She was stressed, unhappy, and anxious; what should have been a period of joy and mutual preparation felt like a lonely slog. I, the Daddy in the story, was in my mid-forties, outwardly a successful physician and columnist. Yet who was I within myself and within the four-walled world of our home? A depressed, anxious,

Gestation Self-Portrait, Rae Maté, 1988, mixed media. Rae created this painting during the first half of the pregnancy depicted in this chapter.

psychologically underdeveloped man, years away from addressing his core wounds; a man whose family bore the burden of his dysfunctional, erratic, and emotionally hostile behaviors; a man whose workaholism took the form at home of physical and emotional absence, even negligence; a man addicted to his own internal drama, not knowing how to be responsible for his actions and mind states or their impacts on his family, least of all his child-to-be.

Rae's diarized correspondence with the baby growing inside her showed how much she intuitively understood, long before I did, about human development and about the dynamics that so often distort its natural course in this culture. In our chapter on trauma, I pointed out that prior to becoming creators of our environment, we are its *creations*. Before we develop the capacity to take part in constructing our universe, the world fashions us. By what medium? At the beginning, through the bodies and minds and circumstances of our parents, who themselves are molded by the state of the world around them and by the histories of preceding generations. In this way, our own bodyminds are products of the larger culture from the start, a life course that begins with conception.

Before proceeding further, a necessary caution. Many readers will feel some alarm at the phrase "begins with conception," which has been heavily politicized in the ongoing cultural/religious debate over abortion rights. It is easy to see how a science-based recognition of the needs of the unborn can become political fodder for an anti-choice/"pro-life" view. All the more reason that I be extremely clear about what I do and don't mean. As a physician, I am well aware of the suffering imposed when women's right to choose is denied. There is no argument in this chapter, or anywhere in this book, for denying the right of autonomy when it comes to making such life decisions.

It has never been more vital that we speak about human development and its womb-to-tomb trajectory. It is also a highly delicate matter. For one thing, looking squarely at anything involving harm to children is difficult, often painful. Worse, when these topics arise, mothers and fathers might get the impression they are being judged, castigated, or impugned, which is doubly unfortunate: first, because in this culture too many parents— and I speak as one myself, three times over—already shoulder crippling guilt, already feel defensive; second, because blame is neither helpful nor remotely justified. We are all doing our best. My contention—really, the thrust of this whole book—is that our best *deserves to be better*, and *can* be if we incorporate the growing body of knowledge now available to us. I aim only to shed light on dynamics our entire culture needs to understand. This and the next chapter begin at our very beginnings, tracing our culture's failure to follow the developmental templates of gestation and birth as laid down by evolution.

The child's "ambivalent or painful memories" that Rae foresaw in her pregnancy journal are no poetic invention. Intrauterine experiences may not be accessible to conscious recall, but they can live on as a different kind of memory: emotional and neurological imprints embedded in the cells and nervous system of the human organism. The psychiatrist Thomas Verny calls this process *"bodywide memory."* A pioneer in recognizing the long-term influence of the intrauterine period on emotional health, Verny published his groundbreaking *The Secret Life of the Unborn Child* in 1982. In his sequel to that book, he wrote, "Before the event of birth, before we have even had a glimmer of sight or sound in the womb, we record the experience and history of our lives in our cells."[1]

In recent decades, a deluge of fresh information has underscored the crucial importance of women's physical environment, health, and emotional balance during pregnancy to the optimal development of the infant. Meanwhile, our era has also brought substantial increases in the number of children, adolescents, and young people facing depression and anxiety and other mental health challenges. Genetics on their own cannot begin to account for such abrupt shifts. If we are serious about reversing trends like these, it is critical that we connect the dots by looking to *the environment.* "Environment does not begin at birth; environment begins as soon as you have an environment," the neuroscientist Robert Sapolsky has said. "As soon as you're a fetus, you are subject to whatever information is coming through Mom's circulation, hormone levels, and nutrients."[2]

A very early factor is the stresses pregnant women are under—emotional, economic, personal, professional, and social. As the physician and psychoanalyst Ursula Volz-Boers points out, "Intrauterine life is not a paradise as some people try to make us believe. We are the receiver of all the happiness and of all the anxieties and difficulties of our parents."[3] But of course, even the earliest factor has its own earlier factors: namely, the intolerable pressures contemporary society places on the rearing milieu, the family, and on the developing young—and, as epigenetics teaches us, on the very activation of DNA itself. We need to consider to what extent our culture, including employment and the health care and insurance systems, supports or undermines women's capacity to hold their unborn infants' needs as a high social priority.

How many women are asked during prenatal checkups about their mental and emotional states, what stresses at home or on the job they may be experiencing? How many future physicians are even taught to pose such questions? How many spouses are helped to understand their responsibility to protect their expectant partners from undue stress and travail? How many businesses make provisions for their pregnant employees' relief? That last question has an especially dismal answer: women frequently report a pregnancy-hostile work milieu, especially in lower-paid jobs. But even in supportive workplaces, women are often burdened by the pressure they have absorbed and put on themselves to perform, advance, even excel in a competence-mad society. Work rarely "stays at work."

As Rae intuited, the baby feels the mother's stress directly. "By listening intently to movements and heartbeats, researchers are finding that the fetuses of mothers who are stressed or depressed respond differently from those of emotionally healthy women," the *New York Times* reported as far back as 2004. "After birth, studies indicate, these infants have a significantly increased risk of developing learning and behavioral problems and may themselves be more vulnerable to depression or anxiety as they age." Essential neurotransmitters such as serotonin and dopamine that later play key roles in mood regulation, impulse control, attention, motivation, and the modulation of aggression—and are implicated in the very learning, behavioral, and mood difficulties the article mentions—are affected by prenatal stress on the mother. Babies of moms stressed in pregnancy have lower levels of these brain chemicals and higher levels of the stress hormone cortisol. Not surprisingly, the same study showed that these newborns also had less developed learning skills, they were less responsive to social stimulation, and they were less able to calm themselves when agitated.[4]

Beyond brain substance levels, there is evidence suggesting that maternal mind states during pregnancy and postpartum shape *the very structure* of the infant's developing brain. In one study, nursing professor Dr. Nicole Letourneau, Canada research chair in parent-infant mental health at the University of Calgary, and her colleagues found that the child's gray matter, the cerebral cortex, was thinner on MRI scanning of the brains of preschool children whose mothers had suffered depression in the middle three months of pregnancy. As they point out, their brain-scan findings may presage later problems such as depression, anxiety, impaired impulse control, and attention difficulties in the child.[5] Postpartum depression had similar effects, indicating that there are certain critical periods in development, both before birth and after, during which the young human is particularly vulnerable to the environment. Such findings align with those of multiple other studies, which point to maternal-stress impacts on such brain structures as, for instance, the fear- and emotion-processing amygdala[6] and on neurological conditions such as autism.[7]

Other findings suggest strongly that many adult health challenges—everything from mental health disorders to hypertension, heart disease to diabetes, immune dysfunction to inflammation, and poor glucose metabolism to hormonal imbalance—are made more likely by intrauterine stress.[8] Among researchers there is a "universal consensus," to cite a major review paper, that what are called the developmental origins of adult disease begin in the womb.[9]

Remember telomeres, the chromosomal markers of health and aging? These structures were shown to be shorter—that is, more prematurely aged—in twenty-five-year-old adults whose mothers had undergone major stress during pregnancy.[10] We also know from our section on epigenetics that a mom's high stress levels during gestation can negatively influence the genetic functioning of the offspring, potentially impairing his lifelong stress-response capacities. Such effects have been shown to last well into midlife.[11]

Maternal stress during pregnancy has even been correlated with a poor makeup of the infant's gut microbial flora—a less healthy mix of bacteria—based on fecal samples taken from newborns days and even months after birth, with a higher incidence of intestinal problems and allergies among these babies.[12] (A deficit in infant gut microbial flora is also seen after many C-sections, when the infant does not travel through the maternal birth canal.)

Though a mother's emotional stress exerts a direct influence on the child's development and future health, it is not an isolated factor: interpersonal biology holds sway once again. As was the case with Rae and me, there is a complex interplay between a woman's psychological states and those of the father. A large Swedish survey recently showed that *paternal* depression in the year from preconception to the end of the second trimester elevated the risk of extreme prematurity (coming between weeks twenty-two and thirty-one of gestation) by nearly 40 percent. This effect was *greater*, in fact, than that of depression in the mother herself, which raised the risk only of moderate preterm birth (thirty-two weeks or after).[13] "Paternal depression is also known to affect sperm quality, have epigenetic effects on the DNA of the baby, and can also affect placenta function," one of the researchers pointed out.

At first blush, the father's melancholy posing a greater risk than the mother's seems an anomaly. As always, context is everything. The social context for procreation in our world assigns women untenably stressful roles in every facet of life, including intimate relationships. Besides being the bearers of children, they've generally been expected to assuage the psycho-emotional stresses of the men in their lives. Mothering a child may be a mandate from Nature, but mothering a grown man is both unnatural and impossible. No wonder the father's stress gets outsourced to the mother, at a cost to children and even to the gestating infant.

There is a predictable socioeconomic link, too: in a recent

Wayne State University study that examined a low-resource, high-stress U.S. urban setting, abnormalities in brain connectivity were identified in scans of yet-unborn infants of mothers who reported elevated levels of depression, anxiety, worry, and stress during the last three months.[14] Needless to say, physical factors such as nutrition and air quality interact with socioeconomic status, predisposing children to such problems as depression, anxiety, and ADHD.[15] "Poor people have more exposure to these things on all counts, whether the bad air, or psychosocial stress and other things," Dr. Shanna Swan, reproductive endocrinologist and vice chair of preventive medicine at Mount Sinai Medical Center in New York, pointed out. "That's a societal problem and the changes are not going to be on an individual level. They're going to be on a societal level."[16] Thus does inequality of opportunity, even in the basic biological sense, begin in the womb.[17]

Long before we had brain scans, blood tests, ultrasounds, and fetal heart monitors, ancient peoples intuitively understood the sanctity of the intrauterine environment. I spoke once about addiction to a First Nations group here in British Columbia, quoting studies on prenatal development such as cited above. A young man came up to me afterward. "You know," he said, "in our clan, tradition was that if you were angry or upset, you weren't even allowed to go near a pregnant woman. We didn't want you to inflict your troubles on her baby." In some African tribal societies, infants were greeted by rituals while still in the mother's belly, including with songs that would later welcome them into the world.[18] Imagine hearing your own melody and lyrics, already familiar to you, as you are ceremonially ushered into your new home, the outside world.

Such collective traditions have mostly been lost to colonialism and atomization, but we can still learn from them and apply their lessons.

"We know prenatal depression and stress and anxiety can predict behavior problems in the child," Professor Letourneau told me. "We can try to fix those behaviors in the kid years later, or we can medicate the child, or we can give pregnant women the support they need in the first place."

Support. If we want to build a world that provides it, we could start by asking its would-be recipients what the word means to them. I recently asked Rae—if I could do it over again, I would have done so long before now—what would have supported her back then. I can't improve upon the wisdom, nor the accuracy, of her answer:

"It would have helped if I had had a community in place. If there existed a larger consensus in our culture of what is required to gestate a baby. It would have helped if I had had a doctor or a social worker or family member who could have stood up for me. If the doctor had asked me, even once, how I was faring emotionally . . . If anyone had phoned my husband: 'Are you aware you are hurting your baby? Whatever problems you have with your wife, your role now is to be protective of her and of the infant she is carrying.' We all need to realize that entering a pregnancy should be like entering a shrine, a sacred place and time: a baby is being built.

"Mental health needs to be on the curriculum as soon as a woman gets pregnant—just as there are prenatal classes for the physical birth, so there should be for the emotional birth. The woman's focus must be on the baby, and not on the husband or even the job; the husband's focus—everyone's focus—must be on supporting the woman. Parents need to know that their job is mutual, that while the wife is pregnant, the husband is also pregnant. Society needs to protect pregnant women because everybody is creating this child. It takes a world to make a baby."

Chapter 11

What Choice Do I Have? Childbirth in a Medicalized Culture

At the beginning of the twenty-first century, we have to rehumanize birth, realizing there are limits to our domination of Nature.

—Michel Odent[†]

Over my decades as a family physician, I attended nearly a thousand deliveries. Standard operating procedure was to perform an episiotomy on every woman giving birth, just as I'd learned in medical school. "Time to make a little cut now," I would announce as the infant's head reached the perineum, ready to exit the birth canal. Having injected local anesthetic near the vaginal opening, I would make an incision a few inches long, "catch" the baby, and hand it to the nurse. I then set about repairing the wound I had inflicted. I knew no other way.

Years later I happened to learn from some midwives—who, in the Dark Ages of the 1980s, were still working illicitly here in British Columbia—that episiotomies are completely unnecessary in most labors. There was an organic process trying to happen, they kindly explained, which allowed a child to be born without my surgical intervention: Who knew? More surprises

---

[†]   Personal communication from the famed French obstetrician and author of *Childbirth and the Evolution of Homo sapiens*, among other books.

followed. Women can, it turns out, deliver babies without their feet in stirrups and even without reclining on a narrow metal contraption. "Try taking a shit while lying down and your legs in the air," a midwife suggested when I questioned her wisdom. Other startling news was that, barring complications, the newborn is best handed to the mother for skin-to-skin contact, rather than being poked and prodded under bright lights and having plastic suction tubes shoved in its mouth. Nor does the cord have to be cut immediately: it can be allowed to complete its pulsations, delivering more oxygen-carrying red blood cells to the infant.[1] It's almost as if Nature knows what it's doing.

These once-heretical practices have since been validated by solid medical research. At long last, doctors now have—more accurately, ought to have—permission to support in good conscience what human beings, with or without any "professionals" assisting, have been doing for hundreds of thousands of years. As the American journalist Anne Fadiman describes in her illuminating work on the clash of medical cultures besetting Hmong immigrants to the United States, these Asian women stubbornly resisted some of our "best practices" in favor of their own ways, including "squatting during delivery and refusing permission for episiotomy incisions to enlarge the vaginal opening . . . Many Hmong women were used to being held from behind by their husbands, who massaged their bellies with saliva and hummed loudly just before the baby emerged."[2] In short, they had tradition, intuition, innate body sense, Nature, and—no doubt unbeknownst to them—the most up-to-date science on their side.[3] Not to mention their husbands, who literally had their backs.

The advent of modern obstetrics has brought much to be grateful for, sparing many women and infants from avoidable suffering, illness, and death. The problem is that, along with its triumphs, and in line with the mechanistic approach of Western medicine in general, obstetrical practice ignores the genuine and natural needs of mothers and babies—in fact, it often runs roughshod over them. Bringing infants into the world is not simply a question of pushing and pulling and cutting and catching. It is a major threshold in human development, and how it is crossed has potentially lifelong consequences. By pathologizing the birth process, present-day medical practice contradicts the wisdom of Nature and of the human body. More damningly, it frequently violates even its own commitments to align itself with science and to, first, "do no harm." We need not abandon the great achievements of medical work to honor traditional wisdom, rooted in age-old experience. We can embrace both.

I will not be advocating for any particular type of birth, "natural" or otherwise, or railing against any other, much less judging any woman's individual choices around this vastly significant event. My interest, in keeping with this book's overall focus, is the cultural context in which, these days, such choices are made—which includes *by whom* and *in what manner* they are made. As the poet Adrienne Rich put it in her book *Of Woman Born*: "In order for all women to have real choices all along the line, we need fully to understand the power and powerlessness embodied in motherhood in patriarchal culture." Reducing women to passive recipients of medical care during perhaps the most momentous passage of their lives is dehumanizing, and not only figuratively: it disrupts physiological, hormonal, and psychological processes that have evolved in our species over millions of years to ensure the necessary bonding of mother and baby and the healthy development of our young.

A few years ago I spoke with Dr. Michel Odent, world renowned for his embrace of and advocacy for demedicalized birth practices. "We have to deindustrialize childbirth, to stop disturbing the first contact between mother and baby," he said in a charming French accent. "Imagine," he said with a laugh, "the mother gorilla giving birth and you try to pick up her newborn baby. And then you will understand what a maternal protective aggressive instinct is. In our civilization we have suppressed that instinct for a long time." Suppression of innate knowledge is one of medicine's unfortunate tendencies.

Medical intervention, which in a sane system would be deployed only when necessary to reduce risk, maximize health, and ensure survival, has become the default approach. A clear example is the steeply rising rate of the cesarean section: a lifesaving intervention when needed, a potentially noxious interference when not. According to the best estimates, about 10 to 15 percent of deliveries ought to end with C-sections to ensure healthy outcomes. Here in my home province of British Columbia that rate now approaches *40 percent*, as it does in many other parts of the world, with some countries exceeding that mark; worldwide, the number of these surgical deliveries doubled between 2000 and 2015. "Markedly high CS use was observed among low obstetric risk births, especially among more educated women in, for example, Brazil and China," noted a detailed, near-global survey by the *Lancet* in 2018.[4]

That would be acceptable if there were some demonstrable "value added" from such procedures being widespread, but there isn't. "Cesarean section use has increased over the past 30 years in excess of the 10–15% of births considered optimal, *and without significant maternal or perinatal benefits*," noted the *Lancet* report.[5] Even the American College of Obstetricians and Gynecologists raised, in 2014, "significant concern that cesarean delivery is overused."[6]

"If we want to find safe alternatives to obstetrics, we must rediscover midwifery," Odent told a birthing conference in 1986, when the medical profession in North America was still fighting a tooth-and-nail battle to keep midwives from fulfilling their traditional role. In many jurisdictions that struggle is far from over, while in many others there reigns a grudgingly observed truce, at best. "To rediscover midwifery is the same as giving back childbirth to women," Odent added. "Imagine the future if surgical teams were at the service of the midwives and the women instead of controlling them."[7] In effect, he was suggesting that medicine be Nature's attendant, not its ruler—a radical reinterpretation of the phrase "attending physician."

The issue is autonomy, an indispensable human need. Birthing practices express the hidden or overt values of a culture in terms of who wields power and how much genuine control people are able to exercise over their own bodies. Modern research finds that maternity-care interventions may disturb hormonal processes, reduce their benefits, and create new challenges.[8] What then, I asked Sarah Buckley—a New Zealand–based physician, advocate, and author of a highly regarded overview of the normal physiology of childbearing—explains the rapidly growing rates of medicalized interference? I expected an answer based purely on medical concerns. In fact, her response was sharply perceptive as to how acculturation into the much broader myth of normal takes place. "Doctors," Dr. Buckley said, "are the agents of our society's expectations that we imprint on mothers, when they are very open and vulnerable, that technology is superior to the body and that women's bodies are intrinsically bound to fail. It really is obvious that the culture wants to impress upon women this view of their bodies as inherently defective and needing high-level technological care." And that will carry on, she added, "*into how she brings up the child to be in accord with the demands of the culture.*"

Though systemic sexism tilts the playing field against women in particular, there is also a broader cause of unnecessary medical interference, one foundational to the Western medical view: a distrust of natural processes and fear of what can, may, or will go wrong.[†] Michael Klein, former head of the family practice department at BC Women's Hospital in Vancouver, has done extensive research on medical birthing. "You learn in a very biased environment that sees childbirth as scary and dangerous," he told me. The paradigm that dominates medical training "sees birth as nothing more than an accident waiting to happen, an opportunity for your pelvic floor to be bent out of shape. The women are unexploded bombs that need defusing." Throughout my medical schooling and internship, I was trained to anticipate the problems, complications, and dangers of birth. All good, as far as it went. The problem was, nothing in my training encouraged me *to align with Nature*. It was left to my patients and my midwife colleagues to teach birth to me as something more than a mechanical procedure of extracting a baby from the mother's body—something with ingrained, evolutionarily derived purposes, both physiological and emotional.

Sherri Dolman, a California woman I've come to know, had to wage an intense and protracted struggle for autonomy around her pregnancies. Despite a triumphant ending, her tale is a medical horror story. "I tried to conceive that child for three years," she told me. "But when I became pregnant, I was no longer able to make decisions for my child or for myself. I will never shake that for the rest of my life." Dolman was coerced into a cesarean section she did not want and, as she subsequently proved, never needed. "My doctor did not respect my decisions," she said, "and I don't think he respected me as an autonomous human being. I believe he thought he knew better than me. I can't think of one

---

[†]   And in the litigious U.S. system, the terror of lawsuits and high insurance premiums.

single instance where a man is told what he can and can't do with his body, but women are told this every day."

At age thirty-four Dolman was already the mother of a seventeen-year-old son, born when she herself was a scared teenager. Because her labor had progressed slowly, likely owing to her stressed state of mind, she'd had a C-section. She was intent on a vaginal birth next time. After three years of trying, she and her partner got pregnant with a daughter. "From the first moment I vowed that I would not have a cesarean section this time around. I would deliver my daughter the way that Nature intended me to. I would trust my body, I would get the proper support I needed to do this." She did her due diligence, interviewing as many doctors as she could. "They all said, 'Once a cesarean, always a cesarean.' They weren't even willing to speak with me about it. 'I'll take you as a patient,' they told me, 'but we're going to be scheduling your cesarean.'"

Medically speaking, the doctors were completely off base. By the time of her daughter's conception, the safety of vaginal birth after cesarean section (VBAC) had long been documented, with the supposed risk—the uterus tearing under the pressure of labor contractions—shown to be negligible, posing no impediment to an unmedicated delivery. Indeed, a high-risk perinatal specialist who had evaluated Dolman's uterus with a detailed scan affirmed that her chance of such a mishap was no greater than if she had never been pregnant. In a sign of how deep the indoctrination runs, the obstetrician still balked at the vaginal option. The one doctor who had finally agreed to support Dolman's preference for natural labor got cold feet at the last possible moment.

Following a routine fetal-monitoring session, which showed no abnormality, Dolman was physically barred from leaving the hospital, threatened with arrest, and browbeaten into accepting the surgical delivery of her daughter. After this harrowing experience, she suffered what she calls "a version of PTSD . . . I was unable to function in my daily life. I felt like a failure as a mother, unable to comfort or touch my daughter in her first moments of life. I felt like I had nothing to do with her even being here. I felt disconnected from her. She cried if she needed me, but I didn't feel that I was enough. Throughout the first year of her life, I cried myself to sleep every night."

Dolman's subsequent two births were her redemption, the reclaiming of full agency.

Under the care of a midwife, she succeeded in a joyful vaginal birth at the completion of her third pregnancy. Though she described it as "very, very painful," she counts it among "the most amazing and exhilarating experiences" of her life. As is the case for so many women, Dolman's license to make her own choices was key to getting to the other side of the suffering. "No matter how painful it got, I had support and I was in control of my own body. That was very empowering to me no matter what came my way—being in charge of my own body was what it came down to." Ten years later, the telling of it still brought tears to her eyes. "Tears of joy," she quickly assured me. "My daughter asks me all the time: 'Tell me the story about how I was born.' She finds it hilarious that while I had the skin-to-skin contact with her, she pooped all over me, and she laughs every time I tell the story. That in itself was a bonding experience, just even sharing that with her. It's part of life." In 2011 Dolman brought forth another child, a healthy nine-pound, three-ounce boy. That birth, too, was vaginal, also in hospital under the care of a midwife, five years after she had been sternly admonished by ten board-certified obstetricians not to attempt such a delivery.

The triumphs don't all look the same, nor should they. "I know from my medical experience that you don't want to hold too fast to anything," said Danielle, a resident in anesthesiology.

"Still, I had beliefs and ideas about how I saw things going . . . I intended originally to have a home birth in water, at a cottage here that we had rented in the forest." It didn't turn out that way. After prolonged labor with little progress at home, the midwife recommended hospitalization and an epidural to allow Danielle some relaxation. The birth hormone oxytocin was given to promote progress, to no avail. After thirty-six hours of intense labor, Danielle accepted the necessity of surgical delivery. To this day, she is elated about her experience.

Although Danielle's process took a different form than Sherri's, the two births resembled each other in one core aspect: the mother felt herself to be in charge. "I was listened to. Everyone made time to hear what I was concerned about. Even the assistant to the surgeon came in to see me, a woman in family practice here. She met me, and she looked me in the eyes, and she was fully present. I just felt safe with everyone in there." In those words we hear the second factor determining the quality of women's experience: safety and support.

A health care system that honors women's strengths and their vulnerabilities gives them the best chance at a childbirth experience they can cherish. This view runs through a little gem of a pregnancy primer, *A Is for Advice (The Reassuring Kind),* by the Brooklyn-born, B.C.-based midwife Ilana Stanger-Ross. "The women who report the most positive birth experiences," she observes, "are those who feel they understood all the decisions made and had a say in the decision-making process. That holds even for complicated births among women who had been hoping for 'natural' deliveries—births that require multiple interventions, births that end in surgery."[9]

To learn about the physiology of childbearing is to marvel at the innate wisdom of Nature and its highest evolutionary achievement, the human body. The biological bottom line is this:

Mammalian labor is more than a process of expelling an infant from a womb. It is preparation for life. Labor, as Nature designed it, promotes the release of hormones such as estrogen, oxytocin, and prolactin that activate a host of neural systems governing the emotions and behaviors, ensuring the baby's well-being in the short and long terms: warmth, nurturing, bonding, protection, and so on. In other words, birth prepares the template for the mother-infant relationship, which itself is the central locus of the child's early development.[10]

Having been out of the baby-catching game for some decades, I was caught off guard by a phrase Stanger-Ross used when we spoke: "obstetrical trauma." "That has become a term," she said. "Unfortunately, a lot of women feel that their birthing experience was one of trauma, which, of course, is going to have impacts on the parent-child relationship. If the birth was traumatizing, then how does that translate when now you have a newborn in your arms?"

Right on cue, I was given a textbook illustration of this alarming trend via a conversation I had the day I finished this chapter. I was being interviewed over video conference by a New York journalist reporting on the COVID-19 pandemic, which at the time was engulfing her city. At one point, Courtney, as I'll call her, proudly showed off her three-month-old cherub. When she learned what I was working on, she poured out the awful story of her recent experience at Mount Sinai Hospital at the hands of one of New York's most prominent and well-regarded obstetricians. It is as clear a tale of normalized obstetrical trauma as can be imagined.

Thirty-seven years old and healthy, Courtney was expecting an uneventful delivery. At thirty weeks the physician phoned her to announce, as if by decree, that, given her age, labor would be induced at thirty-nine weeks. This, the doctor said, was "the office protocol here" for anyone older than thirty-five. "She had known my age from the beginning, since I walked into her office last May," Courtney said. "I was so shocked that I hung up the phone—I barely said a word. I had to have half a glass of wine. I was so upset, I didn't sleep all that night." It went downhill from there. Courtney recalled with pain "the sudden disappearance of flexibility and the imposition of a tyrannical dictate. It was not the kind of care I expected. I'm not used to being bullied by doctors or talked down to. The tone became so toxic . . . and then she also kept saying, 'The baby is *huuuge*. He's going to be *huuuge*.' I said to her, 'Wait, I heard that growth scans are notoriously bad at predicting weight.' She responded, 'Not at Sinai. He's going to be nine pounds at least.'" (The baby's actual birth weight: less than eight pounds.)

Courtney considered looking for a new physician, but this late in pregnancy and still in awe of the specialist's credentials, she stayed put. "By week thirty-eight, she was saying, every week, 'This is really not looking good for vaginal, it's really not. I don't know what to tell you.' I just kept saying, 'I really don't want a C-section.' And this was our dynamic week after week. I was in a terrible state of mind for the last three or four weeks of the pregnancy: sobbing, nervous breakdown . . . At the appointed time, we show up at Mount Sinai, and it's a horrible scene. We're in this waiting room for three hours, a million different things going on, and I kept saying to my partner, 'Why the fuck am I here? We are totally within our rights to go back to Brooklyn and go into labor naturally.'" Feeling disempowered, having her intuition invalidated at this most vulnerable time of her life, being intimidated by a highly extolled medical specialist, and having been raised in a culture where "expert" authority trumps one's own, Courtney lacked the wherewithal to assert herself. She

finally acceded to the induction and, after fifteen hours of fruit-
less labor, the inevitable surgery.

"I was so weak. I'd been throwing up. Everything about this
was like the biggest nightmare. I said, 'Fuck it—let's just do the
C-section. Like, what choice do I have at this point?' So we roll
into the OR, and I'm throwing up on the table, and I'm a basket
case, sobbing. Scared out of my mind, shaking. They start the
surgery; it takes forever. She then says to me, 'Oh, I didn't realize
your abdominal muscles were this strong.' They were, because
I've done Pilates for twenty years. I'm thinking, 'Why didn't you
realize it? You've been examining me regularly for nine months
and anticipating this surgery for weeks.' And the following morning she said to me—can you even make this up?—'I'm going to
call the Mount Sinai scanning department and complain about
how inaccurate your growth scans were!' All that week in the
hospital I would just lie awake at night, sobbing at how violated
I was."

I asked Courtney whether she had thought of working with a
midwife. "I'm not that left-wing," she said. "I'm not that far-out.
I completely bought into the system."

Now consider that this galling story took place in a privileged,
white, middle-class context. For poor women, especially women
of color, treatment of mothers in labor can be considerably more
brutal, with consequences that range all the way to fatal. According to a 2019 World Health Organization report, "42% of the
women [in a global survey] said they experienced physical or
verbal abuse or discrimination during childbirth in health centers, with some of the women being punched, slapped, shouted
at, mocked, or forcibly held down."[11] Nor is this limited to the
so-called third world. In my own country, a cell phone video
emerged recently of hospital staff in a Quebec facility taunting

and verbally abusing an Indigenous woman in labor. Nurses "are heard calling her stupid and saying she's only good for sex and would be better off dead." Minutes later, she was.[12]

———

"For me, the ideal birth situation is a woman alone in a silent room, lights dimmed, with a midwife calmly sitting with her and knitting," Michel Odent told me—a wry but astute comment on the harmful effect of bright lights, noisy machines, and bustling, hectoring medical personnel on the labor process.

This brings us back to the discussion of "inherent expectation" in our chapter on human nature. We, like all organisms, arrive on the scene with the anticipation that life will unfold within certain parameters. Being the adaptable creatures we are, we can endure less than the best—at a cost. "The baby's experiences during a birth without trauma have got to be those, and only those, which correspond to his and his mother's ancient expectations," writes Jean Liedloff in her study of an Aboriginal forest society. Whereas other mammals seek dark, quiet, solitary places for birth, she points out, we invite birth trauma with "the use of steel instruments, bright lights, rubber gloves, the smells of antiseptic and anesthetic, loud voices or the sounds of machinery."[13]

Mothers feel it, even if no one else sees anything out of the ordinary. I still remember my wife whispering to me during our first birth, regarding the nurse who kept haranguing her to "Push, girl, push," to "Please tell that woman to shut up."† A person's body seizes up in the absence of safety and emotional connection, especially under the effect of sensitizing hormones. Oblivious to the woman's needs for silence, safety, and attunement,

———

† That earnest nurse and I became very friendly colleagues years later at the labor and delivery suite of B.C. Women's Hospital.

hospitals create a self-perpetuating cycle, instigating many of the labor complications they then must intervene to resolve.

Ilana Stanger-Ross summed up traditional wisdom and modern science in words that, in a saner system, wouldn't even need to be said: "We need to approach someone in labor as a full person who is experiencing a sacred life passage," she told me. "They're not a sick patient. They are a person in labor—*which is a very normal thing to be.*"

Chapter 12

Horticulture on the Moon: Parenting, Undermined

We've all lost our children . . . Just look at them, for God's
sake—violent in the streets, comatose in the malls, narcotized
in front of the TV. In my lifetime something terrible
happened that took our children away from us.

—Russell Banks, *The Sweet Hereafter*

Modern society is awash in parenting expertise. Peruse any bookstore and you will behold shelves upon shelves of volumes devoted to helping moms and dads navigate this rocky terrain, from conception through college drop-off. Parenting blogs, social media groups, and online lectures abound. A playlist on the TED Talks website offers "Stories from the Front Lines of Parenting." Even if tongue-in-cheek, the war-zone language resonates for many; the struggle to be "good parents" can seem like a protracted battle against time, against ourselves, even against our kids. We arrive at the bookshelf already lost, seeking direction. We want to do right by our children; we just don't know *how*. If only we had some internal compass to guide us.

The good news is, we do: all of us, by virtue of being human, are endowed with a natural drive and talent for child-rearing. The bad news is that our society's guiding assumptions and prevailing prejudices serve to alienate us from that innate knowledge, so inherent to our species that it cannot be taught, only activated or disabled.

In this chapter we'll look at two ways modern Western culture's idea of normal undermines parenting: the erosion of our instinct for the enterprise, and the creation of isolating or stressful conditions inimical to raising healthy children. If it takes a world to raise a child, it takes a toxic culture to make us forget how to.

Suppressing Instinct, by the Book

Recently a parenting manual by an economist with no background in developmental psychology, beyond being a mother herself, became a bestseller. Having crunched the numbers, Emily Oster presents *Cribsheet: A Data-Driven Guide to Better, More Relaxed Parenting, from Birth to Preschool*. It devalues, among other things, such ancient practices as breastfeeding and co-sleeping with one's newborn. As a sympathetic *New Yorker* profile expressed it, "A major refrain of [this] book is that a parent's preferences are important. What do *you* want?" The plaudit is telling: the governing principle is what the parent *prefers*, not what the child *needs*. Here's the problem: any cultural context is bound to shape the preferences of its members in its own image. What we adults "prefer" in unnatural circumstances may well clash with what our nature would have us opt for. It so happens that parents today take their cues from a culture that has lost touch with both the child's developmental needs *and* what parents require to be able to meet those needs.

Oster's intentions are no doubt good. Around the time her book was published, the *New York Times* ran an op-ed by her with the online title "The Data All Guilt-Ridden Parents Need."[1] Freeing fellow parents from shame is a laudable objective. But quite aside from the fact that even the most carefully selected data are a poor antidote for guilt, what if the issue is more complicated? What if the angst parents feel speaks not to a lack of information or figures but to a long-brewing, culturally induced alienation from their own deepest instincts? Quite like the genes in which they are coded, instincts do not assert themselves in an automatic or autonomous way. Rather, they have to be evoked by the proper environment, or else we are liable to lose touch with them. This is as true for human beings as it is for other animals forced to live in unnatural circumstances. We might consider that the proliferation of "parenting experts" in our time is a sign of this disconnect and not its solution.

Of course, early twenty-first-century culture isn't exactly unique in this respect. Just as with theories of human nature, child-rearing attitudes, approaches, and doctrines throughout Western civilization have reflected—and reinforced—their particular time and place. It is a mostly dismal trajectory that includes infanticide, terror, and abuse: all, of course, normalized in their day. Around the fourteenth century, as the psychohistorian Lloyd deMause writes, "there was no image more popular than that of the physical molding of children, who were seen as soft wax, plaster, or clay to be beaten into shape."[2] The intent was to break the child's independent spirit, from birth onward. It was also around this time, he points out, that parenting manuals began to multiply in earnest.

In the mid-nineteenth century arrived what deMause terms the *socializing mode*, the goal of which is the fostering of a socially functional personality, one that "plays well with others"—that is, conforms to society's expectations. This approach became "the source of all twentieth-century psychological models." Among them is one popularized by the iconic Dr. Benjamin Spock, parenting pundit for millions. In *Baby and Child Care*, his bestseller that influenced generations, the good doctor proposed a cure for what he called "chronic resistance to sleep in infancy." The way to ensure that the infant doesn't "get away with such tyranny," he wrote, was to "say good night affectionately but firmly, walk out of the room, and don't go back." That's right: the "tyranny" of a baby who is physiologically and emotionally programmed to crave physical closeness with the parent, as do all mammalian young.

Today the socialization mode still dominates much of the advice parents continue to receive from "experts" and peers. Recently Jordan Peterson weighed in on how to raise "sophisticated denizens of the world outside the family." In his megaselling *12 Rules for Life: An Antidote to Chaos,* Peterson cautions parents: "You love your kids, after all. If their actions make you dislike them, think what an effect they will have on other people, who care much less about them than you. Those other people will punish them . . . Don't allow that to happen. Better to let your little monsters know what is desirable and what is not."[3] To achieve this goal, Peterson recommends gestural and physical intimidation.

"Socialization" may be a kinder approach than treating kids as inanimate putty, yet it still centers something other than their needs: namely, the dictates of the society for which the parents act as the well-meaning but unwitting agents. To see what else might be possible, it is instructive to look at cultures more time-tested and Nature-informed than our own. Such cultures needed no "parenting experts" because the wisdom was passed down generationally, whether by instruction or simple emulation. Contrast Dr. Spock's counsel with what an elderly Cree woman once told me: "In our clan, children weren't even allowed to touch the ground until they were two years old. They were in our arms all the time." Or compare Peterson's tips for managing "little monsters" with the anthropologist Ashley Montagu's description of traditional parenting practices among Netsilik Inuit in Canada's Northwest Territories: "The Netsilik mother, even though she lives under the most difficult of conditions, is an unruffled personality who bestows warmth and loving care upon her children. She never chides her infant or interferes with it in any way, except to respond to its need."[4] Somehow, it seems, these children managed to grow into productive and yes, socialized, members of their communities—even without Dr. Peterson's stern admonishments.

It turns out that our innate parenting instinct is perfectly calibrated to ensure the provision of the thing many "experts" would have us ignore: the child's developmental needs.

And here's a plot twist: we are not talking *only* about children's needs. In a real sense, we cannot even speak about the infant's needs without considering those of the mother. "There is no such thing as a baby," the British pediatrician D. W. Winnicott once said, explaining, "If you show me a baby, you certainly show me someone else who is caring for the baby . . . One sees a 'nursing couple' . . . The unit is not the individual, the unit is the individual-environment set-up."[5] Or, in Ashley Montagu's words, "When a baby is born, a mother is born. There is considerable evidence that at this time, and for months thereafter, her needs for contact exceed those of the infant."[6] Good thing, too: Were there not built-in physiological and emotional incentives for the ones doing the caregiving, parenthood would be even more of a slog than it already is. Fewer babies would have their survival needs met if fulfilling those needs were not rewarding for parents. With its usual brilliance, our interpersonal-biological makeup dictates that our requirements be mutual. (One of the unfortunate impacts of our culture's way of doing things is that stress tends to whittle down these innate rewards, making parenting more frustrating and daunting than it rightly ought to be.)

The poet Adrienne Rich expressed the profound joys of this reciprocal design: "I recall the times when, suckling each of my children, I saw his eyes open full to mine, and realized each of us was fastened to the other, not only by mouth and breast, but through our mutual gaze: the depth, calm, passion, of that dark blue, maturely focused look. I recall the physical pleasure of having my full breast suckled at a time when I had no other physical pleasure in the world except the guilt-ridden pleasure of addictive eating."[7] Neurobiologically, Rich was right on target. On imaging studies, a baby's smile will light up the same reward areas in the mom's brain activated by junk foods or addictive drugs, releasing the same pleasure chemicals and triggering the same high.[8] Nature, that unscrupulous drug-pusher.†

Like all complex brain structures, mammalian bonding systems—whether of whales or chimps or rats or humans—are experience-dependent for their development and activation. For the brain circuits of nurturing to function—to "come on line," as it were—the environment must evoke and then sustain them. Both men and women have latent child-nurturing circuits in their brains, "waiting for the right environment to amplify their potentials," in the words of neuroscientist Jaak Panksepp—he of the PANIC/GRIEF, PLAY, and CARE nomenclature. Dr. Panksepp identified and mapped the specific brain centers, circuits, connections, and associated neurochemicals that choreograph what he called "the enchanting ballet of emotions between a mother and her infant." These include chemical messengers such as vasopressin, oxytocin, and endorphins—the body's natural opiates—all of which awaken in parents nurturing habits that are essential to the survival of the young. Recall,

---

†   I kid, but also not. The connection between the impaired supply of these feel-good chemicals early in life and later patterns of addiction, whether to drugs or compulsive behavior patterns, is a central theme of my previous book *In the Realm of Hungry Ghosts: Close Encounters with Addiction,* and will be revisited here in chapters 15 and 16.

these are the chemicals that, blended, form a "love cocktail" released by natural labor. Skin-to-skin contact and suckling also elicit their flow in the mother. The physiology of infant and parent is thus co-regulated by their interactions, and the effect of these interactions—or their absence—can be imprinted in the young human for a lifetime. Likewise, in the dearth of such interactions, parenting instincts may become muted, with long-term consequences for the parent-child relationship.[9] In this, as in other crucial ways, our culture has become contact-starved.

Let's remind ourselves that civilization, beginning with the Neolithic revolution and the advent of agriculture, is but a blip in the course of our species' existence, no more than twelve thousand years out of the millions that hominins have trod the earth and the estimated two hundred thousand years or less since our own species arrived on the scene. Until then, and in many places until much more recently—even up to today, in a few isolated locations—people lived in small-band hunter-gatherer groups. "The common early experiences of our ancestors (and cousins, the small-band hunter-gatherers) provided *a social commons for the development of human nature*—the essence of being human," writes Dr. Darcia Narvaez. (Italics hers.) The research she has surveyed identified seven early child-rearing practices shared by hunter-gatherer groups, practices that constitute what she calls the "evolved nest." As you read this list, I invite you to compare the experiences it includes with those of the average baby or toddler of our own time.

Amid the stresses generated by our culture, even educated middle-class parents are challenged to provide these needs—if they are even aware of them:

- Soothing perinatal experience
- Prompt responsiveness to the needs of the infant and prevention of distress

- Extensive touch and constant physical presence, including touch with movement (carrying and holding)
- Frequent, infant-initiated breastfeeding for two to five years, with four as the average weaning age
- A community of multiple, warm, responsive adult caregivers
- A climate of positive social support (for mother and infant)
- Creative free play in Nature with multi-aged mates.[10]

"The nest," Dr. Narvaez told me, "includes the mother relaxed and not stressed during pregnancy, gentle birth processes, soothing perinatal experiences, no separation of mom and baby, no infant circumcision,† no painful procedures, breastfeeding, and then affectionate touch constantly in the first year and throughout childhood and life, really." Recall that it was Narvaez whose contention about human beings being *species-atypical* I quoted in chapter 8—the only beings on Earth who routinely thwart their own species' inbuilt needs for healthy growth. "In our culture," she said, "we have pretty much unnested our children. We are missing most of the components of what helps a baby grow into their full potential, their systems to develop properly. That's the unnestedness."

Among the Indigenous people who hosted her in the South American jungle, Jean Liedloff once observed an exception to tribal practices that proved a cardinal rule regarding parental discipline of children: "I saw a young father lose patience one day with his year-old son. He shouted and made some violent motion as I watched and may even have struck him. The baby screamed with deafening, unmistakable horror. The father stood

---

†   I flinched when she mentioned circumcision—I used to perform this procedure myself, one that in the North American context has no health benefit and has been shown to cause suffering to the child, especially in the medical form I was trained in.

chastened by the dreadful sound he had caused; it was clear that he had committed an offense against nature. I saw the family often, as I lived next door to them, but I never saw the man lose respect for his son's dignity again."[11]

The word "dignity" stands out: how many of us think of babies this way? And yet that omission may only underscore our blind spots when it comes to children. Think about it: even if you've never called an infant "dignified," odds are you've met quite a few *indignant* ones. The word is not figurative, either. Even babies—perhaps they especially—know when their physical and emotional integrity is being ignored or violated. Liedloff's anecdote comports with Dr. Narvaez's findings about small-band hunter-gatherers and what has been generally observed about Indigenous cultures: by and large, these did not normalize hitting their kids, and still don't. Landing on the shores of the "New World," the European Christians steeped, or so they believed, in the gentle spirit of Jesus, found it appalling to witness that the "savages" of North America avoided the corporal punishment of children.[12] By contrast, the Puritan ethic was to "engage rod and reproof," in the words of one seventeenth-century Massachusetts minister.[13]

This ethos may have fallen from favor since then, but not entirely. "To hold the *no excuse for physical punishment* theory," writes Jordan Peterson (italics his), assumes "that the word *no* can be effectively uttered to another person in the absence of the threat of punishment."[14] The good professor's "another person" is, in this case, a two-year-old, whom elsewhere he charmingly calls "the determined varmint." For Peterson, steeped in behaviorist ideology, discipline is often a matter of intimidating children, something we can accomplish, he writes, because we are "larger, stronger and more capable than the child" and can, therefore, back up our threats. He proudly boasts, "[When] my daughter was little, I could paralyze her into immobility with an evil glance." In Britain, two headlines in the *Telegraph* from 2011 and 2012, respectively, signaled that such attitudes are far from isolated: "The Rod Has Been Spared for Far Too Long: Allowing Teachers Even the Lightest Touch of Physical Force Will Improve Discipline" and "School Discipline: Sparing the Rod Has Spoiled the Children—What Can Be Done to Reverse the Collapse of Discipline Since the Banning of the Cane?"

Back in the world of science, the American Academy of Pediatrics, having reviewed nearly one hundred studies, issued a statement in 2018 that aligns with ancestral wisdom. It called for the end of spanking and of harsh verbal punishment of children and adolescents. Such treatment, the organization of sixty-seven thousand pediatric specialists pointed out, only increases aggression in the long term and undermines the development of self-control and responsibility. By elevating stress hormone levels, it may cause harm to healthy brain development and lead to mental health problems.[15] More recently, a Harvard study showed that the damage wrought by spanking to the child's nervous system and psyche may be as severe as that caused by more intense violence.[16] The good news is that the tide is turning, with young parents less and less likely to employ corporal disciplining—a welcome instance, perhaps, of the future leading us back to the past.

For another example of the modern disconnection from instinct and body, take breastfeeding. According to massive surveys in North America and internationally, the practice confers physical health benefits on both the child and, in the long term, the mother.[17] As Dr. Lori Feldman-Winter, chair of the American Academy of Pediatrics, told the *New Yorker*, the economist Emily Oster, in devaluing the practice, simply gets the science wrong. "It's basically as bad as the anti-vaxxers," the physician said.[†]

[†]   To clarify, Feldman-Winter's comment regarding anti-vaxxers preceded COVID-19 days.

Elsewhere, Oster writes that "motherhood can be lonely and isolating." Too true—but those attributes pertain not to motherhood itself but to motherhood in an alienating culture. Horticulture on the moon would doubtless be a maddening endeavor, but that tells us nothing about gardening, only that certain conditions must be in place if we hope to succeed. At one point, Oster recounts an experience of attending her brother's wedding, "trying to nurse my screaming daughter in a 100-degree closet." It is hard to conceive of a more apt metaphor for the abnormally stressful conditions our culture imposes on infants and mothers than that closet: shamed or shunned into isolation, hidden away, claustrophobic, cramped, sweltering. Given how interpersonal neurobiology works, is it any wonder the infant is screaming? In a stressed environment, as I often witnessed in family practice, breastfeeding itself can become an onerous and frustrating chore, a source of maternal misery and infant distress.

The same goes for some forms of "sleep training." The assumption that infants need to be trained to sleep is based on a cultural view that the child should adjust to the parents' schedule and agenda—which, for working parents or for stressed parents lacking support, may be a legitimate, even unavoidable longing. But we should be clear on what is being lost. As the psychologist Gordon Neufeld points out, being in physical touch is the infant's only way of connecting with the parent. Her "resistance" to being put down and having the parent follow the Spockian counsel to "say good night affectionately but firmly, walk out of the room, and don't go back" is simply an expression of her essential need. Shutting down our response to a baby's distress may also weaken our own parenting instincts, with consequences that long outlast the child's infancy.

In 2006 I wrote a newspaper article titled "Why I No Longer Believe Babies Should Cry Themselves to Sleep," pointing out that leaving small infants alone stresses their brains, with potential negative effects. It also hurts a mother's heart. I quoted my late mother-in-law, Monica, who had a painful memory of being a young mom in the late 1940s and early '50s and following medical counsel to ignore her infants' cries. "It was torture for me to do it," she told me. "It went against all my motherly emotions." Some years later the paper's website republished the piece, which was quickly shared over eighty thousand times, drawing many responses. One of them was priceless: "This article is nothing more than prefrontal lobe BS. There is no way an infant's brain patterns are permanently psychologically damaged at such a young age. There is no way that your prefrontal cortex will permanently adopt patterns that will translate into adulthood. No way. If that would be the case, then the last 3 generations to rule this earth (boomers, pre-boomers, Generation X) would have all been emotionally unstable and plagued with psychological issues." "Well, then," I thought to myself, "I rest my case."

Why Parental Stress Matters

Especially in infancy, but throughout childhood, the young human uses the emotional and nervous systems of the caring adults to regulate her own internal states. The interpersonal-biological math is elementary: the more stressed the adult, the more stressed the child.

Extensive research has demonstrated that when stressed, parents are less patient and more punishing and harsher with their young children. Stress impairs their capacity to be calm, responsive, and attuned. As a recent review by leading researchers pointed out, "In more stressful environments for parents, children not only experience less protection from environmental stressors but also are more likely to have stress-inducing relationships with caregivers."[18] Another study showed that, while elevated stress induced more punitive attitudes in mothers, increased levels of support favorably diminished them. Contemporary science affirms ancient wisdom once more.

Parental stress expresses itself in less overt ways, too, such as distraction and emotional absence. Many parents, though loving, are frequently preoccupied by genuine concerns about relationship issues or economic troubles or personal problems and, as a result, just aren't as attentive or "present." This affects development as surely as does parental rage or coldness. "Primate experiments show that infants can undergo severe separation reactions even though their mothers are visually, but not psychologically available," reports the renowned researcher, psychologist, and theorist Allan Schore.[19] Dr. Schore calls such noncontact "proximate separation"—so close, but yet so far. It's a dynamic that many children in our society experience, owing to the stresses parents habitually endure. The message the child gets is "You are not worthy of my attention. You must work to earn it." Whether or not we explicitly recall such experiences, their imprints survive in our unconscious and in our nervous systems.

Making matters more stressful is the alienation imposed by financial hardship. "The relentlessness of modern-day parenting has a powerful motivation: economic anxiety," the *New York Times* reported in 2018. "For the first time, it's as likely as not that American children will be less prosperous than their parents. For parents, giving children the best start in life has come to mean doing everything they can to ensure that their children can climb to a higher class, or at least not fall out of the one they were born into."[20] The unintended impact of such fearful, status-driven child-rearing is that the child's irreducible emotional needs fall secondary to the desperation of parents striving to ensure the academic and financial success of their offspring. Recently I was told, by a close eyewitness, of a middle-class mother yelling at her five-year-old son who balked at doing his homework: "You're not thinking of your academic future!" the poor mom shouted at the preschooler. If only the youngster could have retorted, "Yeah? Well, you're not thinking of my psycho-emotional future!"

For some two-parent families of a certain social class, having both parents working may be a choice. "I love my kids! They are amazing," writes Oster. "But I wouldn't be happy staying home with them. It isn't that I like my job better—if I had to pick, the kids would win every time. But the 'marginal value' of time with them declines fast . . . The first hour with my kids is great, but by the fourth, I'm ready for some time with my research. My job doesn't have this nose-dive in marginal value—the highs are not as high, but the hour-to-hour satisfaction declines much more slowly."[21] Oster is wise to value the quality of the hours she spends parenting over their mere number, and has every right to claim her choice, as we all do. For far too long women's self-expression and validation through the fulfillment of meaningful work apart from homemaking were squelched and frustrated.

And of course, neither the opportunity to return to meaningful employment nor the pressure to resume working, no matter what the cost to parenting, is equally distributed among women: class, as always, is a hugely significant variable. Many parents are compelled to enter the workforce from dire economic necessity, or to rejoin it far too prematurely. How can they think of their children's future when they can barely provide for the present? This is particularly the case in the United States, where fewer than 20 percent of new mothers have access to paid leave. The problem is even worse for families of color, Myra Jones-Taylor, chief policy officer at the child development nonprofit Zero to Three, told the *Guardian*. "Parents," she said, "just can't afford to stay home with their babies."[22] There are much more civilized policies in place in some countries, particularly in northern Europe, where even fathers are offered paternity leave.

One in four American women returns to work within two weeks of giving birth, a mere third of the length of postpartum maternal leave suggested by the American College of Obstetricians and Gynecologists. Even that paltry recommendation by the ACOG seems intended only to allow the maternal body to heal and recover from the travails of labor—given especially how many births these days involve surgical intervention. Such a brief postpartum absence from work leaves the needs of the child entirely out of consideration. For healthy child development, according to the child's neurobiological requirements, a much longer period with the mother is necessary—ideally for a *minimum* of nine months until the infant reaches a stage of relative biological maturity. The sudden loss of maternal contact is, for the infant, a shock—as we know from animal studies, even creatures whose period of dependence is much shorter than ours.[†]

All the Lonely Parents

The British anthropologist Colin Turnbull spent three years living with Pygmies in what was then known as Belgian Congo, in Central Africa. Until recently these tribal people followed ways of life dating back, likely with little alteration, for thousands of years. He related his observations in his classic work *The Forest People*. "The infant," he writes, ". . . knows his real mother and father, of course, and has a special affection for them and they for him, but from an early age he learns that he is the child of them all, for they are all children of the forest."[23] In the small-band hunter-gatherer milieu, the extended family and clan formed an indispensable network of warm, responsive support. Far from being

---

† For example, rats weaned just one week earlier than their Nature-appointed times are more likely to get habituated to alcohol as adults.

a two-person show (much less a solo performance), parenting originally functioned within a broad circle of attachments, the multigenerational clan, where consistent affection was modeled, encouraged, and shared.

It was also *supplemented,* in a manner both merciful and utterly commonsense, by a select group of other caregivers that Narvaez terms *allomothers,* the Greek-derived prefix *allo-* denoting "something other than the usual." Allomothers "take the baby when mom needs a break . . . They carry, rock and play with the child. They take care of mundane tasks . . . They are the buffer for the mother-child, father-child relationship." We know from many studies that the more support parents receive, the more responsive they can be to their children. "It used to be the tradition in most every society," Narvaez writes, "to have a 'lying in' period for mom and new baby where women of the community wait on the mother, giving her nutritious teas and foods that promote breastfeeding and healing. They took care of everything in the household so she could stay in her bed and give her full attention to bonding with and breastfeeding her baby."[24] In effect, these cultures had a socialized "Child Care for All" policy, to their great benefit.

As I worked on this chapter, in mid-May 2020, a horrific terrorist assault on a hospital in Kabul, Afghanistan, killed twenty-four people, including some nursing mothers. In one of the most moving news videos I have seen, women arrived to nurture and nourish these orphaned infants. "I have come here today to breastfeed these babies," one young local woman said through her COVID-19 face mask, "because they lost their mothers in this bloody attack. I have a four-month-old baby . . . and came here to give them a mother's love by breastfeeding them."[25] It may be that the allomothering instinct is as natural as that of mothering itself.

Bottom line: It was never Nature's agenda, if we can speak of it as such, that a distressed and confused young mother such as Emily Oster should have to struggle in closeted isolation, or to compromise on her instincts and desires to bond calmly with her child. It's not the job description of parenting that imposes these stresses on mothers and fathers; the problem lies with, so to speak, the sociocultural job site.

To say we have drifted afield from a community-parenting model would be an understatement. Today's insulated nuclear family unit is a distant cry from our "evolved evolutionary niche," traces of which grow fainter with each new decade, with every fresh turn of the wheel of economic or technological "progress." With evolutionary precedents shattered, we are made to endure serial breakages of our instinctual inheritance.

Consider what has happened to local communities within just a very few generations. I and many others in my age cohort can still remember growing up in neighborhoods where nearly everyone knew one another, where children played throughout the day in the streets, and where every adult, known to us all, was a surrogate parent, keeping an eye on us or ready to call us to order when out of line. Families shopped in neighborhood stores; the grocer, the baker, the hardware dealer, and the car mechanic offered their goods and services within walking distance. (A personal note: During my childhood in Budapest, the sidewalk outside our building was almost as wide as a playground, and served as such for the dozens of children from the neighboring apartment houses. I visited my old neighborhood on a recent speaking trip to Hungary, to find the sidewalk now narrow, a multilane freeway coursing along it and, on the other side, a drive-through McDonald's and a gas station.)

How quaint such memories seem now, almost like something out of *Sesame Street*. Local stores are an endangered species.

Notwithstanding thriving communal settings in some localities, in general more and more of us drive, often by ourselves, to work or to shop at some soulless and/or windowless facility far away. In place of people we know, we encounter strangers purveying mass-manufactured products. Economic interactions once informed by personal relationships, whether at the bank, gas station, or large-store checkout counter, have been increasingly replaced by emotionally sterile and ever more mechanized transactions. Suburban sidewalks, largely vacant, are no longer enlivened by the raucous play of children of mixed ages: for the most part, kids attend schools segregated into same-age groupings. The need to make a living impels many people to move far away from their extended families.

Church attendance and other vectors of socially minded participation are on the wane. "Without at first noticing, we have been pulled apart from one another and from our communities over the last third of the century," Harvard professor of public policy Robert D. Putnam wrote in 2000.[26]

Social creatures by natural design, we have become fish out of water.

Mothers, whose need for connection is an especially high-stakes matter, are among the hardest hit by these shifts. Adrienne Rich notes that during the relative affluence of the mid-twentieth century, "the move to the suburbs, to the smaller, then the larger, private house, the isolation of 'the home' from other homes . . . The working-class mothers in their new flats and the academic wives in their new affluence all lost something: they became, to a more extreme degree, house-bound, isolated women."[27] Such tendencies are exerting themselves internationally and with growing force under the sway of globalized capitalism.

While there is no sense in pining for some idealized once-upon-a-time, a decline in cohesion and community support is discernible, and lamentable. "In earlier decades, the social ties were in place," James Garbarino, a lifelong student of child development and a professor of humanistic psychology at Chicago's Loyola University, told me in an interview. "Even though the value of individualism was there, the social structures that bound people together were more evident. Many of those have atrophied or people have chosen to opt out of them, not realizing how important they were for their well-being in the past. These structures—people didn't consciously know how important they were, and so they felt they could get rid of them with no cost." Joni Mitchell was right: we truly don't know what we've got till it's gone.

A culture where Nature has become the exception is a culture in trouble. To do the job evolution has tasked us with, and to access and trust our natural instincts designed for that job, we need each other, and we need communal and social support—just as surely as our children need us. Isolated parenting is stressed parenting, as is trying to keep up with the latest counter-instinctual "expert" advice from the (apologies to Dwight Eisenhower) parenting-industrial complex.[†] Troubled parenting, in turn, is a breeding ground for personal and societal malaise.

---

†   Near the end of his presidency, "Ike" famously warned about the "military-industrial complex."

Chapter 13

Forcing the Brain in the Wrong Direction: The Sabotage of Childhood

*There can be no keener revelation of a society's soul
than the way it treats its children.*

—Nelson Mandela‡

"Do you ever get accused of mother-blaming?" I asked the Harvard-based pediatrician and researcher Jack Shonkoff. "I worry about that a lot," he said. "If we talk about how influential the environment of relationships is, you can end up on a slippery slope, with people saying, 'Parents are doing a bad job—it's their fault.'" Dr. Shonkoff, whose work has illuminated much of the science of early development, then summed up the core dilemma faced by anyone who tries to engage with these issues honestly: "You can't say that parents are incredibly important in the lives of their children, yet if there's a problem it has nothing to do with the parents. But the truth is, parents don't raise their children in isolation from society."

A wiser view requires a wider lens. Yes, parents are responsible for their children; no, they did not create the world in which they must parent them.

---

‡ Address by the South African president at the launch of the Nelson Mandela Children's Fund, Pretoria, May 8, 1995.

Our cultural ecology does not support attuned, present, responsive, connected parenting. As we have seen, the destabilization begins with stress transmitted to infants still in the womb, with the mechanization of birth, the attenuation of the parenting instinct, and the denial of the child's developmental needs. It continues with the increasingly intolerable economic and social pressures on parents these days and the erosion of community ties, and magnifies with the disinformation parents receive on how to rear their young. Reinforced by educational systems that too often stress students with pressures to compete, the process culminates in the exploitation of children and youth for the glory of the consumer market.

Parents do their loving best; I know I did. I also know full well how my "best" was constrained by what I didn't yet know about myself, nor about child-rearing. However noble our intentions, our ability to carry them out is heavily influenced by our own early experiences and unresolved traumas, by the social expectations we are charged with transmitting to our children, and by the stresses of life. Does that knowledge liberate me from feelings of guilt, especially when I see the marks left on my kids by my limitations as a younger man? No, not automatically. But at least I'm aware that guilt and blame are unhelpful and beside the point, especially when we understand the context. As James Garbarino urged in 1995, "We need to put aside blaming parents and take a good hard look at the challenge of raising children in a socially toxic environment."[1]

Garbarino, at that time codirector of the Family Life Development Center and professor of human development at Cornell University, noted that among the many facets of the socially hazardous environment for child-raising were "violence, poverty and other economic pressures on parents and their children, disruption of relationships, nastiness, despair, depression, paranoia, alienation—all the things that demoralize families and communities." He also wrote of "many, many others that are subtle yet equally serious. High on the list is *the departure of adults from the lives of kids*."[2] This radical disruption of evolutionary norms is taken for granted, to the point where we barely even notice it. Worse, we mistake it for the natural state of things.

An automatic consequence of the weakening of communal and family ties is that our kids must seek their attachment needs elsewhere. Children, like the young of many species, must attach to *someone* in their lives: their neurophysiology demands it. Absent a reliable attachment figure, they experience fear and disorientation. Their brain wiring will go, well, haywire. In effect, essential brain circuits having to do with capacities such as learning, healthy social interaction, or emotional regulation will not develop appropriately.

Nothing in a child's brain tells her *to whom* she should attach. Nature's assumption, if we can put it that way, is that the parents will be consistently present. Children are born with this expectation coded into their bodies and nervous systems. The immature brain cannot abide what Gordon Neufeld calls an "attachment void"—a situation in which no attachment figure is there to connect with. Inevitably, just as a newborn duckling, in the absence of its mother, will trustingly follow the first creature it sees—the nearest goose, squirrel, park ranger, or even a robotic toy car—the vacuum must and will be filled by whoever is around.

For our young today, "whoever is around" from an early age onward is most often the peer group. Unmoored by the decline of the multigenerational adult-led community, children and adolescents have to seek acceptance from one another. This is, developmentally speaking, a fool's errand.

To be clear, the desire, even the need, to form close connections with one's own age group is natural and healthy. Such friendships can be among the richest bonds forged in a lifetime. But from the perspective of emotional development, *peer orientation*—the displacement of adults as the *primary* source and locus of attachment for the child, in favor of her own age cohort—is disastrous.[†] The proverbial blind can do a better job of leading the blind than immature creatures can successfully guide one another to psychological maturity. Aaron, the younger of my two sons, now forty-three, sees in hindsight how this dynamic has limited him. "As a teenager I was consumed by what my friends thought of me, how much they liked me, what it took to fit in with their expectations," he recalled recently. "That kept me immature into my adulthood." Of course, his peer orientation was not about his peers per se: it was a natural outcome of his parents' lack of availability as emotionally attuned adults in his early years.

As we've discussed, emotional safety, formed in secure connections with a baseline of unconditional worth, is a prerequisite condition for maturation. Generally, once kids are absorbed into the peer world, they lose the safety of the primary connection with adults.[‡]

In cultures with their priorities in order, young friendships blossom in a community setting, overseen by nurturing adults. In our society, peer interactions occur not in the context of protective adult relationships but away from them.

When children spend much of their waking time away from caring adults, their brains are compelled to choose between competing attachments: the natural call of parental connection or the siren song of the peer world. If parents lose the contest,

---

[†] The phenomenon of peer orientation is documented extensively in Gordon Neufeld's book, which I co-wrote, *Hold On to Your Kids: Why Parents Need to Matter More Than Peers*.

[‡] Assuming, of course, that the adults themselves are emotionally stable, supportive, and available to provide safety. For abused children, the peer group, inadequate as it is, may be a lifeline in some cases.

children must, by default, look to one another. Which means that they, too, lose. All this is exacerbated by the blandishments of a pop culture that holds up immature adolescent celebrities as idols to be "followed"—a telling word—on social media by multiple millions of children and teens. In a previous age, these young people would have seen mature adult figures as the ones to emulate.

Some parents reading this may protest, "But *my* kid's friends seem lovely, accepting, and open-minded!" Real and worth celebrating as those qualities may be, a child finding her *primary* succor and comfort in her peer group is more a sign of "cope" than a cause for hope, especially at younger ages. The noblest of peers are hard-pressed to supply the abiding connection that developmental safety demands. Among other shortcomings, children cannot count on each other to remain internally consistent: many of us can recall an unhappy first day of school when we were shocked to realize that our erstwhile friends had morphed over the summer into something far less friendly. Nor can they offer one another the unconditional positive regard that nourishes healthy growth, a quality even well-meaning adults often find challenging to provide. As a rule, immature peers are constitutionally incapable of accepting each other "as is"; or holding space for the vulnerable experience of emotion, let alone its open expression; or relieving one another's stressed states; or celebrating or even tolerating temperamental differences. Left to its own callow devices, the peer group can offer only acceptance that is highly conditional and thus insecure, often demanding self-suppression and conformity in place of true individuality.

In more dire cases, peer orientation exposes children to the threat of rejection, ostracization, and bullying. According to a 2001 article by Natalie Angier in the *New York Times*, "The news bristles with reports that bullies abound. In one of the largest studies ever of child development, researchers at the [U.S.] National Institutes of Health reported that about a quarter of all middle-school children were either perpetrators or victims (or in some cases, both) of serious and chronic bullying, behavior that included threats, ridicule, name calling, punching, slapping, jeering and sneering."[3] Similar patterns have been reported in Europe.[4] From Spain to Germany, England to the Czech Republic, public officials and school administrators have had to confront the issue. The World Health Organization estimated in 2012 that one-third of children report having been bullied by their peers.[5] These days we hear too many accounts of children or teens manifesting or, at least, feigning indifference at real-life suffering, even finding "kicks" in it. We read frequent reports about bullying or of sexual assaults being shared on social media by adolescents as if they were amusing bits of life, even though the pain caused has also led to suicides and self-harming.

The 2019 overdose death of a troubled adolescent in a Vancouver suburb shocked the world. As the *National Post* reported, "On August 7, Carson Crimeni, a 14-year-old boy described in news reports as lonely and desperate to fit in, took drugs with a group of older teens at a skate park in Langley, B.C. As he grew increasingly incoherent, the older kids filmed him. They mocked him and laughed. They uploaded the clips online and spread them around. '12-year-old tweaking on Molly,'[†] one wrote over a video of a sweaty Carson. He looks tiny in the clip, in his gray hoodie and black pants. He's '15 caps deep,' someone wrote over another clip, according to *Global News*. In later videos, his eyes pop and spin. He sweats through his sweater. He swipes at his nose." Hours later, the boy was found near death, too far gone to be resuscitated. Even at that dire moment, reported the CBC,

---

†   Slang for the psychoactive drug MDMA.

"another teen posted a picture of the ambulance on social media with the jocular caption, 'Carson almost died LOL.'"[6] Very soon after, there was no "almost" about it.

Carson Crimeni's tragedy may have been an extreme case, but many children these days live under the shadow of peer rejection, mockery, or bullying—or may themselves become bullies. In such an atmosphere, a child's protective response is to shut down her vulnerable emotions. That flight from vulnerability— whether instigated by stressful situations at home or in the context of the peer group—inhibits maturation, the emergence of a truly independent self.

"There are indications that children today are losing their tender feelings," Gordon Neufeld said in his penetrating European Parliament address.[7] "Many children have lost their sadness and disappointment . . . their feelings of alarm . . . their feelings of shame and embarrassment. Interestingly enough, research reveals when children lose their blush, they also lose their empathy. It turns out that caring too is a vulnerable feeling as it sets us up for disappointment. We know that the most wounding of all experiences is facing separation . . . Unfortunately, today's children are subjected to more [parental] separation and more peer interaction than ever before." The result, he concludes, is "a significant loss of feeling," as the young brain's defensive apparatus becomes stuck in an effort to "defend . . . against a sense of vulnerability that is too overwhelming." Again, we see the child's emotional apparatus being weakened, their felt sense of being human impoverished.

But why should our children remain open to their own vulnerability? Are we supposed to *want* them to be woundable? Gordon and I addressed the subject in the book we co-wrote:

> Our emotions are not a luxury but an essential aspect of our
> makeup. We have them not just for the pleasure of feeling

but because they have crucial survival value. They orient us, interpret the world for us, give us vital information without which we cannot thrive. They tell us what is dangerous and what is benign, what threatens our existence and what will nurture our growth. Imagine how disabled we would be if we could not see or hear or taste or sense heat or cold or physical pain. To shut down emotions is to lose an indispensable part of our sensory apparatus and, beyond that, an indispensable part of who we are. Emotions are what make life worthwhile, exciting, challenging, and meaningful. They drive our explorations of the world, motivate our discoveries, and fuel our growth. Down to the very cellular level, human beings are either in defensive mode or in growth mode, but they cannot be in both at the same time. When children become invulnerable, they cease to relate to life as infinite possibility, to themselves as boundless potential, and to the world as a welcoming and nurturing arena for their self-expression. The invulnerability imposed by peer orientation imprisons children in their limitations and fears. No wonder so many of them these days are being treated for depression, anxiety, and other disorders.

The love, attention, and security only adults can offer liberates children from the need to make themselves invulnerable and restores to them that potential for life and adventure that can never come from risky activities, extreme sports, or drugs. Without that safety our children are forced to sacrifice their capacity to grow and mature psychologically, to enter into meaningful relationships, and to pursue their deepest and most powerful urges for self-expression. In the final analysis, the flight from vulnerability is a flight from the self. If we do not hold our children close to us, the ultimate cost is the loss of their ability to hold on to their own truest selves.

Why does the flight from vulnerability inhibit maturation? Nothing in Nature "becomes itself" without being vulnerable: the mightiest tree's growth requires soft and supple shoots, just as the hardest-shelled crustacean must first molt and become soft. The same goes for us: no emotional vulnerability, no growth. Even our "tougher" qualities like resilience, determination, confidence, and bravery, if authentic and not mere bluster, have that softer state as a necessary precursor.

Apart from impeding maturation, the shutdown of vulnerable feeling reinforces the sense of emptiness. It fosters boredom, impairs genuine intimacy, undermines curiosity and learning, fuels the demand for distraction from the present moment, and drives a compulsion for overstimulation through competitive games, unrelenting background noise, hazardous social situations and behaviors, the hunger for products, and the pursuit of escape through substances.

The profit imperative animating materialistic society is superbly adept in exploiting these culturally generated pseudo-needs of children and youths. "We should be gravely concerned about our society's soul," the University of British Columbia law professor Joel Bakan writes in *Childhood Under Siege*.[8] As meticulously documented as it is shocking, Bakan's book depicts the multiple ways corporations deploy a sophisticated and sinister understanding of children's emotional needs to generate profit. Here the manipulation has been, and continues to be, very conscious indeed. In 1983 corporations spent $100 million in direct advertising to children. Less than three decades later, that figure had shot up to $15 billion.[†]

Even as parental stress and peer orientation weaken children's connections with nurturing adults, the corporate siege of

---

† Although these are U.S. figures, given the hyper-contagious influence of U.S. culture internationally, the impact is global.

immature minds has exploited and exacerbated the void created by the loss of connection. They act symbiotically to drain child-hood of the emotional richness our development thrives on. A decade ago Bakan warned, "The average child in the United States watches 30,000 television advertisements a year—most of which pitch products directly to them . . . and all conveying a series of subtle, and corrosive, messages: that they will find hap-piness through their relationships with products—with things, not people; that to be cool and accepted by peers, they need to buy certain products; that fast food and toy companies, not par-ents and teachers, know what is best for them; that corporate brands are the true bases of their social worth and identities."[9] These trends have only accelerated since then with the further spread of social media and digital advertising.

Bakan has interviewed some of the world's leading children's marketers. One of them, Denmark's Martin Lindstrom, expressed serious qualms about the results of his work. According to Lind-strom, Bakan writes, "children's constant and deepening expo-sures to marketing is leading to a 'disaster in terms of kids and their futures . . . very unhealthy, and it's just the beginning we are seeing now.' " Lindstrom predicted that his industry would con-tinue to erode children's imaginations and creative capacities. For all that, he stayed on the job. "These marketers are smart, insightful, and quite evil," Bakan told me, "because they under-stand what they're doing. [Lindstrom,] when you talk to him, he has his own kids, and he's quite critical of it all and thinks it's all going in a horrible direction."

Lindstrom's understanding of the child's mind, as summa-rized by Bakan, is alarmingly on point: "Emotions drive every-thing for children . . . and marketers, to be successful, must engage the most fundamental emotions at the deepest level. *Love*, which connotes nurturing, affection, and romance, is one of these fundamental emotions . . . *Fear*—as in violence, terror, horror, cruelty, and war—is another. Then there is *mastery*, kids' aspiration to gain independence from adults." (Italics in original.) This deft analysis is not intended to help the child's mind develop toward health, dignity, genuine mastery, and authentic independence, but the polar opposite: to deliberately turn that mind into prey and a lifelong captive of profit-driven market forces. It aims at the direct sabotage of childhood: the period of growth in which the young human is designed by Nature to move toward her full capacities, mature emotionally, deepen in empathy and self-understanding, learn how to connect with others in mutually beneficial ways, begin to realize her creative potentials, and acquire the template for nurturing the next generation.

Everything the corporate juggernaut foists upon children— prefabricated play options, video games, mass-manufactured toys, gadgets, peer-centric online platforms, and saccharine and superficial television programs targeted at toddlers and preschoolers, along with the mainstreaming of glossy, soulless, porn-inflected depictions of sexuality available to teens and, increasingly, even younger kids—has detrimental effects. "We are forcing the brain in the wrong direction," Lindstrom confessed to Bakan. Psychologically and neurobiologically, the marketing whiz was 100 percent correct. That Facebook (recently rebranded as "Meta"), through its Instagram brand, has knowingly marketed programs that harm the mental health of teenage girls is only the latest revelation of the corporate assault on children's minds.[10]

Although the threat posed to children's brains and minds by the ubiquitous, compulsive, commercialized world of digital devices and media raised profound alarm from the start among those who were observing the impacts, it continues to burgeon and metastasize. I refer here both to the use of digital devices by young children *and* to their compulsive use by adults in their presence.

I spoke with Dr. Shimi Kang, a Harvard-educated psychiatrist, specialist in adolescent addiction, and author, most recently of *The Tech Solution: Creating Healthy Habits for Kids Growing Up in a Digital World.* "Right now we have mothers who are on their phones while they're nursing, or giving an infant a phone during a diaper change," she said. "The diaper change used to be this whole dynamic experience between the caregiver and infant. You'd have to find a way to get them to sit still, and now you just give the child a phone and they lie quietly. You can go to any restaurant and see that many, many, many children are being fed in front of an iPad or a computer. You see it all over the place. The phone is so attractive to that young brain." What gets displaced is the neurobiology of attachment, the release of bonding and mood-regulating brain chemicals like oxytocin, serotonin, and endorphins, present in the cerebral circuits of both parent and baby when they lock eyes in attuned, responsive connection—chemicals, Dr. Kang points out, that are known to be "the key to long-term happiness and success." The unintended but wounding message to the child is, again, "You don't matter."

Although it doesn't take a brain scientist to see what makes these devices "so attractive to that young brain," brain science certainly factors into their design. "Video games, social media, gadgets, and apps are engineered to keep young brains glued to their screens by finding ways to reward them with hits of dopamine," Dr. Kang writes.[11] Dopamine, as we will see, is the essential chemical in the addiction process, whether to substances or behaviors. It is one of the brain's "feel good" chemicals, inducing a state of excitement, motivation, aliveness, and gratification. When Kang asserts that digital apps and gadgets are "engineered" to hit children's brains with bursts of dopamine, she is being very precise. "The phone," she told me, "has been designed by the world's top neuroscientists and psychologists, who have taken all of our most sophisticated brain research and understanding of human motivation and reward cycles and have embedded it into devices." She cited as an example a company with a name and mission so on the nose that one would think it came out of a satirical film or novel: Dopamine Labs. "It was started," she said, "by a neuroscientist and software developers whose entire business platform is to consult companies to help them engage and release dopamine . . . It's called *persuasive design*." Addiction, of course, is the whole point. Viewed from a corporation's bottom line, one could not imagine a more desirable consumer profile than those who can't get enough of what they don't need but feel they must have.

A 2019 study published in the prestigious journal *JAMA Pediatrics* was among the first to investigate the neurobiological effects of screen watching on children. "In a single generation," the authors wrote, "through what has been described as a vast 'uncontrolled experiment,' the landscape of childhood has been digitalized, affecting how children play, learn and form relationships . . . Use begins in infancy and increases with age, and it was recently estimated at more than 2 hours per day in children younger than 9 years, aside from use during childcare and school . . . [The] risks include language delay, poor sleep, impaired executive function and general cognition, and decreased parent-child engagement, including reading together." The study, conducted with preschoolers by means of advanced brain imaging, found increased screen time associated with poorer white-brain-matter functioning "in major fiber tracts supporting core language and emergent literary skills."[12]

Mari Swingle treats many youths with troubled behavior, attention issues, and addictive patterns. A neuropsychologist, she is the author of perhaps the most comprehensive book on the brain and the digital culture, *i-Minds: How and Why Constant*

Connectivity Is Rewiring Our Brains and What to Do About It. "We're seeing autistic-like characteristics in children without autism," she told me. "Lack of smile response, delayed verbal skills, what I used to affectionately call 'busy children': now these are just kids that are kind of running around aimlessly or conversely zombified when they're not on the tech . . . You have kids—for that matter, adults now—that are used to being on the tech for extensive periods of time. A walk won't do it, canoeing won't do it, even speed skateboarding—a lot of things—skiing, even those are now challenged." Dr. Swingle, too, is very concerned about the impacts of relentless screen exposure on brain development: "Less ability to focus on the normal, the baseline, including states of observation, contemplation, and transitions from which ideas spark—what many under the age of twenty now consider a void, proclaiming boredom . . . On a biological as well as a cultural level, such brain state changes affect learning, socialization, recreation, partnering, parenting, and creativity—in essence all factors that make a society and a culture. The neurophysiological processes that regulate mood and behavior are deregulating."[13]

She understands digital media's appeal to well-meaning parents, namely that it acts "as a stress and fatigue mediator." Engaging with it requires little or no pre-planning—it "is instantly available, and provides parents, caretakers, and even educators with much-needed moments of respite and solace." Here we have a case of the solution to one dilemma fueling another. These forms of relief, understandable as they are in these wickedly stressful times, have a cost—and it is our children who pay the lion's share.

As in marketing, the people who invent and propagate these technologies are conscious of the problematic nature of their wares, and even take it to heart—when it comes to their own children, that is. A 2019 *Business Insider* article details how many major Silicon Valley executives—including founders and CEOs of Apple, Google, and even the explicitly kid-targeted Snapchat app (!)—go to concerted lengths to limit their own kids' screen time at home.[†][14] Tellingly, the late Apple CEO Steve Jobs forbade his young children to play with the then newly launched iPad.

Is it all bad news? Of course not; nothing is that simple. Ellen Friedrichs, a Brooklyn-based health educator who works with a diverse array of young people, notes that for some of her students, "the internet has been a lifeline. For that queer kid living in some small town, in a religious community where they have to sit through a homophobic sermon every Sunday . . . you can go online and find 'your people' in a way that you never could." Nor is the "lifeline" solely for marginalized youths. As I write this, for the past year and counting, my primary contact with family, friends, and students worldwide has been via a computer screen. Most of us living through the COVID-19 crisis have newfound appreciation for how technology can promote community and, for many, ease otherwise intolerable isolation. However, we should not be lulled into false optimism or complacency by these upsides. The pleasures and boons of online connectivity can neither keep pace with the burgeoning crises of disconnection nor allay concerns about what the digital world is encoding into our kids' cognitive and emotional operating systems.

When schools in the Canadian province of Quebec reopened after the COVID-19 lockdown in May 2020, omitted from the curriculum were the supposed nonessentials of music, drama, art, and physical education. The assumption was that academic subjects were more important—raising the question,

---

†   Similar sentiments are heard from Silicon Valley execs throughout the hit 2020 Netflix documentary *The Social Dilemma*.

More important for what? Prioritizing "job readiness" is a far cry from foregrounding healthy development, which ought to be the primary agenda of the educational system, as of child-rearing in general. Even on narrow "skill building" grounds, our prevailing educational ideologies miss the boat, since cognitive skills in fact depend on firm emotional architecture, of which play is an indispensable builder.

"We used to think that schools built brains," Gordon Neufeld said in Brussels. "Now we know that it is play that builds the brains that school can then use . . . It's where growth most happens."

Those subjects deemed superfluous by Quebec school authorities tap into essential cerebral circuitry. All young mammals play, and for critical reasons. As the neuroscientist Jaak Panksepp identified, we have a designated "PLAY" system in our brains in common with other mammals. Play is a primary engine of brain development and is also essential to the emotional maturation process. "As a species, we have evolved culturally in a large part because of our playfulness and all that it produces by way of intelligence and productivity," James Garbarino writes.[15] And true play, Gordon Neufeld insists, is not outcome-based: the fun is in the activity, not the end result. Free play is one of the "irreducible needs" of childhood, and it's being sacrificed to both consumerism and the digital culture. "The culture is not respecting normal developmental tasks," the neuroscientist Stephen Porges told me. "Normal developmental tasks are to play with another person, not with an Xbox. Not to talk on a cell phone or text, but to make face-to-face interactions. All these things are neural exercises that provide resilience, creating an ability for an individual to regulate their internal emotional states."

To be up front: I think the influence of the digital/screen problem is almost unfathomably pernicious. In 2016 it was reported that British children ages five to fifteen years were spending three hours a day on the internet, and over two hours watching TV. By contrast, the time spent reading books for pleasure declined from an hour a day (as recently as 2012) to just over half an hour four years later.[16] The vast majority of "gaming" these days takes place alone in front of a screen, with pixelated avatars and disembodied voices standing in for actual playmates. Just what time does all that leave for free, creative, emergent, interactive, individual, or collective play? What kind of brains are we creating?

The same question might be asked about the educational system. In 2016, an American professor and Fulbright scholar named William Doyle, just returned from a semester-long appointment at the University of Eastern Finland, wrote in the *Los Angeles Times* that for those five months, his family "experienced a stunningly stress-free, and stunningly good, school system." His seven-year-old son was placed in the youngest class—not because of some developmental delay, but because children younger than seven "don't receive formal academic training . . . Many are in day care and learn through play, songs, games and conversation." Once in school, children get a mandated fifteen-minute outdoor recess break for every forty-five minutes of in-class instruction. The educational mantras Doyle remembers hearing the most while there: " 'Let children be children,' 'The work of a child is to play,' and 'Children learn best through play.' " And as far as outcomes go? Finland consistently ranks at or near the top of educational test score results in the Western world and has been ranked the most literate nation on Earth.[17]

"The message that competition is appropriate, desirable, required, and even unavoidable is drummed into us from nursery school to graduate school; it is the subtext of every lesson," writes educational consultant Alfie Kohn in his excellent book *No Contest: The Case Against Competition: Why We Lose in Our*

Race to Win, which documents the negative impact of competition on genuine learning, and how competition, praise, grades, rewards, and sanctions imposed on recalcitrant children destroy intrinsic motivation and undermine emotional security.[18] "Does praise motivate kids? Sure it does," Kohn sarcastically remarks. "It motivates kids to get praise."

"And?" you might ask. "What's wrong with well-deserved kudos?" It turns out that there's praise, and then there's praise. Developmental psychologists agree that praising a child's *effort* is helpful and promotes self-esteem, while valuing the *achievement* only programs kids to keep seeking external approval—not for who they are but for what they do, for what others demand of them. It's yet another barrier to the emergence of a healthy self.

For all our love and dedication as parents and educators, the world in which we must rear children these days undercuts our best efforts in a multitude of ways, all masquerading as "just the way it is." There is no "just" about it: the consequences are massive. The present, as it presently is, beggars the future.

Chapter 14

A Template for Distress:
How Culture Builds Our Character

"And that," put in the Director sententiously, "that is
the secret of happiness and virtue—liking what you've got
to do. All conditioning aims at making people like
their inescapable social destiny."

—Aldous Huxley, *Brave New World*

Recall Bessel van der Kolk's crisp remark that "our culture teaches us to focus on our personal uniqueness, but at a deeper level we barely exist as individual organisms." I don't know whether the comparison will discomfit or comfort (perhaps both?), but we humans are, in our lack of an independently self-determined self, not altogether different from our fellow social creature, the ant.

In an ant colony, all larvae are hatched with virtually the same set of genes: the queen, the workers, the warriors are created equal. Which creature becomes what, including what biological features they manifest, depends entirely on the needs of the clan. The oncologist and author Siddhartha Mukherjee described this phenomenon in a fascinating article in the *New Yorker*: "Ants have a powerful caste system. A colony typically contains ants that carry out radically different roles and have markedly different body structures and behaviors." Genetically identical siblings will become differentiated into biologically variable adults based purely on signals from the physical and social environment.

When a queen is removed from a jumping ant hive, for example, the worker ants "launch a vicious, fight-to-the-death campaign against one another—stinging, biting, sparring, lopping off limbs and heads"—until a few workers win and become, well, monarchical. Without any alteration in DNA structure, the physiology of a new queen changes; "she" now becomes fecund and dominant and will live longer than she would have in her previous worker incarnation.[1] Psychiatrist Michael Kerr, formerly of Georgetown University, noted this same dynamic in his book on human family systems. "What each larva becomes is dictated by a colony level process. In this sense, a young larva is born into a functioning position in the colony and his development is determined by that position."[2]

For all our attachment to our individual self-concept, we are rather antlike in this respect. "There is far less autonomy for a human being than we would like to think," Dr. Kerr told me in an interview. "How we function as individuals cannot be understood outside of our relationship to the larger group." In other words, our character and personalities reflect the needs of the milieu in which we develop. The roles we are assigned or denied, how we fit into society or are excluded from it, and what the culture induces us to believe about ourselves, determine much about the health we enjoy or the diseases that plague us. In this, and in many other ways, illness and health are manifestations of the social macrocosm.

If the modern nuclear family forms the primary container for childhood development, that container is itself held within a larger context, formed by entities such as community, neighborhood, city, economy, country, and so on. In our times, the context of all contexts is hypermaterialist, consumerist capitalism and its globalized expressions worldwide. Its fundamental—and, it turns out, quite distorted—assumptions about who and what we are show up in the bodies and minds of those living them out. Given the myriad links between biography and biology, cultural norms can also make themselves known in our physiology.

We see here the attachment/authenticity tug-of-war writ large. Just as we are conditioned to fit into the family, even if that means a departure from our true selves, so we are prepped—one might even say groomed—to fulfill our expected social roles and take on the characteristics necessary to do so, no matter the cumulative cost to our well-being.

I first met Ulf Caap about fourteen years ago. Then vice president of human resources for IKEA North America, Ulf seemed to have everything going for him. And yet this internationally respected business leader had sought me out as part of a personal journey born of deep existential dissatisfaction. He had been visited by a most uncomfortable realization: his well-compensated life—a runaway success by our society's "normal" gauges—and the everyday way of being it demanded of him, amounted, as he recalled, to "a sham, an illusion, a fake . . . There was virtually none of *me* in it." Another wildly successful person by societal standards, the writer-actor Lena Dunham, of *Girls*† fame, said something similar in our interview. In a rehab program for substance addiction, she had been assigned the exercise of writing down her own values. "I realized," she said, "that I could not think of a single value that did not belong to somebody else."

Ulf has since become a friend and sometime collaborator: we have codesigned and led workshops for high-level executives who share that same sense of their authentic selves and their work personas being at diametric odds. I don't mean merely that they leave their true thoughts, feelings, desires, and needs at the office door,

---

† The acclaimed HBO series of which Dunham was both creator and star.

only to retrieve them at day's end as one would a parked car. For the "sham" to be sustainable, these authentic parts of the self must be placed in long-term storage and the key misplaced. "I would negate my personal values to make a success," Ulf admitted. Now in his mid-seventies and the very picture of health, he is convinced his self-suppression and disconnect were draining his life energy: "I recognized that my steps going to work were not so light as they used to be. I was being drawn toward illness."

Ulf has had the good sense—and, he would agree, the privilege—to explore and transcend his alienation. "I spent forty years in insanity," he said, looking back. "My focus was ninety-nine percent on what success looked like in society and in the corporation I worked for. I had no focus whatsoever on what I needed. If I did what the corporation required, I would be successful." He could not have provided a more precise illustration of the insight that the young Trappist monk Thomas Merton, the most influential American Catholic writer of the twentieth century, articulated in his autobiography, *The Seven Storey Mountain*: "The logic of worldly success rests on a fallacy: the strange error that our perfection depends on the thoughts and opinions and applause of other men! A weird life it is, indeed, to be living always in somebody else's imagination, as if that were the only place in which one could at last become real!"[3]

Identity crises such as Ulf experienced are not consciously self-authored—they are the outcome of how we develop in our assorted contexts, from the family outward. "The success I had was one hundred percent external," Ulf said to me. "Totally external—and based on a mental construct I built as a five-year-old and a fifteen-year-old of what it takes to be accepted." In this sense, as the social psychologist Erich Fromm pointed out, the family acts, unwittingly, as the "psychic agent" for society to form what he called the *social character*.

The social character is, in Fromm's words, "the core character common to most members of a culture." This is different from the *individual* character we each possess and display to the world. The social character, to the extent it defines and governs us, assures that we will fit the "normal" mold in our particular culture. Fromm's concept strikes me as a potent rendering of how we function in society—antlike.

I speak here not only of the "we" in an individual sense. The collective "we" is far more blind and dangerous. For example, none of us like to see people sleeping in the streets, but as a society we countenance growing levels of homelessness. Nobody wants life on Earth imperiled, yet the march of climate change seems inexorable. Something in us normalizes such calamities, whether the result is that we actively enable them, deny them, or merely look on in passive resignation. All my life, no doubt spurred by the horrors that shaped my childhood, I have wondered how it is that so many good people can be hypnotized into compliance with the indefensible. There has to be some mechanism to acculturate us to accept as normal what is inimical to ourselves and to the world we inhabit; it is certainly not an inborn inclination. Somehow the system's values and expectations get under the skin, to the point where we confuse them with ourselves.

As Fromm put it, often people's behavior is not a matter of conscious decision to follow the social pattern, but of "wanting to act as they have to act."[4] In this way a culture creates members who will serve its purposes. It is instructive to juxtapose reality with fiction. In Aldous Huxley's *Brave New World,* individuals are "so conditioned that they practically can't help behaving as they ought to behave."[5]

Thus, what is considered normal and natural are established not by what is *good* for people, but by what is expected of them, which traits and attitudes serve the maintenance of the culture. These are then enshrined as "human nature," while deviations from them are seen as abnormal. For the most part, absent an awakening—often of the rude variety—of the authenticity drive, people will develop and behave in ways that seem to confirm the dominant ideas.

What are some of the features of the social character imbued in our culture?

The First "Character" Trait: Separation from Self

I have said that acquired personality traits such as excessive identification with socially imposed duty, role, and responsibility at the expense of one's own needs can jeopardize health. This and other conditioned characteristics are the result of a child's developmental needs being denied, of Nature being thwarted. Culture cements them through reinforcement and reward, encouraging people to perform tasks even if chronically stressful, under circumstances they might naturally want to avoid. My own workaholism as a physician earned me much respect, gratitude, remuneration, and status in the world, even as it undermined my mental health and my family's emotional balance. And why was I a workaholic? Because, stemming from my early experiences, I needed to be needed, wanted, and admired as a substitute for love. I never consciously decided to be driven that way, and yet it "worked" all too well for me in the social and professional realms.

Mechanisms for estranging people from themselves abound. They begin acting on us from the earliest moments of our existence with stresses in the parenting environment and socially sanctioned child-rearing practices that negate the child's needs. The flight from self is powerfully compounded by overt trauma, of course. But even in the absence of personal wounding it can be impelled by a conformist and competition-centered educational system, by social expectations to "fit in," the drive for peer acceptance, and a socially induced, pervasive anxiety about one's status.

In an image-mad culture that sustains itself in large part by making people feel inadequate about themselves—or, more insidiously, capitalizing (pun half intended) on these preexisting feelings—the media holds out ideals of physical perfection against which young and old measure themselves and which lead people to be ashamed of their very bodies. My friend Peter Levine wrote an article some years ago on the cosmetic procedure of injecting people with botulinum toxin; the substance relaxes muscles, temporarily, so as to remove the natural wrinkles from aging. But it also renders the face unnaturally less responsive. "There are nursing mothers taking Botox," Peter told me. "They are not able to communicate their emotions with their babies, or even pick up the babies' emotions. They lose that kind of contact." In many other spheres, including social media, we too often present an artificial, "Botoxed" version of ourselves: an image not of who we are but of how we would like to be perceived by others. "What we have with the internet is sort of a Botox for the masses," Peter said. "We have just lost this capacity to be real, which is fundamentally what makes us human, and what makes us feel connected to each other."

The Second "Character" Trait: Consumption Hunger

Among the great achievements of mass-consumption culture has been to convince us that what we have been conditioned to fervently want is also what we need. In the words of the French-Bulgarian psychoanalyst Julia Kristeva, "Desires are manufactured as surely as are the commodities meant to fulfill them. We consume our needs, unaware that what we take to be a 'need' has been artificially produced."[6] I'm reminded of a response a young Bob Dylan gave on a 1965 tour of England to two desperate autograph seekers. "We need your autograph," one of them begged through the rear-door window of the singer-songwriter's limo. Dylan demurred. "No, you don't *need* it," he said drily. "If you needed it, I would give it to you." And that's just the point: the social character hatched by our consumerist society confuses desire with need, to the point that the nervous system becomes riled when the objects desired are withheld. Supply, meet demand.

As Thomas Merton noted dolefully in 1948, "We live in a society whose whole policy is to excite every nerve in the human body and keep it at the highest pitch of artificial tension, to strain every human desire to the limit and create as many new desires and synthetic passions as possible, in order to cater to them with the products of our factories and printing presses and movie studios and all the rest."[7]

Constantly living at that "highest pitch of artificial tension" leaves many people dissatisfied, on edge, anxious—utterly captured by an addictive process that alienates them from real needs, real emotions, real concerns, real life.

If unable to achieve what we desire, we experience this as a personal failure—even if social conditions are arrayed against us so that success is out of reach. "I remember when I was a kid, I used to love to look at Tide soap commercials," the American actor, director, and political activist Danny Glover told me. "When I look at it now, it was not because I had this affinity to anything about Tide. I would look at it from the vantage point of that I wished my kitchen was like that, I wished my washing machine looked like that, I wished all the things . . . We're put in this situation where we're surrounded by all these things that ninety-nine percent of the time we'll never have, and that creates a sense of valuelessness, because you are not able to have those things." Glover's words track perfectly with social critic Neil Postman's observation as far back as 1985 in his seminal cultural critique, *Amusing Ourselves to Death*. Commercials full of happy-looking people "tell nothing about the products being sold. But they tell everything about the fears, fancies, and dreams of those who might buy them. *What the advertiser needs to know is not what is right about the product but what is wrong about the buyer.*"[8]

Driven by a culturally fueled conviction of insufficiency, we become addicted to consumption. "Consumption is a way in which you mute the pain," Glover said to me. "I know people who have plenty of resources to divert the pain by buying unnecessarily . . . The structure of capitalism creates a situation where people's value relies on their capacity to consume. I don't care if it's consuming from Walmart or from Saks Fifth Avenue. When we talk about addiction, whether it be to drugs or whether it be to other forms of behavior, they all symbolize the sense of being devalued as a human being within a system. That's basically it: feeling alienated within the system."

The Third "Character" Trait: Hypnotic Passivity

Unlike the denizens of Huxley's dystopian fantasy future, we are not automatons, engineered in test tubes to be a certain way and programmed to carry out only certain preordained functions. As citizens in ostensibly democratic countries, we have free will, up to a point—but in practice that freedom rarely strays beyond the frontier of what is socially acceptable. Not daring to rock the boat, we risk sinking with it.

Self-abandonment programmed into the social character makes us passive even in the face of threats to our existence as a species. Healthy people connected to their real emotions and authentic requirements would not be susceptible to blandishments inciting artificial needs and the products to satisfy them, no matter how cleverly packaged. Nor would they accept the unacceptable, except perhaps under threat of force—and even then, they would not be inclined to internalize it as the way things ought to be.

"Children," the great public intellectual Noam Chomsky has remarked, "are constantly asking *why*—they want explanations, they want to understand things." But soon, he says, "you go to school, you're regimented. You're taught this is the way you're supposed to behave, not other ways. The institutions of the society are constructed, so as to reduce, modify, limit the efforts and control of one's own destiny."[9]

The problem originates in how children are raised in the bosom of the modern family, itself a microcosmic representative of the culture. "The family," Erich Fromm pointed out, "has the function of transmitting the requirements of society to the growing child." It does so in all the ways we examined in our chapters on child development. The social character is seeded when children are deprived of breastfeeding; when their Nature-imbued expectations for being held are frustrated; when they are left alone to "cry it out"; when they are compelled to repress their feelings; when they are programmed to fit in with the expectations of others; when they are denied spontaneous free play; when they are "disciplined" by punitive measures such as "time-out" techniques that threaten them with the loss of what they most crave—unconditional positive acceptance; when they are denied a connection with Nature. These all contribute to the inner emptiness, the void that addictions and covetous compulsions will later attempt to fill, even as our independent spirit is subjugated to the demands of an imbalanced, materialist culture.

How lovely it would be if the democratic ideal of "we, the people" creating the society in which we wish to live were true. It's certainly a dream worth pursuing. But believing in it is not nearly enough. It will not and cannot come to pass until we reckon squarely with how things are today: it is *we* who are made in the image of our distorted, disordered, denatured world—the better to keep it running, even as it runs us into the ground.

Part III

Rethinking Abnormal: Afflictions as Adaptations

Much Madness is divinest Sense—
To a discerning Eye—
Much Sense—the starkest Madness—
'Tis the Majority
In this, as all, prevail—
Assent—and you are sane—
Demur—you're straightway dangerous—
And handled with a Chain—

—Emily Dickinson

Chapter 15

Just Not to Be You: Debunking the Myths About Addiction

I have absolutely no pleasure in the stimulants in which I sometimes so madly indulge. It has not been in the pursuit of pleasure that I have periled life and reputation and reason. It has been in the desperate attempt to escape from torturing memories.

—Edgar Allan Poe

Bruce, a vascular surgeon in Oregon, was donning his surgical gown when the police barged in. "I was hauled out of the hospital in handcuffs," he recalled of that sunny day seven years ago. "It was beyond humiliating. I was practicing in a small town, so everybody knew. I was on the front page of the local paper multiple times. It became quite a fall from grace." This trusted local figure had been writing prescriptions in his patients' names, only to retrieve them himself to feed his addiction. "I was using enough, writing enough prescriptions," he recounts, "that the initial suspicion by the police department was that I was running some sort of drug ring." In a few short months, the jig was up.

What could bring a highly trained, accomplished physician like Bruce, married, father of adolescents, to such depths of self-deception, dishonesty, and professional malfeasance? Surely he understood he was jeopardizing his health, family, and livelihood. Why, for that matter, would anyone indulge—if that is the right word—in such self-destructive behaviors?

That question has confronted me almost daily throughout my career but most insistently in my twelve years working in Vancouver's Downtown Eastside, a neighborhood notorious as North America's most concentrated area of drug use. Within its few square blocks dwell thousands of people living lives of desperate dependence on substances of all kinds, inhaling or ingesting or injecting alcohol, opiates, nicotine, cannabis, cocaine, crystal meth, glue, rubbing alcohol. Even visitors from New York or Detroit or Bristol are routinely shocked by what they see there.

"If the success of a doctor is measured by how long his patients live," I would often say, "then I'm a failure, because many of my patients die young." They died from complications of HIV, or from hepatitis C, or infections of their heart valves, brains, spines, bloodstreams. They fell victim to suicide, overdose, or violence, or to vehicles that struck them while they stumbled in a drugged-out haze onto busy streets. Unlike "high-bottom" addicts such as Bruce, now rehabilitated and back on the job, my patients had lost everything—their health, looks, teeth; their families, work, homes. Some had squandered lives of middle-class comfort, and a handful had gone, surprisingly, from riches to rags. All along, they knew full well they were facing the ultimate forfeit: their lives. And still, having struck bottoms lower than most of us could conceive of, they persisted in their habits, as I depicted in my 2009 book on addiction, *In the Realm of Hungry Ghosts*.

Prevailing views about addiction have progressed somewhat in the past decade, in the direction of more compassion, science, and sense. For all that, deceptive and dangerous myths about addiction's provenance and its very nature still reign in many circles, from medical treatment to criminal justice and policy. Even the well-meaning world of rehabilitation and recovery has its blind spots. Given the evident shortcomings and even ruinous harm wrought by our standard approaches, many voices are finally calling for a fresh view.

As a prelude to considering this, let's deal directly with the two leading misconceptions: that addiction is either the product of "bad choices" or else a "disease." Both fail to explain this unrelenting societal plague, just as they hobble our efforts toward remedying it.

The *bad choices* view should by now barely warrant mention, given the scientific advances in understanding, except that it still has a vise grip on many people's thinking and underlies the legal system's assault on drug users. It is so wrongheaded as to be laughable—and it would be, if its consequences were not so tragic. It was expressed succinctly in 2017 by then U.S. attorney general Jeff Sessions, hearkening back to the bad old days of the 1980s drug war: "We need to say, as Nancy Reagan said, 'Just say no,'" he told a Virginia audience. "Educating people and telling them the terrible truth about drugs and addiction will result in better choices by more people."

The precise success of all the war on drugs campaigns, which have had a half century to make good on their stated goals, can be seen in one sordid fact: even as Sessions spoke, his country was losing as many lives to overdoses every three weeks as had been claimed by the 9/11 terrorist attacks. That year, more than 70,000 Americans would die of a drug overdose.[1] Four years later, in 2021, that figure exceeded 100,000.[2] In the same year, my home province of British Columbia saw over 1,700 such deaths, nearly double the number killed by COVID-19 in the province as of this writing.

The "bad choices" view of addiction—which, if we're honest, amounts to little more than "It's Your Own Damn Fault"—is not only disastrously ineffective; it is utterly blind. I have never met anyone who, in any meaningful sense of the word, ever "chose" to become addicted, least of all my Downtown Eastside patients whose lives slowly ebbed away or were rapidly extinguished in the streets, hotel rooms, and back alleys of Vancouver's drug ghetto.

If a socially conservative dissenter were to protest, "Didn't they choose to *stay* hooked?" I would offer this quote by Dr. Nora Volkow, head of the U.S. National Institute on Drug Abuse: "[Recent] studies have shown that repeated drug use leads to long-lasting changes in the brain *that undermine voluntary control*."[3] Translation: when it comes to addiction, "free will" is in many ways a neurobiological non sequitur.

In fact, I would take it much further: most addicted people had little choice even *before* their habits took hold. Their brains arrived on the scene *already* impaired by life experience, especially susceptible to the effects of their drug "of choice" (another dubious expression). Actually, that's true whether the target is a substance or a behavior. In short, the choice model ignores the question of what would drive a person toward addiction in the first place.

Though the *disease* paradigm still embraced by most addiction specialists and treatment programs is more compassionate, it, too, misses the human element. It separates mind from body—or, in this case, brain from mind, seeing the brain in purely biochemical terms. The fact is, personal and social life events, filtered through the mind, shape the brain throughout the lifetime. You cannot, scientifically, cleave biology from biography, especially when it comes to a process as psychologically layered as addiction.

Not that there's no value in considering addiction's neurochemical side. The brilliant work of Dr. Volkow and others has demonstrated that substances of dependence do, over time, change the brain so that essential functions, such as impulse regulation—which would aid someone in resisting addiction's pull—become significantly compromised, even as the circuits of reward and motivation become trained on the desired drugs. In this sense, the brain *does* become an impaired organ, with diminished capacity to make rational choices, obsessively intent instead on satisfying the addictive drives.

We err, however, when we focus on drugs alone: *it does not take a substance addiction to bring about changes in brain chemistry.* Scans have shown similar deleterious changes in the brains of nonsubstance addicts as well, such as inveterate internet gamers.[4] The compulsive intake of foods that trigger the brain's reward apparatus can also produce such effects.[5]

For all that, the equation of addiction with a largely genetically programmed, treatable disease[†6] is, as mentioned, scientifically and humanely a step forward from the shaming "bad choices" model. Just as we wouldn't think of blaming the owner of a diseased kidney, it makes no sense to reproach someone for having a "sick" brain, especially if that "sickness" was inherited.[‡] The problem is that, in typical medical fashion, the disease paradigm turns a process into pathology. Note, too, that "treatable" is a far cry from "healable"—which says less about the nature of addiction than about the medical system's failure to understand it.

The word "disease" also crops up frequently in the world of twelve-step recovery. People in programs like Alcoholics Anonymous or Narcotics Anonymous will speak about "my disease," as in "My disease wants me dead" or "My disease made me hurt the people I love." No doubt such programs have helped millions, and the language used is a big part of helping people think and act

---

†   The American Society of Addiction Medicine defines "addiction" as "a treatable, chronic medical *disease* involving complex interactions among brain circuits, genetics, the environment, and an individual's life experiences. People with addictions use substances or engage in behaviors that become compulsive and often continue despite harmful consequences" (2019).

‡   According to the American Society of Addiction Medicine and the U.S. surgeon general's 2016 report on substance use, up to 50 percent of the "disease" is due to genetic factors. I'll have more to say about the flaws in that view later in this chapter.

in new ways. I will only suggest that "disease" is more therapeutically useful as a metaphor rather than a literal fact. As with most chronic conditions, viewing addiction as a dynamic process to be engaged with rather than a demonic force to be feared or battled can ultimately expand the possibilities for healing.

For a more grounded take on addiction, we need to consider not just people's genes or brain circuitry, but also their real encounters with their world. We need to look closely at people's life experiences.[†] Addictions of any kind are not abnormal ailments, willfully self-inflicted maladies, brain disorders, or genetic short straws. Properly understood, they are not even that puzzling. As with other ostensibly mysterious conditions named in this book, they are rooted in coping mechanisms. To be sure, they may take on some *features* of disease: a dysfunctional organ, tissue damage particularly with extensive drug use, physical symptoms, impairment of certain brain circuits, cycles of remission and relapse, even death. But to call them "diseases" is to miss both the point and the opportunity to deal with them intelligently. Addictions represent, in their onset, the defenses of an organism against suffering it does not know how to endure. In other words, we are looking at a natural response to unnatural circumstances, an attempt to soothe the pain of injuries incurred in childhood and stresses sustained in adulthood.

Two Essential Questions

Over my decades of medical practice and thousands of conversations, I have learned that the first question to ask is not what is wrong with an addiction, but what is "right" about it. What benefit is the person deriving from their habit? What does it do for them? What are they getting that they otherwise can't access?

---

† The American Society of Addiction Medicine's disease-oriented definition, cited earlier, does point to life experiences without naming or exploring them in detail; we need to go further and get more specific.

This inquiry is key to understanding any addiction, whether to substances like alcohol, opiates, cocaine, crystal meth, sniffed glue, or junk food, or to behaviors such as gambling, compulsive sexual roving, pornography, or binge eating and purging. Or to power and profit, for that matter—here, of course, we begin to shade toward addictions that go well beyond individual habits into the realm of collective fixations.

Just as I have never met anyone who chose to become addicted, neither have I met anyone whose addictions did not, at their onset at least, provide for some essential human need. Over and over again, for example, I've heard that people's addictions lubricate the gears of social connection. The Canadian Métis‡ writer, professor, and former inmate Jesse Thistle, author of the memoir *From the Ashes*, told me his substance use gave him "access to friends. And it gave me power, confidence. And it worked for a while—it worked for about the first three years. I became almost, like, bulletproof." For her part, the multitalented television artist Lena Dunham recalled, "It made me more social. It made me more relaxed. It made it easier for me to communicate." In her case, "it" was a dependence on, among other things, tranquilizers: highly addictive medications too freely dispensed by physicians. The boost extended to her creative self-expression: the drugs, she told me, "made me write like a demon because I just completely lost my inhibitions."

"Warmth" is an oft-heard descriptor for the feeling of being high—it captures a felt sense that addicts know well. The actor and children's author Jamie Lee Curtis spoke to me of "this warm bath: the way it feels when you're cold and you step into a warm, not hot, but a warm, really warm bath where that feeling of ease rises as you lower into the warmth. It was a very familiar feeling

---

‡   Métis are people of mixed Indigenous and European ancestry, mostly in the Western Canadian context.

to me, and it was one that I loved. I chased that feeling for ten years in and out of everything from stealing opiates to manipulating doctors for opiates."

Curtis's words reminded me of what I often heard from my hypermarginalized Downtown Eastside (DTES) patients. "What does the heroin do for you?" I once asked a patient just admitted to Onsite, the detox venue above Insite—then North America's only supervised injection site, where I was staff physician. In his late thirties, with weightlifter arms, a shaved head, and a large brass ring piercing his right earlobe, this fierce-looking man looked right at me and said, "Doc, I don't know how to tell you this, exactly. It's like when you're three years old, sick, shivering with fever, and your mother puts you on her lap, wraps you in a warm blanket, and gives you warm chicken soup—that's what heroin feels like." His fellow DTES resident, the poet Bud Osborn, also spoke of the soothing thaw heroin allowed him to experience. "I felt this warmth in the pit of my gut, which had always been really cold."

The rock guitarist[†] and reality-TV star Dave Navarro told me that he found in his addictions "a kind of love and acceptance," another running theme among users. His fellow podcaster and author, the British comedian Russell Brand, also spoke of love. "The first time I took heroin, it felt so sacred and spiritual and warm and maternal," he said. "I felt like I was held . . . I felt like nothing mattered, and I felt safe." His use of the word "maternal" is more than metaphorical: it speaks directly to the neurobiology of opiate addiction.

Others find in their compulsive habits a kind of experience that people spend years pursuing in caves, monasteries, and high-priced retreat centers. "Alcohol," the comedian and former

---

† Jane's Addiction, Red Hot Chili Peppers.

Saturday Night Live mainstay Darrell Hammond said when we spoke, "gives you three or four hours of peace. Just peace. The talk in the head stops, the negative thinking. It's precious." Peace and quiet are not qualities most of us associate with the life of an addict, but these "precious" states are often what is sought—and, for a while, found.

Lena Dunham's tranquilizer dependence provided the temporary illusion of normalcy—an illusion reinforced by the fact that, in our society, her drugs of choice are often acquired via "legitimate" means—a doctor's prescribing pad. "Pharmaceuticals hold this magical promise of making you function normally, or better than normally," she says. "Alcohol, you smell it on someone; crack . . . you end up under a bridge. Klonopin,‡ you can go for a pretty long time thinking, 'Wow, I found the cure to not being able to function in the way that I think people should be able to function in the world.'"

It's worth asking: Who has ever heard of a "disease" that makes you "feel normal"? Or, when's the last time getting sick made you "function better than normally"?

In light of these testimonials, how much more absurd Jeff Sessions's insistence on "better choices" sounds. Shall we do Nancy Reagan one better by erecting more truthful highway billboards and school cafeteria signs: "Just Say No to Pain Relief"? Or "Just Say No to a Warm, Nurturing Feeling in the Belly"? To inner peace; to calmness, empowerment, a sense of self-worth; to community and friendship; to unfettered self-expression; to an elusive sense of comfortable normality; and to love? "I did notice," Navarro told me, "that whenever I started using substances again, I got a sense of *what a human being is supposed to feel like.*" Try saying no to that.

---

‡   Klonopin is a trade name for clonazepam, a tranquilizer of the benzodiazepine class, to which also belong such chemical relatives as Valium (diazepam) and Ativan (lorazepam).

When it comes down to it, all addiction's incentives can be summed up as an escape from the confines of the self, by which I mean the mundane, lived-in experience of being uncomfortable and isolated in one's own skin. Underneath however many surface layers of "normal" functioning, that alienated discomfort can be disturbing to the point of torment: a persistent sense of being abnormal, unworthy, and deficient. Keith Richards of the Rolling Stones, perhaps the world's best-known former heroin addict, crystallizes this escape strategy in his autobiography, *Life*: "It was a search for oblivion, I suppose . . . the convolutions you go through just not to be you for a few hours."[7]

Why would the self need to be escaped? We long for escape when we are imprisoned, when we are suffering. Addiction calls to us when waking life amounts to being trapped in inner turmoil, doubt, loss of meaning, isolation, unworthiness; feeling cold in our belly, devoid of hope; lacking faith in the possibility of liberation, missing succor; unable to endure external challenges or the inner chaos or emptiness; incapable of regulating our distressing mind conditions, finding our emotions unendurable; and most of all, desperate to soothe the pain all these states represent. Pain, then, is the central theme. No wonder people so often speak about the benign numbing effect of their addictions: only a person in pain craves anesthesia.

As a quest for self-escape, the internal logic of addiction is inescapable. *Where I am is intolerable. Get me out of here.*

Here we arrive at the second cornerstone query regarding addiction, one that has become something of a mantra with me: *Ask not why the addiction, but why the pain.* This is the question neither the prevailing disease-based medical paradigm nor popular prejudice can possibly answer or would even think to raise. Yet without it, we can have no clue as to why this affliction of mind, body, and spirit is so rampant.

To map the hard and inhospitable terrain from which addiction springs, it's worth asking the people who have traversed it. Listening to their lived experiences leaves one with no confusion about what needs to be soothed, and why. We lack the space to chronicle all the tragic origin stories of the many individuals I interviewed for this book, from the well known to the unknown; what follows is a brief and representative sample.

- When the Canadian hockey legend Theoren Fleury was fourteen, his coach began sexually abusing him. "He started a routine whenever I was over—masturbate on my feet, then give a blowjob, then let me sleep." And that was far from all, he told me. In his chaotic family of origin, with an alcoholic father, he had no one to turn to. On the contrary, he was desperate to make his economically downtrodden and emotionally dysfunctional parents happy. Years later, earning millions of dollars a year as a scrappy offensive star for the New York Rangers, he was hopelessly addicted to alcohol and cocaine.
- The opiate-dependent surgical specialist Bruce also lived through a childhood bereft of nurturing. "My father was not present," he said. "I did not have a father in my life, growing up. He walked out when I was quite young, four years old. And my mother was too young to assume the duties I needed from her. My mother had me when she was sixteen, and she just was a child herself, essentially. I lived my formative years really not having any support. I lived with a lot of pain."
- The world-renowned photographer Nan Goldin, who says she did drugs "most of my life," was eleven when her older sister died by suicide at eighteen. "That was a huge defining trauma for me," Goldin says. Defining, but

not primary. "I grew up in a very neurotic family," she recalls, understating things by some magnitude. "There was constant turmoil around my older sister . . . Some of my earliest memories were of her throwing things at everyone except me. They put her in mental hospitals, and even sent her to an orphanage. There was a lot of violence, a lot of chaos, a lot of screaming."

– When the late Downtown Eastside street poet Bud Osborn was three years old, his father hanged himself in jail, where the Toledo police had taken him after he tried to throw himself out of a window. "As a child Osborn regarded one person as a refuge: his grandmother," the Vancouver journalist Travis Lupick writes in *Fighting for Space*, his book on the drug policy reform movement, of which Osborn became a prominent leader. "She was shot and killed by his aunt, who then turned the gun on herself." As a five-year-old, Bud witnessed his mother being beaten and raped. A year later he hurled himself off the porch in an attempt to take his own life.

– Former *Saturday Night Live* star Darrell Hammond was physically and emotionally brutalized by his mother, as anyone will know who has watched the painful and self-revealing autobiographic documentary *Cracked Up*.

– Lena Dunham suffered sexual abuse at a young age, along with a factor that ensures such experiences will leave lasting traumatic effects: emotional isolation. In a recent therapy session under the influence of the medication ketamine, she experienced "witnessing this overwhelming grief about being alone in my childhood."

While each life history is particular, and while trauma has many faces, some generalization is both possible and necessary, particularly where abuse and neglect meet the lower strata of racial and class status. During my dozen years in Vancouver's Downtown Eastside, I came to learn that every one of my female patients—many of whom were Indigenous, many caught up in the sex trade—had been sexually abused in childhood or adolescence, one marker of the multigenerational legacy born of Canada's brutal colonial past. Multiple large-scale studies attest to the dynamic of childhood trauma, including sexual abuse, potentiating later addiction. According to one survey published in 1997, looking at more than one hundred thousand students, adolescents who had experienced either physical or sexual abuse were two to four times as likely to be using drugs as those who reported no such molestation.[8] The ones who suffered both physical and sexual abuse were at least twice as likely to be using drugs as others who had been subjected to either abuse by itself. Alcohol consumption has shown a similar pattern: in a national sample of ten thousand adolescents, those with histories of sexual abuse were three times more likely to begin drinking in adolescence.[9]

Now that we have cleared away the thicket of mistaken beliefs about addiction, gotten a sense of what it does for people under its sway, and begun to consider what sorts of life experiences would make those "perks" so palpable and attractive, I propose to pull back the curtain even further in the next chapter. It is yet another myth—at once convenient and highly damaging—that in our world there is a category we can label "addicts," designating some identifiable group of poor, unfortunate souls, and then, neatly segregated from "those people," there are the rest of us "normal" folks.

To twist a line from the great George Carlin, it's a big club—and we're all in it.

Chapter 16

Show of Hands:
A New View of Addiction

We are long overdue for a new perspective—both because
our understanding of the neuroscience underlying
addiction has changed and because so many
existing treatments simply don't work.

—Maia Szalavitz[†]

Having delineated what addiction is and isn't, and recognizing
its impetus and function in people's lives, I'd like to offer a new
working definition, one I believe is truer and more powerful
than its antecedents. In eschewing genetic determinism, it entails the possibility of healing. I should issue a caution, though.
While more precise and more hopeful, my definition is also
more ecumenical—it makes addiction's "big tent" even bigger.
You might just find yourself under it.

Addiction is a complex psychological, emotional, physiological, neurobiological, social, and spiritual process. It
manifests through any behavior in which a person finds
temporary relief or pleasure and therefore craves, but that
in the long term causes them or others negative conse-

[†]   From an article in the *New York Times* by this prolific journalist and author, herself in long-
term recovery ("Can You Get Over an Addiction?," June 25, 2016).

quences, and yet the person refuses or is unable to give it up. Accordingly, the three main hallmarks of addiction are

- short-term relief or pleasure and therefore craving;
- long-term suffering for oneself or others; and
- an inability to stop.

Two things to note right away: First, my definition omits disease—which is not to say that it must exclude it. As I articulated in chapter 6, most illnesses are best understood as complex processes manifesting a person's entire life, rather than discrete "things" in themselves. In the end, as with many conditions, calling addiction a disease may capture relevant aspects of it without coming close to explaining the phenomenon, let alone granting us a workable pathway to healing it at its source.

Second, this definition is not restricted to drugs. The same drive that often devotes itself to substances can activate any number of behaviors, from compulsive sexual roving to pornography; from inveterate shopping to the internet (both of which habits I know well); from gaming to gambling; from any sort of binge eating or drinking to purging; from work to extreme sports; from relentless exercising to compulsive relationship-seeking; from psychedelics to meditation. The issue is never the external target but one's internal relationship to it. Are you craving and partaking of something that affords you temporary relief or pleasure, inviting or incurring negative consequences but not giving it up? Welcome to the meeting. Free coffee in the back.

If you've seen me speak on this topic, whether in person or on YouTube, you'll probably know what I'm about to ask next. I usually pause here to invite a show of hands: "Who, by the definition just given, is now or ever has been addicted?" No matter the audience size, virtually no one's hand ever stays lowered—except, I like to jest, for the occasional liar's. That is how downright normal addictions are in our culture today. I invite you, fearless reader, to put yourself to the same test, with or without the hand-raising.

Of course, not all addictions are created equal, except in the broadest of broad strokes. My HIV- and hepatitis-C-ridden patients in the Downtown Eastside surely stand apart from most of us in the degrees of suffering that hurled them into their habits, in the extent to which their dependencies dominate their lives, and, too, in the dire consequences their habits visit upon them. This is to say nothing about the diminished inner or outer resources available to them, often for socioeconomic and racialized reasons not of their creation. They differ also in the degrees of ostracization and punishment society has inflicted and continues to inflict on them.

These acute differences of degree do matter, and we should not flatten or erase them. But they do not change the fact that the addiction process has certain intrinsic features known to all who live it. It spares no one, not even people at the top. That includes those whose destructive habits, in our culture's topsy-turvy value system, are spun as "success." Nor do these differences obviate the fact that most of us "normal" citizens bear far more resemblance than we'd be inclined to admit with those we deride or pity for their more severe or glaring dependencies. It's not even a fine line that separates "us," the upstanding, from "them," the downtrodden: it's a made-up one.

Here it helps to remember the severity spectrum when it comes to trauma. All kinds of suffering, from the less obvious developmental wounds we have called small-t to the more overt big-T traumas, can cry out for addictive pain relief. Again, trauma/injury is about what happens *inside* us, and how those effects persist, not what happens *to* us. An inquiry into "Why the pain?" has to leave space for the kinds of emotional injuries that may elude conscious recall or, much more often, seem unremarkable to the person doing the remembering.

It is not uncommon for people to tell themselves they enjoyed a "happy childhood." As long as life is going reasonably well, we may lack any reason to question this narrative. When addiction is present in oneself or a loved one, some inquiry is definitely in order.[†] Looking inward with compassion, most people will be able to locate themselves somewhere on the trauma/ psychological-injury spectrum. Genuine happy memories do not rule out emotional suffering, but the usual bias is to recall the former and to suppress awareness of the latter. It has been my experience that even people with the most insistent "happy childhood" narrative will, if asked the right questions, very quickly come to realize that their autobiography has been riddled with blind spots.

In 2015, the writer and theater artist Stephanie Wittels Wachs lost her younger brother, Harris, to an overdose. She herself is a self-acknowledged workaholic, to the detriment of her family life. Until she invited me onto her *Last Day* podcast, she was convinced—adamant, in fact—that she and Harris had grown up in a normal, happy home. Her remembered evidence for that normalcy and happiness included their mother's involvement in many school activities—field trip chaperone, president of the PTA, and so on—and a home life where the spousal roles were stable in the traditional sense: working dad, housewife mom. The sense of security inspired by all these arrangements may well have been real; it certainly sounds like Wittels Wachs

---

† This inquiry, of course, need not be exclusive to uncovering the sources of addiction: anyone manifesting any of the signs of developmental injury covered in this book, from mild to severe, mental or physical, stands to benefit from a compassionate self-investigation into their own histories of distress.

grew up with a mother and father who loved their children as best they could and provided for their physical and social needs. Yet embedded in that "normalcy" were experiences of profound emotional hurt she had completely discounted, until they were conjured up from the depths by my questions. "This whole exchange caught me off guard," she confessed to her listeners afterward. "He is absolutely fucking correct. My talking points on my happy childhood are incomplete."

David Sheff was likewise "caught off guard" by a similar realization. His book, *Beautiful Boy: A Father's Journey Through His Son's Addiction,* which depicts his son Nick's nearly fatal stimulant habit, was a bestseller and, more recently, the subject of a poignant film starring Steve Carell and Timothée Chalamet. There had been no big-*T* trauma in this family, no child abuse or dire adversity. Perplexed, Sheff was forced to ask himself uncomfortable questions to understand what had impelled his talented, vivacious, highly sensitive eldest child into a life-threatening addiction. Looking back, Sheff saw that Nick's pain must have originated early on, in the crucible of a dysfunctional parental relationship. "We shouldn't have been together," he told me. "We had terrible, terrible problems in our marriage." Self-delusion played a major role: even while engaging in an extramarital affair with a family friend, Sheff harbored "this fantasy in my mind that, you know, if I was happy and she was happy, the kids would be together and then we'd have this happy family and we'd be sort of freeing them from these two traumatic families . . . I actually believed that I was doing this in some ways for Nick. I was justifying it, trying to make it okay." It is to Sheff's credit that he has been willing to look back with open eyes at how it actually was. I don't know the details, but Sheff did say that he and his son are now having candid and mutually compassionate conversations about those days, with the shared understanding that the pain of Nick's childhood was a major driver of his later difficulties.

As I have, Dr. Dan Sumrok has met the occasional trauma skeptic. With a long, graying beard hanging mid-chest and a passionate oratory style, this friend and colleague of mine in addiction medicine seems the very vision of a biblical prophet. But if Dan is an evangelist for anything, it's sanity. Over his career as a family physician, first at the University of Tennessee medical school in Memphis, then in Nashville, and more recently in a rural area, he has treated nearly twenty-five thousand people with opiate addiction. He, too, sees past the medical view of addiction as disease, genetic or otherwise; in his experience, too, trauma is the foundational factor. "I began writing about this in 1980 when I was just discharged from the military. I was a first-year medical student, and my life was flying apart. I would say my best friends were George, Jack, and Jim—the whiskey brothers."[†] "Some people," Dan relates, "the real militant Twelve-Steppers, will say to me, and some of the treatment programs have said, 'You know, it's not all about trauma, Dr. Sumrok.' I do want to reassure them, so I say, 'I promise you, I'm keeping an open mind. I'm waiting to see the first person for whom it's not all about trauma.'" One would have to wait a long time.

Whatever the degree of injury, all addiction is a kind of refugee story: from intolerable feelings incurred through adversity and never processed, and into a state of temporary freedom, even if illusory. Again, try saying no to that.

It may surprise many to learn that no drug is in itself addictive, not even the most notorious "high risk" ones like crack or methamphetamine. Most people who try drugs, any drug, even repeatedly, never become addicted. The reasons why throw further light on the nature of addiction.

---

†   The Tennessee whiskey brands George Dickel, Jack Daniel's, and Jim Beam.

I often ask audiences, "Is alcohol addictive: yes or no? Is food addictive: yes or no? Or work: yes or no? Or sex: yes or no? Or pornography, or shopping: yes or no?" The right answer, embedded in the question, is "yes or no," depending on the degree of pain one needs to soothe.

San Diego internal medicine specialist Dr. Vincent Felitti was one of the lead investigators of the now famous (though not famous enough) Adverse Childhood Experiences (ACE) Study. The study emerged after Felitti decided to listen to the life histories of patients at an obesity clinic who all reported childhood traumas. Carried out in the 1990s in California's Kaiser Permanente health care network, the research showed that among a cohort of over seventeen thousand mostly Caucasian, middle-class persons, the more adversity a child had been exposed to, the greater the risk of addictions, mental health issues, and other medical problems they faced in adulthood.[1] Adversity was categorized under three general headings: abuse (psychological, physical, sexual); neglect (physical, emotional); household dysfunction (alcoholism or drug use in the home, divorce or loss of a biological parent, depression or mental illness in the home, mother treated violently, imprisoned household member). The impacts of such experiences did not merely add up; they multiplied each other. An adult reporting an ACE score of 6 had a risk of intravenous drug use forty-six-fold greater than a child with none of the adversities named.

"It is commonly believed," Felitti said, discussing his research, "that repeated use of many street drugs will in itself produce addiction. Our findings challenge those views . . . Addiction has relatively little to do with the supposed addictive properties of certain substances, other than their all providing a desirable psychoactive relief . . . In other words, this is an understandable attempt at self-treatment with something that *almost* works, thus creating a drive for further doses."[2]

Felitti's childhood adversity findings lay further waste to the myth of genetic determinism that I began debunking in the chapter on epigenetics. No single addiction gene has ever been found—nor ever will be. There may exist some collection of genes that predisposes people to susceptibility, but a predisposition is not the same as a predetermination. What's true of physical illness is just as true of addiction: genes are turned on and off by the environment, and we now know that early adversity affects genetic activity in ways that create a template for future dysfunction. Human and animal studies have both confirmed that any genetic risks for substance abuse can be offset by being reared in a nurturing environment.[3]

One of the happiest email acknowledgments I ever received was from the grateful mother of a four-year-old. Her husband, a former alcoholic, refused to have children, so afraid had he been of passing the "alcoholism gene" to his offspring. Having read my book on addiction, he recognized the traumatic sources of his alcohol habit and gave up his fear of this nonexistent gene. And just in time—his wife had been nearly past the child-bearing age. I couldn't suppress a self-satisfied chortle. I'd been thanked before for "saving" the lives of people I had never met, but never for having been the cause of one at long distance.

The way childhood adversity engenders the neurobiology of addiction has to do with the interpersonal-biological science we have already examined. Experiences of stress in the womb can predispose to addiction, for example, by altering the brain's ability to respond to stress in functional ways. They can also have long-term influence on the parts of the brain that modulate the incentive-motivation system impaired in all addictions, whether to drugs or behaviors.[†] As the psychiatric practitioner, neuroscientist, author, and leading trauma researcher Dr. Bruce Perry told me, "We've done work, and a lot of other people have done work, showing that essentially the number and density of dopamine receptors in these [brain] areas is determined in utero."[4]

Whoever coined the slang term "dope" for drugs was onto something, because all addictions, whether to drugs or behaviors, involve *dopamine*. Dopamine is the essential neurotransmitter in the motivation system, without which all mammals are inert, inactive, and lacking all incentive. A hungry laboratory mouse whose brain is artificially denuded of its dopamine apparatus will starve himself while standing in front of a plate of food. In fact, every addict is a dopamine fiend, outsourcing the hunt for the homegrown chemical hit that makes the present moment exciting and vibrant. For virtually every "positive" feeling or quality people derive from their substances or behavior of choice, there are endogenous—naturally occurring—brain chemicals implicated. Addiction begins as an attempt to induce feelings that we were biologically programmed to generate innately, and would have—if unhealthy development hadn't got in the way.

Sex addiction, for example, has nothing to do with a "high sex drive" and everything to do with dopamine. New York social worker and former Fordham and Rutgers Universities adjunct professor Zachary Alti specializes in sex therapy and behavioral addictions, particularly addiction to porn. "Studies are suggesting," he told me, "that when viewing a pornographic image, we get a dopamine spike in our brain. When viewing images after images, we get spike after spike after spike. Whereas with substance addictions you typically get one or a few spikes just before use, with behavioral addictions dopamine itself is the substance,

---

†   Or what Dr. Jaak Panksepp identified as the brain's SEEKING apparatus.

the primary component. Especially in pornography addiction, these dopamine spikes happen over and over and over again." As with smartphone and app companies, pornographers are well aware that their profits rest on the hijacking of their consumers' brains. The sociologist Gail Dines, author of the bracing 2010 book *Pornland: How Porn Has Hijacked Our Sexuality*, reports on an article in the trade publication *Adult Video News*, in which an industry insider trumpets a Stanford University study on cyber-sex addiction showing that 20 percent of porn users are hooked. "In a true capitalist approach," she notes, the article is cheerfully headed "Exploiting the Data."[5]

What about the feelings of love that people find in addictions, particularly with opiates—the warmth Jamie Lee Curtis and others spoke of? That is, in large part, a function of the brain's internal opiate apparatus in which endorphins, our own natural, endogenous opiates, are the neurotransmitters. Dr. Jaak Panksepp suggested twenty years ago that opiate addiction is rooted in the evolutionary brain mechanisms that promote social bonding: nurturing, emotional closeness, and social affiliation. "We would anticipate," he wrote, "that individuals who experience especially intense social distress and insecurities would be especially vulnerable to opiate abuse, and this prediction has been affirmed by some clinical research. Indeed, the same dynamic may help explain why opiate addictions are especially prevalent among the socially disenfranchised."[6] The current opioid overdose crisis in the United States, and to lesser degrees in Canada and the U.K., has tragically borne out the acuity of this observation.

The endorphin system, too, is dependent on supportive, attuned relationships early in life for its development. "Face-to-face interactions activate the child's sympathetic nervous system," writes Louis Cozolino, a clinical psychologist, neuroscientist, and professor of psychology at Pepperdine University. "These higher

levels of activation correlate with increased production of oxytocin, prolactin, endorphins, and dopamine; some of the same
biochemical systems involved in addiction."[7] A child's closeness
with the attuned, emotionally available parent promotes the
optimal growth of brain systems; the lack of it inhibits healthy
development.

Work has been the main, but not only, addiction of singer-
songwriter Alanis Morissette. In endorphin-friendly terms, she
now speaks of it as a compensation. "There's an attachment-
craving in being famous," she said when we spoke. "If you think
about it, eyeballs are on you. Everyone's hyper-responsive. Everyone's paying attention to you . . . You keep chasing that sense
of being loved and adored and stared at." Morissette was seeking
to attain through her fame that state of infant bliss so many miss
out on or experience all too briefly.

When Robert Palmer sang about being addicted to love, he
might have been speaking to all of us with our hands raised—all
the drug addicts, all the workaholics, all the compulsive gam-
blers and shoppers and eaters, all those hopelessly chasing the
next exciting high or soothing low. Except it's not really love we
get hooked on but our desperate attempts to cope with its lack,
by any means necessary.

Sobering stuff, I know. But we might as well face it.

Chapter 17

An Inaccurate Map of
Our Pain: What We Get Wrong
About Mental Illness

We don't understand any major mental disorder biologically.

—Professor Anne Harrington[†]

At age nineteen, a freshman journalism student at the University of Florida, Darrell Hammond was plunged into his first experience of searing mental distress. "I was in unspeakable terror," the comedian recalled. "That level of fear—I don't even know how I survived it. The doctors were treating me for depression and paranoia, and for psychosis because I told them that I had seen someone talking, and the words didn't come out at the same time their mouth was moving." He was prescribed an antidepressant, amitriptyline, as well as the antipsychotic thioridazine. Over the subsequent decades, Hammond estimated that he was evaluated by up to forty psychiatrists and labeled with multiple diagnoses, including depression, bipolar disorder, and complex PTSD, and he didn't recall what else. The assumption that guided his treatment was the same one that dominates much of medical thinking: that such torments are caused by a biological disease of the brain. Accordingly, he was treated with an ever-changing cocktail of medications. Throughout

---

†   Historian of science at Harvard University and author of *Mind Fixers: Psychiatry's Troubled Search for the Biology of Mental Illness*. CBC Radio interview, October 2019.

years of professional success, including an unprecedented fourteen-year run on *Saturday Night Live*—his range expressed in roles from Bill Clinton to, perhaps most belovedly, a jocularly vulgar Sean Connery—he continued to feel lost, irritable, isolated, and despondent. The only recourses he could find to interrupt his misery were self-medicating with alcohol and overt self-harm: his body still bears the scars of over fifty self-inflicted cuts.

Thirty-five years into his psychiatric odyssey, Hammond met a clinician, Dr. Nabil Kotbi at New York City's Weill Cornell Medical College, who changed his life with two short sentences: "I don't want you to call what you have a mental illness. You have been injured." The insight that his symptoms were not the manifestations of some mysterious medical condition, Hammond told me, "was a 'Hallelujah Chorus' moment . . . What [Dr. Kotbi] seemed to be saying to me was that mental illness comes from somewhere very specific. It has a story, and in that story, you're the only one that has no power." In the decades between his first encounter with the mental health system and his meeting this particular psychiatrist, no one had asked Hammond about traumatic childhood experiences. "I can't describe what it was like to go into a doctor's office, in acute pain, and have them look at me and go, 'You shouldn't be feeling this way.' No one at the time was saying, 'Hey, you're probably a victim of child abuse.' At that time, if you felt bad for no apparent reason, they called you bipolar. That's all they knew. 'He has unexplainable highs and lows,' you know. They treated me with [the mood stabilizers] lithium and then Depakote. Neither of those were successful. *Nothing* was really successful until the truth about my life was acknowledged." The truth of Hammond's life included a cavalcade of abuse at the hands of his mother.[†]

---

† The hit Netflix documentary *Cracked Up!*, directed by Michelle Esrick, catalogs the real-life horror show Hammond endured as a child. Dr. Kotbi is interviewed in the film.

While mental ailments certainly exhibit some features of ill-ness—the brain seeming to function like a disordered organ—mainstream psychiatry takes the biological emphasis too far, reducing everything mostly to an imbalance of DNA-dictated brain chemicals. Psychiatrist Kay Redfield Jamison, one of to-day's most eloquent authors on manic-depressive illness, also known as bipolar disorder, wrote the memoir *An Unquiet Mind*. This book is essential reading for anyone wanting to appreciate the experience of an exquisite consciousness oscillating from ep-isodes of hyper-elation to immobilizing despair. And yet, embed-ded in Dr. Jamison's gorgeously rendered recollections are faulty assumptions that exemplify the simplistic genetic narrative to which psychiatry still clings. Here she recalls a manic episode: "My mind was flying high that day, *courtesy of whatever witches' brew of neurotransmitters God had programmed into my genes.*" In truth, neither God nor genes have much to do with it.

In her *Touched with Fire*, an equally poignant book, Jamison puts it more explicitly, asserting that "the genetic basis for manic-depressive illness is especially compelling, indeed almost incontro-vertible."[1] Twenty-five years on, we know that the hard, scientific evidence is not only not compelling; it is nearly nonexistent. The "almost incontrovertible" proof Dr. Jamison relied on is the liter-ature on family histories, adoption, and twin studies, all of which are riddled with false assumptions.[‡] The proof she alludes to for

---

[‡] Traits can be passed on from one generation to the next without any DNA sequences being involved; and in identical twins, one cannot separate genetic effects from environmental ones, given identical siblings were gestated in the same uterus and most were brought up in the same family. If adopted to different families, they had still shared the same uterine environment and the same trauma of separation from their birth mother. I won't fatigue the reader here with a further critique of adoption studies, a subject I covered extensively in two of my previous books, on ADHD and addiction, respectively. See especially *In the Realm of Hungry Ghosts: Close Encounters with Addiction*, Appendix 1: "Adoption and Twin Study Fallacies." In brief, for all the attention they have received, twin and adoption studies prove very little, if anything. For an exhaustive refutation of twin-study "findings," see *The Trouble with Twin Studies*, by the psychologist Jay Joseph.

genetic causes is only "compelling" if one is already a believer: on the evidence itself, it is pure science fiction.[2] It is also inelegant: in my work with mental distress and addictions—including my own—I've always found more than enough in people's personal histories to account for their psychic suffering, without super-imposing a narrative dominated by genetic predetermination.

The term "mental illness," even as it describes real phenomena, focuses our attention centrally on brain physiology, analogous to how, say, anginal pain connotes a restriction of oxygen supply to the heart muscle, owing to narrowed cardiac arteries. It also implies that the problem necessarily falls within the domain of medicine. Despite whatever partial truths they contain, these assumptions are highly questionable and limit our understanding. Worse, they generate harm, both in the sense that they leave many people subjected to inappropriate treatments and in that they displace perspectives that could be far more complete, humane, and helpful. The biological determinism that governed Darrell Hammond's physicians also placed his condition beyond his own agency to heal, thereby rein-forcing the "You are the only one that has no power" story he spoke of. Such a view threatens to keep the sufferer largely in the position of passively receiving treatment, his symptoms ameliorated by med-ications to be ingested, in many cases, for a lifetime.

In its predominantly biological approach, psychiatry com-mits the same error as other medical specialties: it takes complex processes intricately bound with life experience and emotional development, slaps the "disease" label on them, and calls it a day.

Little in the training of doctors prepares them to wonder about their patients' lived experience, much less to seek the sources of their malaises therein. Simplistic explanations, which require lit-tle time or emotional energy, are an attractive fallback position. Many doctors are intensely uncomfortable facing their own hid-den sorrows and wounds—what Carl Jung called our shadow side. And not only doctors: as a well-known colleague told me, "Patients play into this as well. They don't want to look at their lives, either. It would involve getting into recovery, changing something. It's enormous work to recover from our childhoods. It's incredibly worthwhile, but it's a lot of work." The gospel of genetic causation shields us from having to confront our hurts, leaving us all the more at their mercy.

If anything, this limitation is especially calamitous in the realm of mental suffering, and even less justified. After all, unlike in cancer or rheumatoid arthritis, no physical findings, blood tests, biopsies, radiographs, or scans can either support or rule out psychiatric diagnoses. That statement may surprise many readers, so it bears repeating. There are *no measurable physical markers* of mental illness other than the subjective (a person's description of their own mood, say) and the behavioral (sleep patterns, appetite, etc.).

Like all concepts, mental illness is a *construct*—a particular frame we have developed to understand a phenomenon and explain what we observe. It may be valid in some respects and erroneous in others; it most definitely isn't objective. Unchecked, it becomes an all-encompassing lens through which we perceive and interpret. Such a way of seeing can say as much about the biases and values of the culture that gives rise to it as about the phenomenon being seen, whether a religious concept like "sinful" or a biomedical one like "mentally ill."[3] In some cultures, for example, people with visions may become prophets or shamans. In ours, most likely they would be deemed insane. One wonders how a Joan of Arc or the medieval saint and composer of sacred music Hildegard of Bingen would fare at the hands of the contemporary mental health system. I once speculated out loud, in front of an audience of hundreds, what would happen if I strode up to the prime minister of Canada and pronounced, Joan-like, that I have seen the future in which he leads the global fight against climate change, beginning with giving up his reliance on campaign funding from the fossil fuel industry.

Other than modern culture's typical, left-brain materialist bent, how did we arrive at this view of mental illness as an essentially biologically rooted phenomenon? In part, it seems to be a holdover from a once tantalizing aspiration in medical science, a mission unaccomplished. "Psychiatry today stands on the threshold of becoming an exact science, as precise and quantifiable as molecular genetics," wrote the journalist Jon Franklin in a Pulitzer Prize–winning series in 1984.[4] As with the ultimately unfulfilled promise of the genomic revolution to explain health and illness, the initial enthusiasm for the prospect of a science-based psychiatry was virtually unbounded. Nearly forty years later we are no closer to crossing this imagined threshold; if anything, we are further away. When the fifth edition of the *Diagnostic and Statistical Manual of Mental Disorders (DSM-5)* was published by the American Psychiatric Association in 2013, Dr. David Kupfer, head of the task force responsible for it, acknowledged as much. "In the future," he stated in a press release, "we hope to be able to identify disorders using biological and genetic markers that provide precise diagnoses that can be delivered with complete reliability and validity. Yet this promise, which we have anticipated since the 1970s, remains disappointingly distant. We've been telling patients for several decades that we are waiting for biomarkers. We're still waiting."[5]

The journalist and author Robert Whitaker, formerly the director of publications for Harvard Medical School, was a firm believer in the chemical-imbalance theory of mental illness—until he wasn't. "When I first started writing about psychiatry, I believed that to be true," he told me. "I mean, why wouldn't I?" His disillusionment arose from research he uncovered while reporting for the *Boston Globe*. "I said to people, 'Can you just tell me where you found that depression is due to serotonin or where you actually found that schizophrenia is due to too much dopamine?' I asked to read the source materials and, I swear to God, they said, 'Well, we didn't really find that. It's a metaphor.' The most amazing thing was, when you trace it in their own research, you find they didn't find it! The divergence from what you're being told from what is in their own scientific literature— that's the key—it was just stunning to me." These conspicuous non-findings are documented in Whitaker's book *Anatomy of an Epidemic* and have been corroborated in other literature.[6]

Contrary to what I, too, used to believe, a diagnosis like ADHD or depression or bipolar illness explains nothing. *No diagnosis ever does.* Diagnoses are abstractions, or summaries: sometimes helpful, always incomplete. They are professional shorthand for describing constellations of symptoms a person may report, or of other people's observations of someone's behavior patterns, thoughts, and emotions. For the individual in question, a diagnosis may seem to account for and validate a lifetime of experiences previously too diffuse or nebulous to put one's finger on. That can be a first and positive step toward healing. I know this from firsthand experience.

The dead end comes when we assume or believe that the diagnosis equals an explanation—an especially futile view when it comes to illnesses of something as inherently abstract as the mind. As the British psychologist Lucy Johnstone said to me, "In physical illness you have, in principle, a way of checking it out. You can say, 'Let's look at the blood test or the enzyme levels.' And you could, in most cases, confirm or disconfirm it. But in psychiatry, it's simply a circular argument, isn't it? Why does this person have mood swings? Because they have bipolar disorder. How do you know they have bipolar disorder? Because they have mood swings." My mind goes to A. A. Milne's Pooh and Piglet walking in the snow in an unwitting circle, shuddering as they come across yet more "Heffalump" tracks at every turn.

An oft-heard objection to mental health diagnoses, particularly with regard to children, is that they "pathologize" or "stigmatize" ordinary, healthy feelings or behaviors. Aren't kids supposed to get bored or antsy, angry or sad? My answer would be yes—and it's not that simple. While overdiagnosis is certainly a risk, I don't see the spike in, say, ADHD cases over the past decades as being due solely to gullible parents, hapless teachers, overzealous school shrinks, and unscrupulous drug companies. As I discussed in earlier chapters, the world into which kids are being born these days might as well have been designed to promote disruptions of cognitive function and emotional self-regulation. Everything I have seen tells me we *are* witnessing a sea change in children's mental well-being.

Why, then, do I persist in my critique of the diagnostic model? Because diagnoses reveal nothing about *the underlying events and dynamics that animate the perceptions and experiences in question.* They keep our gaze trained on effects and not their myriad causes. There could be multiple reasons why a child may have trouble paying attention or be restless, disengaged, and fidgety: anxiety, stresses at home, boredom with material she finds uninteresting, resistance to the constraints of sitting in a classroom, fear of bullying, an authoritarian teacher, trauma—even birth month, believe it or not. A University of British Columbia study looked at the prescription records of almost one million B.C. schoolchildren over an eleven-year period and found that kids born in December were 39 percent more likely to be diagnosed with ADHD than classmates born the previous January. The reason? December kids entered the same grade nearly a year younger than their January counterparts—they were eleven

months behind in brain development. They were being medicated not for a "genetic brain disorder" but for naturally delayed
maturation of the brain circuits of attention and self-regulation.[7]

Or consider the *DSM-5* diagnosis of oppositional defiant disorder (ODD), often tacked on to ADHD and other "diseases."
"If your child or teenager has a frequent and persistent pattern of
anger, irritability, arguing, defiance or vindictiveness toward you
and other authority figures, he or she may have oppositional defiant disorder," advises the Mayo Clinic.[8] The clue is in the word
"toward": oppositionality, by definition, can arise only in the
context of a relationship. I can suffer symptoms of a cold in isolation, or break my ankle on my own. I cannot oppose anyone or
be angry or irritable with anyone unless that "anyone" is in some
relationship with me. "If you don't believe me," I sometimes tell
audiences of therapists, parents, teachers, or medical professionals, "just lock yourself in your room tonight, make sure you
are absolutely alone, and oppose somebody. If you succeed, put
it on YouTube—it'll go viral in no time."

Given that a child develops in the context of relationships,
her behavior will be intelligible to us only if we look at the relational environment. Seen this way, these so-called ODD kids
turn out to be ones who lack sufficient connection with nurturing adults and have a natural resistance to being controlled by
people they do not fully trust or feel close enough to. This aversion, furthermore, is only magnified by all attempts to shame or
cajole it into submission. To call this "disordered" says nothing
about the child's inner experience; it reflects only the perspective of the ones who find his recalcitrance inconvenient. It is also
completely obtuse about how emotional power dynamics work:
there is nothing disordered in resisting authority figures that, for
whatever reason, we do not feel confident in and safe with.

If we are today seeing more youngsters in automatic resistance mode, the question we must return to is, How does this culture disrupt healthy adult-child relationships? Why are we diagnosing children with a disorder, instead of "diagnosing"—and treating—their families, communities, schools, and society?

The psychiatrist, author, and leading trauma researcher Bruce Perry[†] has come to disdain diagnoses almost completely. This is no knee-jerk prejudice: his dim view of the norms and practices of his field follows decades spent assessing tens of thousands of troubled children, and extensive contributions to the vast literature on adversity and what we define as "disorders." "When I got into psychiatry," Dr. Perry told me, "it became clear really quickly that the diagnoses were not connected to the physiology, that they were just descriptive, and that there were hundreds of physiological routes to somebody having an attention problem, for example. And yet the profession acted as if these descriptive labels were *really a thing* . . . I knew that if we were doing 'research,' if we were using these hollow descriptors which we call 'diagnoses' and then study interventions and outcomes, we would just get garbage. And that's what we've done."

These days Dr. Perry is adamant that "even playing the *DSM* game is completely wrong." When invited to contribute to one of the manual's editions, he refused. "I said, 'Listen, in twenty-five years they are going to look back and won't believe that we thought about people that way.' It's not a valid way to think about the complexities of human beings." He practices what he preaches in the clinic he helps run. "We haven't used diagnoses for fifteen, twenty years," he said, "and it really has not interfered with our ability to do good clinical work. In fact, we're able to do better clinical work without using those labels."

[†]   Currently senior fellow of the Child Trauma Academy in Houston, Texas, and an adjunct professor of psychiatry and behavioral sciences at the Feinberg School of Medicine in Chicago, and, most recently, coauthor, with Oprah Winfrey, of the bestselling *What Happened to You?*

Based on my observations in family practice and my understanding of human development, I have followed the same lines. When I work with any mental health condition, say depression or anxiety or ADHD or addiction, I'm not so interested in the formal diagnosis as such. My "diagnostic" focus goes to the specific challenges the person is facing in their life and the traumas animating those challenges. As for "prescriptions," I am primarily interested in what will promote the healing of the psychic wounds the ongoing traumatic patterns represent.

Now, here's a perhaps surprising assertion: I'm not anti-pharmacology. No one who's felt or witnessed the beneficial effects of psychiatric drugs can deny that neurobiology must, indeed, play a role in the dynamics and potential easing of mental distress, just as it does in all our experiences. Sometimes the healing of which I just spoke can be helped along—not made to happen, certainly, but assisted—by the intelligent use of these medications. That is not just my professional opinion but my personal experience as well.

In my mid-forties, I decided to go on the serotonin-enhancing drug Prozac. (Among the brain's principal neurotransmitters, or chemical messengers, serotonin is believed to be active in such functions as mood regulation and the dampening of aggression.) The skepticism I harbored about this growing trend to medicate millions was eclipsed by my hunger for respite from the daily severities of my state of mind, as summed up grimly in a diary entry from that time: "*I have no energy for life. I have spent every weekend for the past two months—every free weekend—in an enervated, passive, demoralized state, depressed and depressing to be with.*"

I was soon a different person. Within days, my wife noted with relief the softening of my facial features. I now greeted mornings with vim instead of venom, lost my irritability around my family, smiled and laughed a lot more, and could feel and express tenderness where before I'd been cold and brittle. It was as if someone had bandaged my aching heart so that it no longer hurt or bruised at the slightest touch. I found myself marveling to my sister-in-law: "You mean people can feel like this normally? I had no idea!" My experience was similar to what, some years later, the writer Elizabeth Wurtzel would depict in her 1994 personal account *Prozac Nation*. "One morning I woke up and really did want to live," she wrote. "It was as if the miasma of depression had lifted off me, in the same way that the fog in San Francisco rises as the day wears on. Was it the Prozac? No doubt."

As happens with many new converts, my initial reticence quickly gave way to a period of outsize enthusiasm. In my medical practice I became something of a Prozac booster, succumbing to the error of looking for pathology where there was only everyday unhappiness. "You have a chemical imbalance in your brain—you are lacking serotonin," I would earnestly explain to patients in whom I detected symptoms of depression, prescription pad at the ready. Little did I know that I was uttering scientific nonfacts. Yes, the medication was helping me, at least in the short term. And yes, I have witnessed other cases where psychiatric drugs were life-enhancing and even lifesaving. But we have to avoid the fallacy of inferring from medication's (in some cases) observable benefits that the proven *origin* of mental illness rests in the biochemistry of the brain, let alone that physiological disturbances are genetically caused.

That a medication has a certain positive effect reveals nothing about the genesis of a symptom. If aspirin eases a headache, can the headache be explained by an inherited brain deficiency of acetylsalicylic acid, the pill's active ingredient? If a shot of bourbon relaxes you, is your tense nervous system suffering from a DNA-dictated whiskey shortage? There are fifty or more neurotransmitters in the brain whose complex interactions we are only now beginning to explore, not to mention the almost infinite possibilities inherent in the lifelong intersection of experience with the biology of body and brain. Once again, the physiology of the brain is a manifestation and a product of life in motion and in context.

Further, as Bruce Perry writes, "The brain is a historical organ. It stores our personal narrative." Since it does so in the form of its chemistry and its neural networks, it is no wonder that difficult experiences may result in disturbed neurobiology. Even when brain scans show certain abnormalities—as they do, for example, in many traumatized people—these do not prove that the "disorder" has a neurochemical *source*. A recently published thirty-year study followed people from early life to age twenty-nine. Poor quality of care in infancy was, nearly three decades later, associated with a higher volume of the emotionally key brain structure, the hippocampus, as well as with an elevated risk for "borderline personality" features and suicidality. In other words, the brain's genetics did not "cause" either the "illness" or the neurophysiological differences: all were the result of life experience.[9]

The British author Johann Hari has explored addictions and depression from both the personal and journalistic points of view. In his bestselling work *Lost Connections*, he relates his own experience of devastatingly low moods, followed by his initial elation at the depression diagnosis that, at last, "explained" his disturbing mind states. "This will sound odd," he writes, "but what I experienced at that moment was a happy jolt—like unexpectedly finding a pile of money down the back of your sofa. There is a term for feeling like this! It is a medical condition, like diabetes or irritable bowel syndrome."

Like mine, Hari's first experience of medications was positive.

"It was only years later," he relates in *Lost Connections*, "that somebody pointed out to me all the questions the doctor didn't ask that day. Like: Is there any reason you might feel distressed? What's been happening in your life? Is there anything hurting you we might want to change?" The answers would have been yeses all around: Hari was carrying both past trauma and present stress that he took to be part of his "normal." Over time, he came to recognize that the narrow medical model that had helped him manage his symptoms was also leaving him far short of healing. He is not entirely jaded about the biological approach, he told me, but he also noted with sorrow that "it has crowded out the much more common-sense insights that people have about why they become distressed and how to resolve their distress. Really—how do I put it—it's given us an inaccurate map of our own pain."

It is known beyond controversy that the greater the degree of childhood adversity, the higher the risk of mental disturbances, including psychosis. One study found that people who had suffered five types of maltreatment in childhood were multiple times more likely to be diagnosed with psychosis than those who had not experienced such traumatic events.[10] A major review in 2018 in the *Schizophrenia Bulletin* concluded that the severity of childhood traumas was correlated with the intensity of delusions and hallucinations.[11] Richard Bentall, a clinical psychologist, academic, and Fellow of the British Academy, summed up the science a few years ago: "The evidence of a link between childhood misfortune and future psychiatric disorder is about as strong statistically as the link between smoking and lung cancer," he wrote. "There is also now strong evidence that these kinds of experiences affect brain structure, explaining many of the abnormal neuro-imaging findings that have been reported for psychiatric patients."[12] This mirrored a Harvard study that concluded,

"These brain changes may be best understood as *adaptive responses to facilitate survival and reproduction in the face of adversity*. Their relationship to psychopathology is complex."[13]

There is something scientists reviewing research papers will not say, although it is manifestly evident to many clinicians working with mental distress: overt maltreatment is not necessary to exert negative impacts on the neurobiology of the brain or the functioning of the mind. Neurobiology is a continuum, as are "mental illness" and health. Emotional injury during development can have physiological consequences, even *without* abuse or neglect. As Bruce Perry explains, adverse childhood experiences—of the big-ticket kind that merit the official ACE designation—are of consequence, but "not as determinative as your history in relationships . . . The most powerful predictor of your functioning in the present is your current relational connectedness and then the second most powerful component that we see is your history of connectedness."

_____

"Don't be so sensitive," people are often told. In other words, "Don't be so yourself." Genetic vulnerabilities do not code for illness, but they may confer sensitivity for a person being more impacted by life's vicissitudes than someone else with a hardier predisposition—a far from trivial effect. Sensitive people feel more, feel deeply, and are more easily overwhelmed by stress, not just subjectively but physiologically. Both monkeys and humans, for example, can inherit genes involved in the production of certain brain chemicals such as serotonin that can make them more susceptible to negative experiences—or, on the other hand, more amenable to the effect of positive ones. (And, of course, sensitivity, too, is a continuum.)

"Genes affect how sensitive one is to environment, and environment affects how relevant one's genetic differences may be," the leading geneticist R. C. Lewontin has said. "When an environment changes, all bets are off."[14] Some people will feel more pain and will therefore have greater need to escape into the adaptations that mental illness, or addiction, represent. They will have more need to tune out, to dissociate, to split into parts, to develop fantasies to account for realities they are unable to endure. But that's a far cry from saying that they have a heritable neurobiological disease. These are the children that Tom Boyce, a professor of pediatrics and psychiatry at the University of California, San Francisco, describes as *orchids*, "exquisitely sensitive to their environment, making them especially vulnerable under conditions of adversity but unusually vital, creative, and successful within supportive, nurturing environments."[15] The same "sensitivity" genes that in a stressed environment can help potentiate mental suffering may, under positive circumstances, help promote stronger mental resilience and therefore happiness.[16] Sensitive people have the potential to be more aware, insightful, inventive, artistic, and empathic, if their sensitivity is not crushed by maltreatment or disdain. The most sensitive of our kind have made some of the most lasting cultural contributions; many of these have also suffered the most intense pains during their lives. Sensitivity can be the quintessential combo package: gift and curse, all in one.

Many of the people I've met with mental illness exhibit this quality, sometimes to astounding degrees. I'll never forget a conversation I had as a medical student with a psychotic young man about my age. Tall and disheveled, he gazed at me with piercing eyes as I lobbed him some questions related to a meaningless research project for which I was getting paid. Inwardly, I was awed by his insights into life, society, the secrets of existence, into human beings. I was wishing as I listened that I could have access to such awareness. "It's not true what you're thinking," he abruptly interjected. "It's not true I'm more intelligent than you are."

———

Despite the genetic hoopla in the popular media and all the lavishly funded DNA-hunting in the scientific world, no one has ever identified any gene that causes mental illness, nor any group of genes that code for specific mental health conditions or are required for the presence of mental disorder. Professor Jehannine Austin, an academic and researcher, leads a genetic counseling clinic for mental health in Vancouver.† "Everybody has some genes that predispose to mental illness," she told me, but these are "a very, very long way away from causing anything . . . Literally what separates those of us who do suffer from those of us that don't is *what happens to us during our lives*."

I believe there is more than meets the eye when it comes to the persistent appetite for genetic causes. There are the factors I've already covered: reticence to face trauma on the one hand, and the neglect of developmental science on the other. There is also the standard-issue preference for a simple and quickly understood explanation, along with our tendency to look for one-to-one causations for almost everything. Life in its wondrous complexity does not conform to such easy reductions.

Other psychological and sociological dynamics add to the adhesive appeal of genetic theories. The first shouldn't come as any news: we all hate feeling culpable. Whether as individuals for our own actions, as parents for our children's hurts, or as a society for our many failings, we have our ten-foot poles at the ready when accountability comes to call. Genetics—that neutral, impersonal

———

†   Full credentials: Ph.D., FCAHS, CGC; professor and Canada research chair, UBC Departments of Psychiatry and Medical Genetics; executive director, BC Mental Health and Substance Use Services Research Institute.

handmaiden of Nature—seems to absolve us of responsibility and of its ominous shadow, guilt. If genes truly rule our fate like capricious, microscopic gods, then we are off the hook.

The genetic argument is used to justify social inequalities and injustices that are otherwise hard to defend. Much like junk sciences of the past—phrenology, eugenics, and so on—it serves a deeply conservative function: if phenomena like addiction or mental distress are determined mostly by biological heredity, we are spared from having to look at how our social environment supports, or does not support, the parents of young children, and at how social attitudes, prejudices, and policies burden, stress, and exclude certain segments of the population, thereby increasing their propensity for suffering. The writer Louis Menand said it well in a *New Yorker* article: " 'It's all in the genes': an explanation for the way things are *that does not threaten the way things are*. Why should someone feel unhappy or engage in antisocial behavior when that person is living in the freest and most prosperous nation on earth? It can't be the system! There must be a flaw in the wiring somewhere."[17]

There is a stark paradox in all this. To the extent that we cling to genetic fundamentalism to avoid the discomforts of personal responsibility or societal reckoning, we radically—and unnecessarily—disempower ourselves from dealing either actively or proactively with suffering of all kinds. It is entirely possible to embrace responsibility without taking on the useless baggage of guilt or blame. Even more regrettably, we miss the excellent news that if our mental health is not dictated by our genes, then we are not their victims. On the contrary, there is much we can do, each and all.

Chapter 18
The Mind Can Do Some Amazing Things: From Madness to Meaning

Perhaps the line between sanity and madness must be drawn relative to the place where we stand. Perhaps it is possible to be, at the same time, mad when viewed from one perspective and sane when viewed from another.

—Richard Bentall, *Madness Explained: Psychosis and Human Nature*

If we are not to see mental distress solely as illness, then what is it? The view I have come to favor is of a piece with how I approach many other conditions under the "illness" umbrella: rather than seeing it as an intruder from the outside, consider what it might be expressing about the life in which it arises. This framework is, if anything, all the more intuitive when it comes to afflictions that take up unwanted residence in the mind, in a person's emotional world, in the personality.

Let's begin with something rather simple, now on the rise: depression, a state I know intimately. The word's literal meaning is quite telling. To *depress* something means to push it down, as one might a beach ball in a swimming pool. I like that analogy especially because one can easily feel how much concerted force it takes to keep the ball submerged, and the way it "wants" to find a way back up to the surface. Keeping it down takes a toll.

What is pushed down when a person is depressed is easily identified by its absence: emotion, the continual flow of feelings that remind us we're alive. Unlike the wrangler of the beach ball, a depressed person doesn't choose this submersion of life energy—it imposes itself, turning a once-vibrant emotional landscape into arid desert. The only "feeling" that remains, typically, is more sensation than emotion, a thrumming, indistinct pain that threatens to consume everything, and sometimes does. If we label this depression of feeling a disease, we risk not recognizing its original adaptive function: to distance oneself from emotions that are unbearable at a time in life when to experience them is to court greater calamity. Recall what I called the tragic tension between authenticity and attachment. When experiencing and expressing what we feel threatens our closest relationships, we suppress. More accurately, *we* don't: our mind does that automatically and unconsciously on our behalf.

The origin story of my own depression is easy to trace. It is documented in the trove of family photographs, from infancy onward, in which there is hardly ever even a hint of a smile on my face. Gazing at you from these pictures is a child who, at best, is serious beyond his age, when not morose. Under the conditions of war and genocide, I absorbed the feelings of my grief-stricken and terrorized mother; in my earliest photos I see my little self almost mirroring them. "The child can . . . feel the tension, rigidity and pain in the body of the mother or of anyone else he is with," writes the psychological thinker and spiritual teacher A. H. Almaas. "If the mother is suffering, the baby suffers too. The pain never gets discharged."[1] I could not have endured such emotional torment if I had felt it fully—no infant could. Nor was there room for my own sorrow and rage at the separation from my mother at less than one year of age.

As I have noted before, such extreme circumstances as beset my infancy and childhood are not required to induce a splitting from self. The riskiest emotions, and thus the most frequently exiled, are acute grief and healthy anger, two feelings that often get tarred as "negative."† Of course, a child may also have cause to banish her joy, enthusiasm, or pride if these arouse disapproval, envy, or just blank incomprehension on the part of parents too stressed, distracted, or depressed themselves. Either way, repressing the rejected emotion is the surest way of escaping overwhelming levels of vulnerability, of avoiding a too-painful rift between oneself and the ambient world. There is a catch, however: we cannot select which emotions to force below consciousness, nor willfully reverse the mechanism even after it has outlived its usefulness. "Everybody knows there is no finesse or accuracy of suppression," wrote the American novelist Saul Bellow in *The Adventures of Augie March*; "if you hold down one thing, you hold down the adjoining." Thus the repression of emotion, while adaptive in one circumstance, can become a state of chronic disconnect, a withdrawal from life. It becomes programmed into the brain, embedded in the personality.

The neuroscientist Jaak Panksepp, who studied the biology of the brain's emotional systems as thoroughly as anyone, had scathing words for the physiological disease model. "Popular depictions of depression as a 'chemical imbalance' are trivial . . . [All] problems in living, including death, are accompanied by 'chemical imbalances,' " he pointed out. He, too, saw depression as an adaptation of the brain to the loss of connection, as a physiological "shutdown mechanism" to terminate distress, "which, if sustained, would be dangerous for infant mammals."[2] In other

---

† By contrast, recall that we are born with evolution-programmed RAGE and GRIEF circuits in our brains.

words, far from expressing inherited pathology, depression appears as a coping mechanism to alleviate grief and rage and to inhibit behaviors that would invite danger. It is not that neurotransmitters are not involved in depression—only that their abnormalities *reflect* experiences, rather than being the primary *cause* of them. Brain disturbances manifest the stresses of existence during formative periods and, once established, become a source of further stress. Hence follow, Dr. Panksepp concluded, "the diverse symptoms and variants of depressive illness."

It has been transformative for me to realize that my own mental health issues carry genuine meanings that arose from my life within my family of origin in a particular historical context. I have found the same to be true universally, no matter where I look, whose mental "illness" I consider, or indeed how extreme the condition happens to be. If anything, the more flagrant ones are easier to decode. When examined, the manifestations of all the various mental health diagnoses have meaning, from depression through what is called schizophrenia to attention deficit hyperactivity disorder, from troubled eating patterns to self-cutting.

"Before becoming a clinical psychologist, I was considered by some to be a seriously mentally ill patient," New York therapist Noël Hunter recalls in her book *Trauma and Madness in Mental Health Services*. Prior to seeking help in early adulthood, she had been living with intense distress and a sense of "being controlled." "I was just all over the place," she told me, "and was very scared of being hospitalized. I saw about six or seven different psychologists, social workers, psychiatrists at that time, and accrued about eight different diagnoses throughout all of that as well." She was placed on five medications, which she was assured she would have to rely on for the rest of her life. "I feared having my own children one day lest I pass on my genetic faults," she writes. "The fact that there was unfathomable abuse throughout my entire family, that coldness and greed superseded nurturance and love, and that emotional neglect was balanced only by an intrusive lack of boundaries all seemed irrelevant."[3] The meaning, once sought, was crystal clear and had nothing of the insane in it: Hunter's "paranoia" was a faithful, unerring emotional imprint of childhood. Without getting into the details, there had been a time in her life when, young and helpless, she *was* controlled by powerful, hostile figures in ways she found hurtful and scary, ways that violated her neural expectations and distorted her sense of reality.

The mind is a meaning-making machine. It will generate stories that "make sense" of the emotions that, at a vulnerable time, it could not contain and perhaps still cannot. Yet in the individual's unspoken history, the emotions were real, and therefore still are. They can surface in a number of different ways, such as Dr. Hunter's belief in being "controlled" as a young adult. To other minds, such narratives appear as madness itself. "It comes out as somewhat fantastical, so we say, 'That's totally non-understandable,'" Hunter remarked. In my experience, the story underneath diagnostic labels like hers is always perfectly coherent if one seeks the truth in the emotional texture and the biographical record rather than in the *content* of the paranoid fantasy. Coming to see this coherence and integrate it into her sense of self has enabled Hunter to understand and regulate herself differently. Today she is long off her "lifetime" pharmacological agents. I have witnessed many such examples and know of many more.

Forty-year-old Leslie, a recently certified therapist who is now pursuing an MA in psychology, made over a dozen suicide attempts or serious suicidal gestures from age seventeen to her mid-thirties. Leslie was plagued by chronic insomnia, cried uncontrollably, and could not maintain relationships. Her medical chart was a smorgasbord of *DSM* nomenclature: chronic depression, borderline personality disorder, dysthymia, panic disorder, ADHD, and, briefly, bipolar disorder. She had also been diagnosed with chronic cystitis and fibromyalgia. At one point she was on five different psychiatric medications, including two antidepressants, an antipsychotic, and a benzodiazepine tranquilizer, and was prescribed a third antidepressant intended to soothe her physical pain, along with an anti-inflammatory.

Leslie's healing journey—she, too, is no longer on any medications—has centered on finding the meaning in her multifaceted sufferings. Her crushing belief in her unworthiness revealed itself to be a self-protective strategy gone awry. Odd as it may sound, it was the best worst option. A suffering child, as Leslie was—again, the details matter less than the contours— has two possible options when it comes to processing her experience. She can conclude either that the people she relies on for love are incompetent, malicious, or otherwise ill-suited to the task, and she is all alone in this scary world; or that she herself is to blame for, well, everything. As painful as the latter explanation is, it is far preferable to the other one, which paints a life-threatening picture for a young being with zero power or recourse. The first option is not an option at all. Better to believe "It's my fault; I'm bad," which lets you believe there's the chance that "if I work hard and be good, I will be lovable." Thus, even the debilitating belief in one's unworthiness, nearly universal among people with mental health diagnoses and addictions, begins as a coping mechanism, a topic we will revisit in chapter 30.

What of Leslie's chronic state of panic? Her supposed "brain disorder" was, in fact, the expression of a mind alarmed by early hurt. It is adaptive for the brain of a child in her situation to be in a state of hyperalert fear, even when no immediate danger is present. These adaptations to adversity, once habitual, cannot discern between major and minor threats—or no threat at all. The capacity to recognize safety or threat will evolve in a healthy way under conditions of safety but be disrupted by prolonged early insecurity. Possible outcomes include feeling besieged when there is no threat, or conversely, remaining oblivious to danger when it is present.[4]

Leslie has even learned to have compassion for her self-hurting compulsions. "They were actually trying to protect me from the deep pain that I was in or trying not to feel," she said. These included hitting herself with a leather belt, as her mother had done when Leslie was a child. When I asked her what that did for her, she answered: "It would kind of calm me down a bit. I would be *less dysregulated.*" Surprising but true: the very mental patterns and behaviors that seem to throw our lives into such chaos originate as an attempt, a temporarily and partially effective one, to *regulate* our nervous systems, to bring our bodies and minds to equilibrium.

The incidence of self-cutting is rising, particularly among young people. If we resist the default to "mental illness" as an explanation for such acts, we might ask instead: Why do people harm themselves? As in Leslie's case, these behaviors play the role, paradoxically enough, of self-soothing. They bring short-term relief. That more and more people are resorting to self-harm is a marker of the growing prevalence of stress and trauma. The comedian Darrell Hammond told me that cutting himself afforded him "a crisis that's more manageable than the terror inside you, the one that's going on in your head . . . You look at a cutter's arms; those aren't suicide cuts. Those aren't death cuts. Those are either 'I want someone to know I'm in distress,' or 'When I start patching this arm up, running and finding the Band-Aid, and cleaning myself up, I have a crisis, but it's manageable, and the one in my head was not.'" The Canadian Indigenous writer Helen Knott depicts the same process with scorching eloquence: "Those brief moments of the sharp blade dragging across skin provided me with a relief from the hate that I felt for myself. It was as if the moment the skin opened up, it became a vent that poured out all of my fucked-up whirling emotions . . . I didn't want to die at that time—that's not what cutting was about. I was doing it so I could put up with living."[5]

Thus, many actions and beliefs that look like pure insanity from one perspective make sense from another—and *always made sense at the start*. It is our task, if healing is the goal, to make sense of them newly, now, with the benefit of adult discernment and compassion.

We can derive this same lesson from the tragic life of the great comic actor Robin Williams. On August 10, 2014, the night before he died by suicide, Williams attended a soiree in his posh San Francisco Bay Area neighborhood. The others at the party would have seen the effervescent, people-loving persona for which he was so well known. Underneath that mask, he was in despair.

Williams was in the throes of Lewy body disease, a neurodegenerative brain disorder characterized by Parkinsonian symptoms and advancing dementia. Unlike depression or anxiety, this ailment does have distinct physiological markings, even if they can be identified only in an autopsy. "Robin was losing his mind and he was aware of it," his wife revealed after his death. "He kept saying, 'I just want to reboot my brain.'" The thought of suicide, however, was not new to him; in a 2010 interview he recriminated himself for "not having the balls to do it."

In addition to the madcap, on-the-fly brilliance of his work as a comic, he had a sweetness and vulnerability that touched many hearts, a love that poured out into the world but that he could never extend to himself.

The founts of the comedian's anguish can be located in his

childhood. The author Anne Lamott grew up near Williams in Illinois. In a much-circulated Facebook post, she wrote that, as children, "we were in the same boat—scared, shy, with terrible self-esteem and grandiosity." His lifelong dilemma, she said, would remain "how to stay one step ahead of the abyss."

In the same post, Lamott alluded to heredity as a likely cause of her friend's sufferings. Yet I hear in Williams's own words more than enough information to account for his mental-emotional woes without resorting to genetic superstitions. "My only companions, my only friends as a child were my imagination," he once said, an admission of profound loneliness.[6] He initially honed his extraordinary capacity to generate strange and hilarious imaginary characters as a way of breaking his isolation, in a family with an emotionally distant mother and a father he recalled as "frightening." As many sensitive kids are in the peer culture, he was bullied at school. He found some freedom in fantasy, as his characters "could say and do things I was afraid to do myself." His comic skills had the original function of gaining him some closeness with his mother. "You get this weird desire to connect with her through comedy and entertainment," he told the podcaster Marc Maron in 2010. His wording was unkind to himself: there is nothing weird about a child seeking attachment with his parent. What is abnormal is that any child should have to do so. Hence the same coping mechanisms that potentiated his greatest gifts ended up becoming the bars of his prison—the double bind of the hypersensitive child, once again. Underneath his brilliantly turbulent comic persona, he learned to suppress his real feelings. He was past master at that, until his death.

Cocaine, he once implied, gave him respite from his super-charged energy, just as a hyperactive child may be given the stimulant Ritalin to settle him. He had the addict's lifelong discomfort with the self, the need to flee from his consciousness of himself:

"sleepwalking with activity," he called it. In an episode of the hit 1970s television series *Mork & Mindy*, he played both the outer space arrival Mork and his real self. "You know, if you learned to say no, you'd probably have a lot more time to yourself," Mindy tells the comedian. "Maybe that's the last thing I want," Robin replies, with an ineffably sad expression on his face.

It wasn't for lack of self-awareness that the abyss got the better of Williams in the end. Long before he developed a degenerative disorder, he suffered from what he called "please-love-me syndrome," a self-diagnosis far more penetrating than anything a *DSM*-toting psychiatrist could come up with. I find myself wishing someone had guided him to connect the dots, to see that "syndrome" as the emotional endoskeleton of his manic-depressive swings, addictions, and suicidality, and very likely his terminal brain condition as well.[†] From there, he could have traced the links back even further to the scared, isolated child he once had been. He might have found the meaning that could have saved him.

What, then, of conditions widely believed to be brain diseases, largely rooted in genetics, such as the group of diverse behaviors and thought patterns called schizophrenia, marked often by psychoses, delusions, and hallucinations? The science is clear and, again, belies popular prejudice. No "schizophrenia gene" has ever been found—or, more accurately, claims of its discovery have had to be serially retracted. Broad surveys have found that at most only about 4 percent of the risk can be attributed to a wide variety of genes—none of them specific to this condition, as they are also seen in cases of ADHD or autism.[8] Again, what

---

[†] A scientific aside to Williams's story is that research has now linked the onset of Parkinson's—a close relative of Lewy body disease—with chronic depression and stress. See endnote 7 to this chapter.

is being transmitted, if anything, is sensitivity and not disease. Even the nomenclature should give us pause: the Greek origin of "schizophrenia" means "split mind." The question follows naturally: Why would a mind need to split itself?

Self-fragmentation is one of the defenses evoked when the experience of how things are cannot be endured. Only those who know real life to be an insufferable bane are impelled to check out from it. No fixed genetic destiny here, but a survival need composed of constitutional vulnerability and overwhelming life experience. One way for an organism to escape that agony, whatever its source, is to disconnect whenever the distressing emotions are triggered. In the face of trauma, splitting from the present is a form of instantaneous self-defense.[9] From that perspective, it is a miraculous dynamic allowing vulnerable creatures to survive the unendurable.

In psychoses there occurs a prime feature of severe mental illness, disintegration. In such extreme states, with normally related mental processes utterly separated, the person may be completely detached from the here and now. Such is the case in schizophrenia, but absenting oneself from reality can show up in a range of forms from mild to severe, depending on the degree of hurt and the genetic sensitivity of the individual.

A milder flight from reality is dissociation. Helen Knott, subjected to sexual exploitation when very young, describes it well: "My feelings left my body. My spirit sat outside of me like an unacknowledged apparition. I didn't know whose life I was living, whose body I inhabited. This wasn't my story, my life, my reality . . . I was scared that if I tried to lean into my feelings, I would fall off the emotional edge and I didn't know what I would do to myself."[10] What we call a disorder is revealed to be an ingenious means for an assaulted psyche to absent itself from agony.

Such is also the recollection of the former National Hockey League star Theoren Fleury, who was sexually assaulted by his coach as a teenager and went on to become an advocate for childhood victims of sexual abuse. "The first few times he got at me weren't so bad because I was gone. I would open my eyes and he would be standing over me, cleaning himself up. I knew something had happened, but I was not sure what. The mind can do some amazing things. Even years later in therapy, when telling the counselor about it, I would check out—leave my body. She'd have to literally shake me to bring me back."[11] Horrific though the inciting circumstances were, I hear in Fleury's use of the word "amazing" an appreciation for the parts of himself that mobilized way back when to protect him from pain—an attitude I heartily recommend to anyone making similar discoveries.

———

A chronic, reflexive tuning out is one of the hallmarks of attention deficit hyperactivity disorder (ADHD),[†] now being diagnosed worldwide with increasing and alarming frequency. This is not dissociation-level "out of body"–ness, but it does disconnect one from oneself, from one's activities, and from other people in ways that disrupt functioning and are, as I personally attest, often highly frustrating. ADHD's features include poor attention span, distractibility and low boredom threshold, poor impulse control, and (mostly in males) difficulty being still. Millions of children are receiving stimulants as a result, and hundreds of thousands are even being treated with antipsychotic medications—not for psychosis, but simply to calm them, to make them more pliable. This amounts to a vast and uncontrolled social experiment in the chemical control of children's behavior, since we don't know the

———

[†]   Also known as ADD, to denote that the hyperactivity may not always be present. In practice, and confusingly, the two acronyms are often used interchangeably.

long-term effects of such drugs on the developing brain. What we do know from adult research should give us pause. It has been understood since at least 2010 that prolonged use of antipsychotics is associated with shrinkage of brain volume in adult subjects.[12] In children we are already witnessing some short-term systemic harm. Here in Vancouver, British Columbia Children's Hospital has had to establish a special clinic just to deal with the metabolic consequences of such drugs, which include obesity, diabetes, and threats to cardiovascular health.

ADHD is sometimes said to be the "most heritable" mental illness, which in my view is a bit like calling quartz the most chewable crystal. Some experts estimate—I should say misestimate—the heritability of ADHD traits to be in the range of 30 to 50 percent.[13] The genetic thesis never made sense to me, even though two of my children and I myself have been diagnosed with this "brain disease." Tuning out is dissociation's less extreme cousin, part of the same family of escapist adaptations. It is invoked by the organism when the circumstances are stressful and there is no other recourse for relief, when one can neither change the situation nor escape it. Such was the imperative in my own infancy. Such, too, was the situation for my three sensitive children—a trait they may well have inherited, as discussed in the last chapter—in an emotionally chaotic home characterized, amid plenty of love, by parental anxiety, depression, and conflict. This adaptation then becomes wired into the brain, without the brain itself being the original source of the problem.

It's true that we are seeing more troubled children these days, but blaming a child's behavior on her brain makes no sense—nor does blaming the parents. As we have seen with other conditions, when a syndrome rises sharply in frequency over a short period of time, genetics cannot possibly be the cause. Jaak Panksepp suggested that ADHD is not a brain disease but a problem stemming partly from the thwarted development, in modern societal conditions, of what he called the innate PLAY system. His proposed solution: more play opportunities for children, to encourage the "construction of the social brain."[14]

Just as depression is "explained" by the biologically minded as resulting from a lack of the neurotransmitter serotonin, ADHD is chalked up to an insufficiency of dopamine, the brain's incentive-motivation molecule. So we prescribe dopamine-enhancing stimulants, such as Ritalin or Adderall. While dopamine certainly seems to be implicated, here, too, medical practice ignores the interaction of physiology and environment. Today, voluminous research has linked the symptoms of ADHD to trauma or early stress, and has shown that both can impact the dopamine circuits of the brain and that adversity can interfere with a child's subsequent capacity to focus and to organize tasks.[15, 16] Such trauma or early stresses can include maternal depression or more overt disturbances in the family milieu. One study reviewed data involving sixty-five thousand children aged six through seventeen years. The parents of those diagnosed with ADHD reported much higher prevalence of adverse events.[17]

The time has come to address the swiftly changing and ever more stressful environments our children are growing up in, before we interfere chemically with children's brain physiology. When I saw children who met the criteria for this condition, my approach was to consider the family milieu and to help parents understand the stresses they were unwittingly transmitting to their offspring. These children were in every case the proverbial canaries in the coal mine. Sensitive to the nth degree, their "symptoms" expressed the unresolved travails of the entire family system, itself often overwhelmed by the pressures exerted by a culture increasingly unfriendly to development. If we saw the condition and its associated traits as manifestations of biopsychosocial underdevelopment rather than as symptoms of a disease, we would ask ourselves how to provide the right conditions for healthy brain plasticity and psychological growth. We—physicians, parents, educators—would honor the neurobiology of relationship above all.†

We might well learn from our canine friends. A veterinary publication in 2017 reported that some "problem dogs"—more hyper, more distractible, and less obedient than others—can be treated with stimulant medications to abate the "symptoms," rendering them more trainable. "Of more interest is the fact that certain environmental and social conditions affect the appearance of ADHD symptoms," reported *Psychology Today*. "Dogs which have lots of social contacts with other dogs and many interactions with people seem to show fewer symptoms [typical] of ADHD. The more that you physically connect with and play with the dog, the fewer the problems. Dogs that are left alone for extended periods of time are also more likely to show hyperactive symptoms on your return. Another interesting association the researchers found is that dogs who sleep alone (isolated from their owner or other dogs) have more problems."[18] If only psychologists, physicians, and educators had as much insight and empathic imagination as these veterinarians, perhaps fewer children would be medicated.

———

Meaning, when sought, readily shows up as well in bipolar illness, also known as manic-depressive disorder. "I got sick for the first time when I was twenty-one," Caterina recalled. "It turned into a full-blown psychotic episode. I thought I was the epitome

———

†   Though I am not categorically against the use of medications in ADHD, I decry the automatic, extensive, long-term, and almost exclusive reliance on them. For more, see my book *Scattered Minds: The Origins and Healing of Attention Deficit Disorder*.

of evil. I felt I was this horrible thing that doesn't deserve to exist. I would go into catatonic states and hear voices, all telling me about my unworthiness, my evil nature."

This interview was unique in that it took place in the presence of Caterina's parents, instead of the usual one-on-one. They had intuited that their daughter's problems arose from something beyond her brain chemistry and requested my input.

Caterina's manic episode ensued after a hostile argument with her mother. "I felt hurt and angry at something she said," Caterina reported. "I thought I had ruined my family and that we were all going to fall apart. At first it was scary . . . but then it started feeling really good, and it progressed and progressed until I felt like I was very powerful—I could save the world. I wasn't a force of destruction anymore; I could put all the art back in the world." (Now twenty-six, she studies art in Toronto.) Typically for the manic state, Caterina felt hyperenergized and did not sleep for a week until she was admitted to a psychiatric hospital. The medications she was prescribed eased her symptoms, but she was not guided to ponder the source of her delusions of malevolent or magnificently benign power. "Do you think that is something we have to look at?" she asked me. "My psychiatrists thought that delusions are just like having a fever." I replied with a question of my own. "What if your delusions are perfectly accurate? Not accurate in a concrete sense, but accurate to your emotional reality?" I pointed out that both fantasies—"I had ruined my family" and "I could save the world"—have something in common. Caterina was quick to catch the similarity: "In both, I have a sense of control! I'm very powerful."

The source of that sense of overweening power soon began to surface. "My parents went through a really hard time when I was eleven," Caterina recalled. "They would have horrible fights at night . . . and they would scream at each other. My dad would cry to me . . . *understandably,* because he was going through a lot, and we were really close." That "closeness," really an unhealthy lack of boundaries that psychologists call "fusion," had persisted throughout Caterina's formative years. Harmful as the dynamic was, in Caterina's mind it was her moral duty to protect her parents: she wore her inability to hold her family together like a badge of shame, proof of her unworthiness. Absorbing a parent's sorrow is not the Nature-given responsibility of a child. "The reversal of roles between child, or adolescent, and parent, unless very temporary, is almost always not only a sign of pathology in the parent but *a cause of it in the child,*" wrote the great pioneer of attachment research and personality development, the British psychiatrist John Bowlby.[19]

Caterina's psychotic phase can be seen as a kind of inner haunting wherein all the intense emotions she'd had to stuff away as a child in order to carry out her "understandable" role came to take over her adult mind. Her parents, who had themselves been traumatized in their families of origin and by political tragedies in their home countries, were unable to handle their own emotions, never mind their young daughter's. All in all, her self-accusations of ungodly wickedness and her delusions of near-divine potency were two poles of a "power" she never should have been burdened with.

A study in 2013 looked at nearly six hundred French and Norwegian subjects with a bipolar diagnosis. "Our results demonstrate consistent associations between childhood trauma and more severe clinical characteristics in bipolar disorder," the researchers reported. "Further, they show the importance of including emotional abuse as well as the more frequently investigated sexual abuse when targeting clinical characteristics of bipolar disorder."[20] Once again, let's note that the subtler forms of emotional injury, such as those Caterina sustained as a child, while more difficult to study, are no less harmful to the sensitive youngster.

"So, do you think people should focus on the emotional content of delusions and try to understand them?" Caterina asked me as we wrapped up. "Do you think that's a way of healing, rather than medicating them?" "It's not necessarily a question of *rather than*," I suggested. "If you weren't on medication, you'd not be able to have this conversation right now. My problem with the usual approach is not that doctors give medication; only, too often, that's all they do."

I advised the family to pursue therapy to sort out their individual traumas and mutual enmeshment.

Extensive scientific literature now links disordered relationships to food, as well, with early trauma and family stress. Recall that the seminal Adverse Childhood Experiences (ACE) Study began after the lead investigator, Dr. Vincent Felitti, began to pay heed to the life histories of patients at the obesity clinic where he served as medical director. "We could help them lose weight," Dr. Felitti told me, "but not to keep it off. I kept wondering why, until I finally got the message. 'Don't you get it?' they said. 'We're stuffing down our pain.' "

As with other people with "genetic" mental health problems, which anorexia is often considered to be, the personal histories of individuals always reveal meaning. A medical colleague who suffered from anorexia as a teenager, for example, is a self-described perfectionist, a trait that nobody is born with. Rather, it arises as an adaptation to fit in with an environment where one perceives no welcome for being just who one is, with all one's "imperfections."

Much as with addictions or self-harming behaviors, or conditions like obsessive-compulsive disorder, there is always a "pay-off" with disordered eating patterns. At age seventeen, Andrea, now twenty-seven, became "super, super meticulous" about what she would eat. "I would cook for other people, and I would never eat it. But everything that I would eat for myself was always weighed out, measured out. When I was in university, I remember eating Greek yogurt and granola or muesli for breakfast, and I would measure out absolutely everything in measuring cups. Everything would go into a tracker so I knew what I was eating. It was the ultimate form of control." At five feet seven, Andrea went down to 106 pounds.[†] She did not menstruate for seven years.

When asked what she "got" from her self-denial, she said: "It's that sense of control, and also self-acceptance. It made me feel better about myself, because I had control of what I was doing, essentially." Although she recalled a "not bad" childhood, her mother, Cathy—who participated in our interview—was able to correct the record. She and her husband divorced when Andrea was six, after years of intense marital stress. A child in such circumstances is prone to lack self-acceptance and yearn for agency in an emotionally unstable environment.

This desperate drive to seize some command at least of their own body amid turmoil is almost universal among people with anorexia or bulimia that I have interviewed. The psychologist Julie T. Anné, who specializes in treating eating disorders, nails it: with her clients, she says, "three lacks" are typical—lack of control, identity, and self-worth—along with a need to numb pain. "In a relational world . . . the human psyche devises a brilliant means to emotionally survive," she told me. "In our culture, this becomes the pursuit of perfection vis-à-vis the body and self. Also known as anorexia." And yet these deeply wounded individuals, like the

---

† 170 cm and 48 kg, respectively.

bearers of every mental-emotional burden we have touched on, are all too rarely asked the key questions: *Where did this come from?* and *What valid problem is it trying to fix?*

One of Robin Williams's most beloved performances, for which he won an Academy Award, is in *Good Will Hunting*, where he appears in the role of a kindly psychologist tasked with helping an angry Boston janitor after the latter assaults a cop. Played by Matt Damon, this gifted man—he turns out to be an intellectual diamond in the rough—has stuffed his vulnerability underneath a layer of ossified rage and defiance. The most iconic scene from the movie features Williams's therapist getting right in Damon's face and repeating a simple but powerful statement, "It's not your fault," until the latter finally collapses, sobbing, into his embrace. That message, "It's not your fault," conveys not just undaunted compassion, for which Damon's character was starving inside, but wisdom, too. From behavioral problems to full-blown mental illness, it's not *anyone's* fault—nor, as we've seen, the fault of their brains or their genes. It is an expression of untended wounds, *and it is meaningful.*

The meaning extends beyond people's individual lives, their families of origin, and their childhoods. If we are going to address the myriad afflictions to which this book has devoted its attention so far, we need to look through a wider lens at the bigger story. If I could distill my message and insert it into that beautiful cinematic moment, I would have Robin Williams look all of us in the eye—including himself—and say with assurance: "It's not your fault . . . *and it's not personal.*" It's about our hurting world, manifesting the illusions and myths of a culture alienated from our essence.

We turn to that bigger picture next.

Part IV

The Toxicities of Our Culture

Making an injury visible and public is often the first step in remedying it, and political change often follows culture, as what was tolerated is seen to be intolerable, or what was overlooked becomes obvious.

—Rebecca Solnit, *Hope in the Dark*

Chapter 19

From Society to Cell: Uncertainty, Conflict, and Loss of Control

The history of the world is the history of a ten-thousand-year
war of brains between the rich and the poor . . . The poor
win a few battles . . . but of course the rich have won the
war for ten thousand years.

—Aravind Adiga, *The White Tiger*

We know that chronic stress, whatever its source, puts the nervous system on edge, distorts the hormonal apparatus, impairs immunity, promotes inflammation, and undermines physical and mental well-being. I see it on a daily basis, and I agree with János Selye, the father of stress research, who "without hesitation" asserted "that for man the most important stressors are emotional."[1] At this stage in our exploration of trauma, illness, and healing I would only add that the main determinants of human emotional stress extend from the personal to the cultural. We are, in effect, biopsycho*societal* beings.

To review what we've seen about stress so far: First, its physiology and consequences include the acute or chronic activation, potential overactivation, and even exhaustion of the hypothalamic-pituitary-adrenal (HPA) axis that connects our brain's emotional centers and the body's entire physiological apparatus.[†] Then there's what Bruce McEwen has called "allostatic load": the wear and tear on the body of having to maintain its internal equilibrium in the face of changing and challenging circumstances, trauma salient among them. In this culture many people are fated to be bearers of heavy allostatic loads, to the detriment of their mental and physical health, as demonstrated, if more proof were needed, by a recent Yale study showing the cumulative impact of stress on accelerated biological aging. "Our society is experiencing more stress than ever before, leading to both negative psychiatric and physical outcomes," the researchers noted.[2]

Of course, there is no "equality of opportunity" in stress, any more than there is in economic life. The structure of a society based on power and wealth, with built-in disparities along racial and gender lines, leaves some people far more physiologically burdened than others. It is true that in a culture that recruits individuals and groups into a fearful competition against others, the psychological triggers for stress spare no social tier, but the fact remains that their effects are unevenly distributed. And while the *personal* stresses of a disconnect from the self and the loss of authenticity may cut across class lines, the allostatic strain imposed by imbalances of power falls most onerously on the politically disempowered and economically disenfranchised.

What, in our society, are the most widespread emotional triggers for stress? My own observations of self and others have led me to endorse fully what a review of the stress literature concluded, namely that "psychological factors such as *uncertainty, conflict, lack of control, and lack of information* are considered the most stressful stimuli and strongly activate the HPA axis."[3] A society that breeds these conditions, as capitalism inevitably does, is a superpowered generator of stressors that tax human health.

[†]   Chapters 2 and 3.

Capitalism is "far more than just an economic doctrine," Yuval Noah Harari observes in his influential bestseller *Sapiens*. "It now encompasses an ethic—a set of teachings about how people should behave, educate their children, and even think. Its principal tenet is that economic growth is the supreme good, or at least a proxy for the supreme good, because justice, freedom, and even happiness all depend on economic growth."[4] Capitalism's influence today runs so deep and wide that its values, assumptions, and expectations potently infuse not only culture, politics, and law but also such subsystems as academia, education, science, news, sports, medicine, child-rearing, and popular entertainment. The hegemony of materialist culture is now total, its discontents universal. We explore how it affects our very health in this and the following chapters.

In medical school I was trained to think of life and health in purely individualistic terms. That we have a hard time *not* seeing things this way is, itself, a quintessential feature of the "normal" worldview engendered by capitalism.

In this, as in much else, the medical system mirrors and reinforces the prevailing ethic. In an atomized, materialistic culture people are induced to take everything personally, to see their own mental and physical distress as misfortunes or even failures belonging to them alone. Take the picture painted by the former British prime minister Tony Blair, to this day a sought-after, well-remunerated spokesperson for the desocializing ethic—that is, for bleaching the "social" out of society. Many health problems, he said, are "not, strictly speaking, public health problems at all. They are questions of lifestyle: obesity, smoking, alcohol abuse, diabetes, sexually transmitted diseases . . . These are not epidemics in the epidemiological sense—they are the result of millions of *individual decisions*, at millions of points in time."[5] This perspective denotes a blithe unawareness of the many studies linking all these "millions of decisions" to trauma and stress, including the stresses imposed by low socioeconomic or occupational status, and poverty—a festering sore in British society since the dismantling of the "welfare state" and communal institutions, along with the disempowering of labor unions. That underlying such "individual decisions" is the social milieu fostered by late-stage capitalism seems not to have occurred to Mr. Blair, despite considerable evidence. This is no surprise: a refusal to recognize broad economic and political conditions as relevant to individual health and happiness is a core feature of materialistic ideology. No one inclined to connect those dots would ever be entrusted with the keys to the kingdom.

Culture acts on our well-being via all manner of biopsychosocial pathways, including epigenetic causes; stress-induced inflammation; impairment of telomeres and premature aging; how and what we eat; toxins we ingest or inhale. It exerts its influences through many other outside-in mechanisms, too: through effects passed on from parents to children; from one person to another; from social, political, and economic conditions to individual bodies—"from society to cell," in the words of the molecular scientist and researcher Michael Kobor. Contra the Blairite view, it also powerfully influences and constrains nearly all the "individual decisions" most of us make with regard to our well-being.

All stressors represent the absence or threatened loss of something an organism perceives as necessary for survival. An impending loss of food supply, for example, is a major stressor for any creature. So is, for our species, the absence or threatened loss of love, or work, or dignity, or self-esteem, or meaning.

In 2020, a few weeks before the novel coronavirus metastasized to devastate the world economy, no less a figure than Kristalina

Georgieva—head of the International Monetary Fund, that executive planning committee of international capital—was already warning that the global economy risked returning to the woeful conditions of the Great Depression, owing to inequality and financial-sector instability. "If I had to identify a theme at the outset of the new decade," she said, "it would be increasing uncertainty."[6] The majority of the population in my own country, for one, did not require this alarming forecast to know that things were not looking up. Just a month before the IMF head issued her prediction, nearly 90 percent of Canadians expressed the concern that food prices were rising faster than their incomes. About one in eight Canadian households experienced food insecurity in the previous year.[7] In my home province of British Columbia in 2017, 52 percent of women reported "extreme emotional stress" regarding their financial situation.[8] Such trends are international and have been growing for decades.

The burgeoning of chronic mental and physical health conditions across many countries in the past decades, from depression to diabetes, can be no coincidence. "Neoliberalism[†] has made the world of work far less secure and consequently more stressful and health damaging," write two British health academics, ". . . resulting in a myriad of chronic diseases including musculoskeletal pain and cardiovascular disease."[9] I find that unsurprising, living as we do under a system that habitually foments the stress of mass uncertainty. Globalization, with its ruinous policies dictated to so-called developing countries by bodies like the International Monetary Fund and the World Bank—such as cutting back social supports, suppressing workers' rights, and

---

[†] Although the term "neoliberalism" is mostly employed nowadays by critics of the erosion of social programs, the increasing power of the corporations, their laissez-faire ideology, and their sway over governments under late-stage capitalism, it was originally coined in the 1930s by prominent advocates of just such policies. My use of it is in itself neither critical nor laudatory: it refers to an objective reality whose health impacts we are investigating.

encouraging privatization—has also permeated the industrialized nations. It's what the Canadian political philosopher John Ralston Saul called "the crucifixion theory of economics: you had to be killed economically and socially in order to be reborn clean and healthy."[10]

The health impacts of our economic system are neither hard to understand nor difficult to track. A 2013 study comparing the health and stress status of young Swedes to young Greeks during the financial catastrophe then engulfing Greece found the Athens students to be at a marked disadvantage. They reported higher levels of stress, harbored "lower hope for the future," and suffered "significantly more widespread symptoms of depression and anxiety," as well as, ominously, *lower* cortisol levels.[11] The latter is a marker of long-term stress: a sign that people's healthy, protective stress-response mechanism was burning out. It often augurs future disease.[†] "One can suspect that the social crisis in Greece is beginning to have biological effects on the residents of the country," the study warned. Similarly, in Canada it was found that when women are under economic pressure, their children's stress-hormone levels rise markedly by age six, elevating the risk of illness later in life.[12]

Many people exist at the mercy of forces completely beyond their power to affect, let alone control. Who knows when the next cyclic recession will strike or when yet another megabusiness will downsize, merge, or relocate so that livelihoods are jeopardized with barely a day's notice. Even prior to COVID-19's economic ravages, one had become almost inured to news that yet another corporation was declaring masses of employees redundant. "High Street Crisis Deepens as 3,150 Staff Lose Jobs in a Week" was a headline in the *Guardian* in January 2020, a few

---

† To clarify, both chronically elevated *and* lowered cortisol levels signal overburdening of the body's stress apparatus: the former its excessive activation, the latter its debilitation.

weeks before the pandemic arrived in Britain. Only months earlier, the *New York Times* had reported on the deepening insecurity of American families: "The costs of housing, health care and education are consuming ever larger shares of household budgets and have risen faster than incomes. Today's middle-class families are working longer, managing new kinds of stress and shouldering greater financial risks than previous generations did."[13] As the famed anthropologist, researcher, and author Wade Davis remarked recently in a broadly circulated *Rolling Stone* piece, "Though living in a nation that celebrates itself as the wealthiest in history, most Americans live on a high wire, with no safety net to brace a fall."[14] A better blueprint for allostatic overload could not be imagined.

Although the world's most advanced capitalist country evinces the rawest individualistic ethic, leaving the majority of its people mired in insecurity, we are not speaking of a uniquely American trend. Such is the overweening economic and cultural influence of the U.S. throughout the world that, as Morris Berman has argued, "If the twentieth century was the 'American century' the twenty-first will be the 'Americanized century.' "[15] The Organisation for Economic Co-operation and Development reported that pressures on the middle class around the world have increased since the 1980s.[16] Thus on the very terrain in which capitalism stakes its greatest claims to success—economic achievement—we find many people in a state of chronic uncertainty and loss of control, subject to stress-inducing fears that translate into disturbances of the hormonal apparatus, of the immune system, and of the entire organism.

No wonder, then, that insecurity about work or the loss of it can instigate disease. Studies in the United States showed that the risk of stroke and heart attacks in people fifty-one to sixty-one years of age more than doubles in the aftermath of prolonged job loss.[17] The results hold even after the expected increase in stress-related behaviors such as smoking, drinking, and eating are taken into account. In fact, multiple job losses have been shown to raise the risk of heart attacks as much as cigarettes, alcohol, and hypertension.[18] Even the *fear* of losing one's job is just as strong a predictor of an older person's health as it actually happening. In the decade and a half between the late 1970s and the mid-1990s, the proportion of American employees of major corporations who professed themselves "frequently concerned about being laid off" nearly doubled, from 24 to 46 percent.[19] Jobs with time pressure, fast pace, and high workload, coupled with decreased control over such factors, are also associated with increased stress and ill health.[20]

A signature marker of stress is inflammation. I've encountered the links between the two in many of the patients under my care. Inflammation is implicated in an extensive range of pathologies, from autoimmune conditions to vascular disease of heart and brain, from cancer to depression. One of my most penetrating interviews for this book was with the scientist Dr. Steven Cole. "A theme that comes up over and over and again," Cole said, "is this increase in inflammatory gene activity in people confronting a sense of threat or insecurity for more than a short period of time. We can detect these same in mice, in monkeys. As far down as in fish, you can see that the more stress or threat or uncertainty you're exposed to, the more the body turns on this defensive program that involves more inflammation."

While most people experience loss of control and waning security, others enjoy a surfeit of these. For this stratum of society, even conflict is not such a source of stress—in any struggle, the greater the power, the less the threat. It used to be that only people accused of Marxist tendencies would speak of "class war." In recent years, though, the actuality of elite dominance and the assault on the middle and lower classes has struck home across ideological lines. No less an authority than the multibillionaire investment tycoon Warren Buffett has seen the writing on the wall. "There's class warfare, all right," he told the *New York Times* in 2006, "but it's my class, the rich class, that's making war, and we're winning."[21] The ice-cream magnate Ben Cohen, a wealthy man with a social conscience, put it even more frankly, telling the same paper in 2020: "What we have in America is a democracy that's run for the benefit of corporations. That's a disaster. We're looking at it, we're living it and it continues to get worse."[22] In our globalized world, America's way of doing things is the template for many countries.

Even Nobel Prize–winning economists like Joseph E. Stiglitz have joined the chorus. Stiglitz is as credentialed an expert as they come: apart from his Nobel laurels, he was chief economist for the World Bank and chairman of President Bill Clinton's Council of Economic Advisers. As such, he used to formulate many of the policies whose effects he has now come to rue. Currently a professor at Columbia University, he has documented and decried the social, political, and health impacts of rising inequality throughout the elite-ruled globalized world. He laments what he calls a shift "from social cohesion to class warfare."

"The political system seems to be failing as much as the economic system," Stiglitz writes in his 2012 book, *The Price of Inequality*. In the eyes of many, he continues, "capitalism is failing to produce what was promised, but is delivering on what was not promised—inequality, pollution, unemployment, and *most important of all*, the degradation of values to the point where everything is acceptable and no one is accountable."[23] (Italics in original.)

Here the analysis by Stiglitz and other latter-day critics of capitalism reveals its limitations. What if, I would put to them, the system is not failing at all but succeeding magnificently? To suppose that its demonstrated harms represent a "failure" is to ignore that for some people—who also happen to be the class gaining most of the wealth and wielding the most power—the system is functioning smoothly indeed. The Swiss bank UBS reported in October 2020 that during the COVID-19-induced market turmoil the international billionaire stratum had grown their fortunes to over ten trillion dollars between April and July of that year. The world's then richest individual, Amazon founder Jeff Bezos, had increased his wealth by over $74 billion; Tesla owner Elon Musk by up to $103 billion.[24] "Canada's top 20 billionaires collectively have become $37 billion richer," the *Toronto Star* reported. "That's in the midst of an economic crisis that has left millions of Canadians unemployed or working reduced hours and struggling with bills, and our governments are borrowing to fund emergency financial aid for individuals and businesses to stave off even greater hardship."[25]

The notion that capitalism is *meant* to provide equality and opportunity for all must be taken on faith, since history and material reality provide no evidence for it.

In the realm of political decision-making, a widely circulated U.S. study showed that the views of ordinary people make no difference to public policy: a lack of control on a mass scale.[†] "When a majority of citizens disagree with economic elites or with organized interests, they generally lose," the authors concluded, adding that "even when fairly large majorities favor policy change, they generally do not get it."[26]

"Why do the rich have so much power?" asks a *New York Times* piece by Stiglitz's fellow Nobel laureate in economics Paul

---

†   Reported extensively, for example, in the *New York Times*, the *New Yorker*, and in many other publications, not to mention the academic literature.

Krugman—another erstwhile advocate, since reformed, of the globalizing impetus fueling the dominance of multinational corporations over governments and the public. Because, he answers his own question, "America is less of a democracy and more of an oligarchy."[27] In this light, I find little reason to question the astute assertion of consumer advocate and social crusader Ralph Nader that the two leading political parties in the United States are, in practice, "one corporate party wearing two heads and different makeup." In many other countries, too, behind the democratic facade real power is wielded by the moneyed few.

Where does that leave the rest of us? When he was installed as rector at Glasgow University in 1972, the spirited Scottish labor leader Jimmy Reid gave an address that the *New York Times* called "the greatest speech since President Lincoln's Gettysburg Address."‡ Reid may not have studied the psychology or neurobiology of stress, but he understood everything about uncertainty, loss of control, and conflict in the lives of the people he represented. "Alienation is the precise and correctly applied word for describing the major social problem in Britain today," he declared. "People feel alienated by society . . . Let me right at the outset define what I mean by alienation. It is the cry of men who feel themselves the victims of blind economic forces beyond their control. It's the frustration of ordinary people excluded from the processes of decision-making. The feeling of despair and hopelessness that pervades people who feel with justification that they have no real say in shaping or determining their own destinies."[28]

Keep in mind, Reid's speech was given at the tail end of a brief postwar era of relatively enlightened social programs, at a time the system he excoriated was exhibiting its most benevolent face. What might he say today?

---

‡ A Scottish friend of mine opined that the *Times* thereby flattered the American president.

Chapter 20

Robbing the Human Spirit: Disconnection and Its Discontents

Whereas individual people can become dislocated by misfortunes in any society, only a free-market society produces mass dislocation as part of its normal functioning, even during periods of prosperity.

—Bruce Alexander, *The Globalization of Addiction*

As a speaker on stress and trauma I'm often asked what lessons we may derive from the COVID-19 pandemic. Chief among them, surely, is the indispensability of connection—a quality globalized materialism has increasingly drained from modern culture, long before the isolation imposed by the virus reminded us of life's spiritual impoverishment without it. The health impacts are immeasurable.

It is now de rigueur for observers of all political hues and philosophical persuasions to bewail the glaring, growing absence of social feeling. "That basic sense of peoplehood, of belonging to a common enterprise with a shared destiny, is exactly what's lacking today," the oft-insightful conservative columnist David Brooks wrote recently in the *New York Times*.[1] Lacking, we might say, by design: qualities like love, trust, caring, social conscience, and engagement are inevitable casualties—"sunk costs," in capitalist argot—of a culture that prizes acquisition above all else.

A society that fails to value communality—our need to belong, to care for one another, and to feel caring energy flowing toward us—is a society facing away from the essence of what it means to be human. Pathology cannot but ensue. To say so is not a moral assertion but an objective assessment. "When people start to lose a sense of meaning and get disconnected, that's where disease comes from, that's where breakdown in our health—mental, physical, social health—occurs," the psychiatrist and neuroscientist Bruce Perry told me. If a gene or virus were found that caused the same impacts on the population's well-being as disconnection does, news of it would bellow from front-page headlines. Because it transpires on so many levels and so pervasively, we almost take it for granted; it is the water we swim in. We are steeped in the normalized myth that we are, each of us, mere individuals striving to attain private goals. The more we define ourselves that way, the more estranged we become from vital aspects of who we are and what we need to be healthy.

Among psychologists there is wide-ranging consensus about what our core needs consist of, some of which we have already explored. These have been variously listed as:

- *belonging, relatedness,* or *connectedness;*
- *autonomy:* a sense of control in one's life;
- *mastery* or *competence;*
- *genuine self-esteem,* not dependent on achievement, attainment, acquisition, or valuation by others;
- *trust:* a sense of having the personal and social resources needed to sustain one through life; and
- *purpose, meaning, transcendence:* knowing oneself as part of something larger than isolated, self-centered concerns, whether that something is overtly spiritual or simply universal/humanistic, or, given our evolutionary

origins, Nature. "The statement that the physical and mental life of man, and nature, are interdependent means simply that nature is interdependent with itself, for man is a part of nature." So wrote a twenty-six-year-old Karl Marx in 1844.[2]

None of this tells you anything you don't already know or intuit. You can check your own experience: What's it like when each of the above needs is met? What happens in your mind and body when it's lacking, denied, or withdrawn?

Bruce Alexander is the author of the essential volume *The Globalization of Addiction: A Study in Poverty of the Spirit* and a professor emeritus of psychology at Simon Fraser University. We both worked with the socially ostracized drug-user community in Vancouver's Downtown Eastside in the early 2000s. To hear Bruce tell it, such a choice of career path would have confounded his younger self, enthralled as he was by the ideology of materialist selfishness. "As I saw it then," he said, "it doesn't matter if a few people are going to die around the edges, but us strong guys, we're going to make it good for ourselves and for everybody. Now I've converted. Those ideas are incredibly toxic. They simply do not allow people to be people."

Just as I have named authenticity and attachment as two basic needs, so Bruce has identified people's "vital need for social belonging with their equally vital needs for individual autonomy and achievement" and calls the marriage of the two *psychosocial integration*.[3] A sane culture, Bruce and I agree, would have psychosocial integration as both an aim and a norm. Authenticity and attachment would cease to be in conflict: there would be no fundamental tension between belonging and being oneself.

Dislocation, in Bruce's formulation, describes a loss of connection to self, to others, and to a sense of meaning and purpose—all of which appear on the roster of essential needs above. Lest the word "dislocation" conjure something hazy like "being lost," he is quick with a graphic metaphor. "Think of a dislocated shoulder," he said, "a shoulder disarticulated, out of joint. You didn't cut off the arm, but it's just hanging there and not working anymore. Useless. That's how dislocated people experience themselves. It's excruciatingly painful." More than an individual experience, the same intense pain often occurs at the social level when large groups of people find themselves cut off from autonomy, relatedness, trust, and meaning. This is *social dislocation,* which, along with personal trauma, is a potent source of mental dysfunction, despair, addictions, and physical illness.[†] Abnormal from the perspective of human needs, such dislocation is now an entrenched facet of "normality" in our culture. Extreme examples include the physical and psychic dislocation forced upon North America's Indigenous populations by colonialism and, more recently, the globalization-induced economic hollowing out of entire regions in the United States, from the Rust Belt to the mining towns of the Appalachians—which has resulted in a vast increase in suicides and overdose deaths among the working class. The latter have been called "deaths of despair" by the Princeton economists Anne Case and Angus Deaton, her Nobel laureate spouse.[‡]

Dislocation spares no class of people, even if it shows up differently in different strata of society. Societal privilege may insulate some of us from being outwardly wrecked by dislocation's

---

[†]   Alexander acknowledges the Hungarian American economist Karl Polanyi as the originator of the concept of social dislocation, in the latter's 1944 work, *The Great Transformation.*

[‡]   As in their much-lauded 2020 book, *Deaths of Despair and the Future of Capitalism.*

gale-force winds, but it cannot exempt us from the inner impacts of having our needs for interconnection, purpose, and genuine self-esteem denied. Neither achievements nor attributes nor external evaluations of our worth can possibly compensate us for such a lack.

———————

Recall that the Scottish labor leader Jimmy Reid defined "alienation" as the estrangement of people from a society that bars them from shaping or determining their own destinies. The word has other meanings as well, including estrangement from our essence, from ourselves, and from others. Already in the mid-nineteenth century Karl Marx recognized all these and added one more: disconnection from our labor as a meaningful activity over which we have agency and control. In this, Marx was prescient. Work encompasses several of the core needs noted above, including competence, mastery, and a sense of purpose. Just 30 percent of employees in the U.S. feel engaged at work, according to a 2013 report by Gallup; across 142 countries, the proportion of employees who feel engaged at work is only 13 percent. "For most of us," wrote two leading economic consultants in the *New York Times*, "work is a depleting, dispiriting experience, and in some obvious ways, it's getting worse."[4]

Alienation is inevitable when our inner sense of value becomes status-driven, hinging on externally imposed standards of competitive achievement and acquisition, and a highly conditional acceptance—I should say "acceptability"—in others' eyes. With the erosion of the middle class in recent decades, people who judged themselves in terms of worldly success have sustained a perceived loss of worth. The promise of the middle-class dream has largely evaporated, to the distress and deep anger of many. But even people perched atop the economic pyramid can experience a devaluation of self, for the simple reason that materialistic values run counter to the need for meaning, for purpose beyond self-serving endeavors.

There are no moral fingers to wag here. Objectively, it is the case that centering on the self's evanescent desires to the exclusion of communal needs results in a diminished connection to our deepest selves, which is to say the parts of us that generate and sustain true well-being. Whatever "wins" our personality can rack up, whatever momentary sense of security we gain through our various identities, however much we burnish our image or self-image with material gains—these are a flimsy replacement for the rewards (and challenges) of being alive to one's humanity. An investor dabbling daily in millions told Pulitzer Prize–winning journalist Charles Duhigg, "I feel like I'm wasting my life. When I die, is anyone going to care that I earned an extra percentage point on my return? My work feels totally meaningless." That loss of meaning, Duhigg says, afflicts "even professionals given to lofty self-images, like those in medicine and law." Why would this be? the author wondered. The answer: "Oppressive hours, political infighting, increased competition sparked by globalization, an 'always-on culture' bred by the internet—but also something that's hard for these professionals to put their finger on, an underlying sense that their work isn't worth the grueling effort they're putting into it."[5] It's simple economics, really: artificial inflation (of self-concept, of identity, of material ambition) is bound to lead to a downturn or even a crash when the bubble inevitably bursts.

Like our other needs, meaning is an inherent expectation. Its denial has dire consequences. Far from a purely psychological need, our hormones and nervous systems clock its presence or absence. As a medical study in 2020 found, the "presence [of] and search for meaning in life are important for health and well-being."[6] Simply put, the more meaningful you find your life, the better your measures of mental and physical health are likely to be. It is itself a sign of the times that we even need such studies to confirm what our experience of life teaches. When do you feel happier, more fulfilled, more viscerally at ease: when you extend yourself to help and connect with others, or when you are focused on burnishing the importance of your little egoic self? We all know the answer, and yet somehow what we know doesn't always carry the day.

Corporations are ingenious at exploiting people's needs without actually meeting them. Naomi Klein, in her book *No Logo*, made vividly clear how big business began in the 1980s to home in on people's natural desire to belong to something larger than themselves. Brand-aware companies such as Nike, Lululemon, and the Body Shop are marketing much more than products: they sell meaning, identification, and an almost religious sense of belonging through association with their brand. "That presupposes a kind of emptiness and yearning in people," I suggested when I interviewed the prolific author and activist. "Yes," Klein replied. "They tap into a longing and a need for belonging, and they do it by exploiting the insight that just selling running shoes isn't enough. We humans want to be part of a transcendent project."

Whatever one might say about the corporate, social, or ecological ethics of firms like Ford or General Motors, the unionized jobs they provided did keep generations of families employed gainfully and, for many, even meaningfully. The rapid deindustrialization of the working class in North America has led to a loss not only of income security but also of meaning, exacerbating the dislocation epidemic. The proliferation of service jobs and Amazon warehouse gigs hasn't replaced the sense of belonging these company jobs fostered in many communities. The eviscerating effect of these trends on people's sense of purpose and connection was expressed with heartbreaking candor by the dockworker character Frank Sobotka on HBO's *The Wire* two decades ago, who wistfully lamented to a lobbyist friend: "You know what the trouble is, Brucey? We used to *make* shit in this country, *build* shit. Now we just put our hand in the next guy's pocket."

Not only does our individual and societal sanity depend on connection; so does our physical health. Because we are biopsychosocial creatures, the rising loneliness epidemic in Western culture is much more than just a psychological phenomenon: it is a public health crisis.

A preeminent scholar of loneliness, the late neuroscientist John Cacioppo and his colleague and spouse, Stephanie Cacioppo, published a letter in the *Lancet* only a month before his death in 2018. "Imagine," they wrote, "a condition that makes a person irritable, depressed, and self-centered, and is associated with a 26% increase in the risk of premature mortality. Imagine too that in industrialized countries around a third of people are affected by this condition, with one person in 12 affected severely, and that these proportions are increasing. Income, education, sex, and ethnicity are not protective, and the condition is contagious. The effects of the condition are not attributable to some peculiarity of the character of a subset of individuals, *they are a result of the condition affecting ordinary people*. Such a condition exists—loneliness."[7]

We now know without doubt that chronic loneliness is associated with an elevated risk of illness and early death. It has been shown to increase mortality from cancer and other diseases and has been compared to the harm of smoking fifteen cigarettes a day. According to research presented at the American Psychological

Association's annual convention in 2015, the loneliness epidemic is a public health risk at least as great as the burgeoning rates of obesity.[8] Loneliness, the researcher Steven Cole told me, can impair genetic functioning. And no wonder: even in parrots isolation impairs DNA repair by shortening chromosome-protecting telomeres.[9] Social isolation inhibits the immune system, promotes inflammation, agitates the stress apparatus, and increases the risk of death from heart disease and strokes.[10] Here I am referring to social isolation in the pre-COVID-19 sense, though the pandemic has grievously exacerbated the problem, at great cost to the well-being of many.

The rise of loneliness as a health hazard tracks with the entrenchment of values and practices that supersede any notion of "individual choices." The dynamics include reduced social programs, less available "common" spaces such as public libraries, cuts in services for the vulnerable and the elderly, stress, poverty, and the inexorable monopolization of economic life that shreds local communities. By way of illustration, let's take a familiar scenario: Walmart or some other megastore decides to open one of its facilities in a municipality. Developers are happy, politicians welcome the new investment, and consumers are pleased at finding a wide variety of goods at lower prices. But what are the social impacts? Locally owned and operated small businesses cannot compete with the marketing behemoth and must close. People lose their jobs or must find new work for lower pay. Neighborhoods are stripped of the familiar hardware store, pharmacy, butcher, baker, candlestick maker. People no longer walk to their local establishment, where they meet and greet one another and familiar merchants they have known, but drive, each isolated in their car, to a windowless, aesthetically bereft warehouse, miles away from home. They might not even leave home at all—why bother, when you can order online?

No wonder international surveys show a rise in loneliness. The percentage of Americans identifying themselves as lonely has doubled from 20 to 40 percent since the 1980s, the *New York Times* reported in 2016.[†][11] Alarmed by the health ravages, Britain has even found it necessary to appoint a minister of loneliness.

Describing the systemic founts of loneliness, the U.S. surgeon general Vivek Murthy wrote: "Our twenty-first-century world demands that we focus on pursuits that seem to be in constant competition for our time, attention, energy, and commitment. Many of these pursuits are themselves competitions. We compete for jobs and status. We compete over possessions, money, and reputations. We strive to stay afloat and to get ahead. Meanwhile, the relationships we prize often get neglected in the chase."[12]

It is easy to miss the point that what Dr. Murthy calls "our twenty-first-century world" is no abstract entity, but the concrete manifestation of a particular socioeconomic system, a distinct worldview, and a way of life.

———

Is it possible nevertheless that our consumer culture does make good on its promises, or could do so? Might these, if fulfilled, lead to a more satisfying life?

When I put the question to renowned psychologist Tim Kasser, professor emeritus of psychology at Knox College, his response was unequivocal. "Research consistently shows," he told me, "that the more people value materialistic aspirations as goals, the lower their happiness and life satisfaction and the fewer pleasant emotions they experience day to day. Depression, anxiety, and substance abuse also tend to be higher among people

---

†   Ironically, this pre-COVID-19 article, in its online version, was titled "How Social Isolation Is Killing Us."

who value the aims encouraged by consumer society." He points to four central principles of what he calls ACC—American corporate capitalism: it "fosters and encourages a set of values based on *self-interest*, a strong desire for *financial success*, high levels of *consumption*, and interpersonal styles based on *competition*."[13]

There is a seesaw oscillation, Tim found, between materialistic concerns on the one hand and prosocial values like empathy, generosity, and cooperation on the other: the more the former are elevated, the lower the latter descend. For example, when people strongly endorse money, image, and status as prime concerns, they are less likely to engage in ecologically beneficial activities and the emptier and more insecure they will experience themselves to be. They will have also lower-quality interpersonal relationships. In turn, the more insecure people feel, the more they focus on material things. As materialism promises satisfaction but, instead, yields hollow dissatisfaction, it creates more craving. This massive and self-perpetuating addictive spiral is one of the mechanisms by which consumer society preserves itself by exploiting the very insecurities it generates.

Disconnection in all its guises—*alienation, loneliness, loss of meaning*, and *dislocation*—is becoming our culture's most plentiful product. No wonder we are more addicted, chronically ill, and mentally disordered than ever before, enfeebled as we are by such malnourishment of mind, body, and soul.

Chapter 21

They Just Don't Care If It Kills You: Sociopathy as Strategy

Not all psychopaths are in prison. Some are in the boardroom.

—R. D. Hare, Ph.D.[†]

Rob Lustig asserts that endocrinologists are the unhappiest of doctors, the most prone to suffer burnout. He would know, being one himself. Endocrinologists specialize in metabolic diseases, those of the hormone-producing glands such as the adrenals, the thyroid, the pituitary, and the pancreas. I asked him why gloom is such an occupational hazard for him and his colleagues. "Increasingly, we look after people who don't get better," Dr. Lustig replied. "It's like we're ladling water out of the proverbial leaky boat with a teaspoon while it keeps pouring in through a gaping hole at the bottom." He is all the more saddened by such futility since his subspecialty is working with children, among whom rates of obesity, diabetes, and related conditions have been escalating over the past several decades. Increasing numbers of children are showing markers of cardiovascular disease previously found only in adults.[‡]

The tide that keeps flooding the ship, Dr. Lustig says, stems from a culture in which many major corporations, unregulated

---

[†]   Professor emeritus, University of British Columbia, and a world-renowned expert on psychopathy.

[‡]   As Dr. Lustig documents in his book *The Hacking of the American Mind: The Science Behind the Corporate Takeover of Our Bodies and Brains.*

by governments, have deliberately and with the utmost ingenuity targeted the brain circuits of pleasure and reward to foster addictive compulsions. "That's why they hire neuroscientists and use fMRI machines," he told me. Neuroscience, originally meant to unlock the mysteries of consciousness and the brain, has become another handmaiden of the profit motive. There is actually a field called—and I'm not making this up—*neuromarketing*. "Their aim is to market happiness in a bottle," Lustig added. Or in a hamburger, or in a new smartphone or one of its many apps. In short, these corporations are acting as unscrupulous pushers in the open-air, perfectly legal market of mass addiction.

What the system sells as happiness is actually pleasure, a philosophical and economic distinction that makes all the difference between profit or loss. Pleasure, Rob Lustig pointed out, is "This feels good. I want more." Happiness, on the other hand, is "This feels good. I am contented. I am complete." This tracks perfectly with my understanding of addictions and brain chemistry. While similar in some ways, pleasure and happiness run on different neurochemical fuels: pleasure employs dopamine and opiates, both of which operate in short-term bursts, while contentment is based on the more steady, slow-release serotonin apparatus. It is very hard to get addicted to serotoninergic substances or behaviors. *All* addictions, however, commandeer the dopamine (incentive/motivation) and/or opiate (pleasure/reward) systems of the brain. Pleasure in the absence of contentment, and especially when sought in instant gratification, may be addictive, hence profitable. Contentment sells no products—except when evanescent, in which case it is no contentment at all, rather the bogus kind of "happiness" meant by *Mad Men's*[†] fictional ad whiz Don Draper when he

---

† The critically acclaimed cable TV series about the mid-twentieth-century advertising business.

muses, "What is happiness? It's a moment before you need more happiness." True happiness, being a non-commodity, does not make itself obsolete.

Neuromarketing is a strategic invasion of human consciousness, consciously aimed at the hyperactivation and constant agitation of the dopamine/endorphin functions of the brain. This endeavor was abundantly cataloged, for example, in Michael Moss's 2013 work of investigative journalism on the food industry, *Salt Sugar Fat: How the Food Giants Hooked Us*, one of the most widely read books of the year. He, too, documented a deliberate corporate conspiracy to hook people on addictive junk foods, with no regard for health consequences. Painstaking work combining the expertise of scientists and marketing wizards was undertaken to find the "bliss spot," that perfect blend of sugar, salt, and fat‡ that would most excite the brain's pleasure centers. This mind-hacking—in today's parlance—to induce mass addictions directly undermines free will, and I mean that neurochemically. By design, the power of the prefrontal cortex to override cravings is dampened, and the capacity of the lower emotional circuits to subvert rational thought ratcheted up. It's an appalling example of how rampant free-enterprise materialism has hijacked the science of neurophysiology to deregulate the brain, just as it "deregulates" the financial markets.

To call such activities a "conspiracy" is no hyperbole, even if the word has lost some of its meaning through overuse, particularly in post-9/11 and COVID-19 times. Yet if nonsensical conspiracy theories take hold too readily among the credulous and the enraged, the underlying fear of being manipulated is downright sensible. The history of corporate wrongdoing, including

---

‡   Or, as the case may be, other addictive substances such as caffeine: for example, the dopamine-boosting drink Red Bull, which, if advertising were honest, would add a qualifier to its label, billing itself as a "*non-renewable* energy drink."

direct assaults on health, is a compendium of well-documented schemes to deceive the public for profit. Each one is secret until it's not. Far from aberrations, they are all rigorously faithful to the system's acquisitive logic. Life-impairing but lucrative deceptions have been repeatedly exposed in virtually every industry and in the most prestigious firms, from pharmaceuticals to the extraction of raw materials, from air travel to car manufacturing to food production. We need not belabor the point here, except to remind ourselves that the folks in control are powerful and "respectable" people, even philanthropists, in whose minds the denial of prosocial values has become acceptable, more virtue than sin, and either way, a requirement.

It no longer surprises me that even when exposed, such manipulations do not create any significant long-term pushback from a public too desensitized to protest, or too resigned to imagine meaningful alternatives. Popular outrage, even when it bursts into flame temporarily, does not translate into structural change. Massive public assaults on human health and humane ethics are, for lack of a better word, entirely normalized. "The greatest conspiracies are open and notorious," the whistleblower Edward Snowden told British comedian and podcaster Russell Brand in 2021. "They are not theories but practices: practices expressed through law and policy and systems of government, technology, finance . . . We become inured to it. This leaves us unable to relate *the banality of the methods of their conspiracy to the rapacity of their ambitions*."[1] This is conspiracy realism, not conspiracy theory. That widespread chicanery in the top rungs of society is ignored or, at best, tolerated by much of the population speaks to the effectiveness of elite control and to the passivity of the social character inculcated by our culture.†

---

†   Social character was the topic of chapter 14.

Rob Lustig calls the United States "the drug capital of the world," and he isn't talking about cocaine, heroin, or methamphetamine, nor even mass-marketed opioids like OxyContin. He is referring to sugar, a substance that, in 2013, the chief health officer of the Netherlands declared to be "addictive and the most dangerous drug of all times." "Addictive" is not too strong a term. A Harvard Medical School study found that people ingesting foods with a high glycemic index—meaning, in practice, junk foods that rapidly elevate blood sugar levels—got hungrier faster. On fMRI scans, they showed activation of the same brain regions stimulated by drugs such as cocaine or heroin.[2] Never missing a profitable beat, multinational corporations vigorously market sugar-laden concoctions to children, and prey on people who, owing to trauma, penury, and grinding oppression, are especially vulnerable to addictive substances. The latter include poor Black people in the United States and the denizens of Brazil's makeshift villages, the *favelas*. In many "developing" countries—a term that manages to be both condescending and euphemistic—troops of impoverished women are recruited to go door-to-door, selling such junk products to already undernourished compatriots.

The costs in health and longevity are far greater than even the worst projections for the COVID-19 pandemic. A report published in the *Lancet* found that eleven million deaths worldwide in 2017 could be attributed to diets deficient in vegetables, seeds, and nuts but laden with salt, fat, and sugar.[3] According to another study presented to the American Heart Association, sugary drinks alone may be responsible for up to 180,000 deaths around the world.[4] Coca-colonization, this has been called.

As a result of the corporatization of agriculture, a built-in outcome of the North American Free Trade Agreement, Mexico now vies with the United States for world leadership in obesity and its related diseases. "About 73% of the Mexican population is overweight, compared to one-fifth of the population in 1996, according to a study by the Organisation for Economic Co-operation and Development," the BBC reported in August 2020.[5] "Childhood obesity tripled in a decade and about a third of teenagers are [overweight] as well," according to CBS News. "Experts say four of every five of those heavy kids will remain so their entire lives."[6] More than four hundred thousand cases of diabetes are diagnosed in Mexico every year, with the numbers dying exceeding those killed in that country's appalling drug wars.†

Canada is swiftly catching up, with Australia, New Zealand, and Asia also in the race. In China, the adult obesity rate doubled in the two decades between 1991 and 2011, from 20.5 to 42.3 percent. There, too, Coca-Cola has wielded major influence in shaping government policy to enhance its profits.[7]

British prime minister Boris Johnson, formerly a man of notorious girth, became a weight-loss evangelist in the wake of his close encounter with the novel coronavirus, which, for a few days in 2020, had him in intensive care. "I'm not normally a believer in nannying, or bossing type of politics," said the PM after his recovery. "But the reality is that obesity is one of the real co-morbidity factors. Losing weight is, frankly, one of the ways you can reduce your own risks from COVID." He instituted government policies advocating healthier eating habits and regulating the advertisement and marketing of junk food. Spot-on, one might say. Yet, had he chosen to be scientific, Johnson might have listed poverty and being BAME—Black, Asian, or minority ethnic—as major risk factors for coronavirus morbidity and death. He might also have

† In a desperate and probably futile attempt to reduce high obesity and diabetes rates, the Mexican state of Oaxaca has banned the sale of junk food and sugary drinks to children.

recognized obesity itself to be a socially engendered condition, dramatically on the rise internationally since the advent of the austerity and laissez-faire policies his party has championed for almost a half century now. Nearly two-thirds of adults in his country are obese or overweight, as are a third of children six years of age. According to the National Health Service, in the statistical year 2018–2019 there were 876,000 hospital admissions in Britain in which obesity was a factor, an increase of nearly 25 percent over the preceding twelve months.[8]

Not all food- or tobacco-related ill health can be ascribed directly to the commercialized "hacking" of the public mind, any more than the epidemic of prescription drug deaths is due exclusively to corporate manipulation. It is truer to say that the manipulation is made possible by the very stresses, disconnections, and dislocations of life entrenched by globalized capitalism. Ted Schrecker and Clare Bambra—professors of public health policy and of public health geography, respectively, at Durham University—have studied the health impacts of recent economic trends. "The countries which are currently the most neoliberal and experienced the greatest increases in neoliberalism during 1980–2008 . . . had correspondingly higher rates of obesity and overweight," they note. "This shows that the timing and international spread of the obesity epidemic mirror the rise and diffusion of neoliberalism."[9] That's the issue Boris Johnson was not about to confront in his weight-loss promotion campaign.

The worldwide obesity epidemic is a marker of the international stress epidemic discussed in our previous chapters, and of the attendant lifestyle challenges endemic to our modern era: lack of time, lack of exercise, growing insecurity, lack of family connection, loss of community, and erosion of the social network. There are many aspects of life that drive people to follow unhealthy diets and engage in self-harming habits, the main culprits being emotional pain, stress, and social dislocation. And as we have seen, compulsive overeating—like all addictions—is itself a response to stress and a way of soothing the impacts of trauma. "It's not what you are eating," someone cleverly said, "it's what's eating you." Stress induces people to "choose" unhealthy foods and to put on weight in the wrong places, promoting disease. It also depletes the serotonin/contentment circuits, shifting the brain's functioning toward the short-term, dopamine-fueled pleasure mechanisms.

The corporate elite, served by their amply compensated minions in the fields of science and psychology, well know how to profit off the stress generated by the system that gives them power. They wouldn't be doing their jobs if they didn't.

Big Food is no outlier when it comes to hoodwinking the public. The pharmaceutical industry "systematically manipulated the entire country for 25 years," wrote Nicholas Kristof in the *New York Times* in 2017, "and its executives are responsible for many of the 64,000 deaths of Americans last year from drugs—more than the number of Americans who died in the Vietnam and Iraq wars combined. The opioid crisis unfolded because greedy people— Latin drug lords and American pharma executives—lost their humanity when they saw the astounding profits that could be made." And the government response? In Kristof's words, "Our policy was: 'You get 15 people hooked on opioids, and you're a thug who deserves to rot in hell; you get 150,000 people hooked, and you're a marketing genius who deserves a huge bonus.' "[10] It has been broadly established that Big Pharma, such as Purdue, the company controlled by the Sacklers, promoted opiates like

OxyContin to doctors as relatively safe analgesics. They did so in full awareness of their drugs' addictive potential. Over the years, hundreds of thousands of people have died.

All the while, the Sacklers garbed themselves in the cloak of virtuous public benefactors: an established phenomenon in the world of major-league philanthropy. The drug-profiteering family bestowed their largesse—and their names, beautifully embossed—on hospitals, medical schools, and museums around the world, from North America to Europe to Israel.

Kristof's point about differential consequences was all too close to my own experience. If any patient of mine in the Downtown Eastside was arrested selling a couple of ounces of cocaine—as many were, in their desperation to fund their arbitrarily illegalized habits—they were subject to imprisonment. Meanwhile, this week as I write, a court settlement was announced that infuriated many: at the cost of a paltry $4.5 billion fine, the Sacklers get to keep their wealth and face no criminal charges. Free as birds—vultures, perhaps—holding billions in their beaks.†

To be fair, the drug companies were only following their tobacco-industry exemplars who for decades, and with equally casual disregard for human life, denied and actively concealed the health hazards of their product, and who continue to resist efforts at regulation.[11] Tobacco kills about forty-five thousand Canadians annually, ten times as many as die from opioid overdoses—not to mention the hundreds of thousands who suffer smoking-related illness and debility. The worldwide death toll due to tobacco use exceeds seven million each year.[12] For every person who dies, thirty live with chronic illness.

---

†   This settlement has since been overturned on appeal and, as this book goes to edits, the court saga continues. More on the Sacklers in chapter 33.

Like the skilled pushers they are, the tobacco corporations miss no angle, targeting the most vulnerable. "For decades, menthol cigarettes have been marketed aggressively to Black people in the United States," reported the *New York Times*. "About 85 percent of Black smokers use menthol brands, including Newport and Kool, according to the Food and Drug Administration. Research shows menthol cigarettes are easier to become addicted to and harder to quit than plain tobacco products."[13] (As of this writing, the Biden administration has indicated plans to ban the sale of menthol cigarettes.) Now restricted, though far from curtailed, in hawking their products in the wealthier countries, the multinational merchants of tobacco, alcohol, sugary drinks, and junk food have cast their gaze on the so-called developing world, where rules are more lax and governments even more pliant. Millions will fall ill, millions will die—not "will," are dying.

What kind of people would knowingly cause the illness and deaths of countless millions? Law professor Joel Bakan,[†] whose book *The Corporation: The Pathological Pursuit of Profit and Power* became the basis of the award-winning documentary of the same name, set out to assess corporations in the light of standard mental health measures we would apply to people. The appraisal is entirely fair, given that U.S. law has, since the late 1800s, regarded corporations as "persons." "Viewed from such a vantage," he told me, "many corporations meet the criteria of 'sociopaths,' acting without a conscience: not caring about what happens to other people as a consequence of their actions, having no compulsion to comply with social or legal norms, not feeling guilt or remorse." It's an airtight case—from a mental health perspective, how else to regard nonaccountable "persons" with limitless power, quite willing to obscure truths and broadcast lies, sowing illness and death?

---

† See chapter 13.

If anyone requires a second opinion, the New York psychoanalyst Steven Reisner is ready with one.[‡] "Narcissism and sociopathy describe corporate America," he told me. "But it's flat-out wrong to think in twenty-first-century America that narcissism and sociopathy are illnesses. In today's America, narcissism and sociopathy are *strategies*. And they're very successful strategies, especially in business and politics and entertainment." Call it the myth of abnormal, this notion that somehow these antisocial traits go against the grain; truer to say they are the grain.

Why would such strategies be pursued? That patron saint of unbridled free-market ideology, the Nobel Prize–winning economist Milton Friedman, put no fine point—nor any ethical handbrake—on it. "Well, first of all, tell me," he once remarked in an interview, "is there some society you know that doesn't run on greed? You think Russia doesn't run on greed? You think China doesn't run on greed? . . . The world runs on individuals pursuing their separate interests."[14] Friedman also laid down as an iron-clad rule that "there is one and only one social responsibility of business—to use its resources and engage in activities designed to increase its profits."[15] Note the use of the phrase "social responsibility": Friedman believed to his bones that self-interested, minimally regulated corporate capitalism is *what's best for everyone*. Thus spoke not a mustache-twirling movie villain self-aware of his perfidy, bound to get his comeuppance by film's end, but a theorist whose still-eminent standing in "normal" political-economic circles speaks volumes about what sort of society we are.

Bakan told me that he originally imagined corporations as unhealthy life-forms plaguing "a basically healthy, democratic society." He no longer believes that. "The pathology has metastasized— the pathogen has infected the host," he said.

---

‡ Reisner hosts *Madness: The Podcast*, an engaging look at "where psychology and capitalism collide."

Humanity faces no challenge of more gravity and consequence than the climate crisis that, as of this writing, is devastating many areas of the world and threatens planetary life itself. To my mind, no issue illustrates more vividly the sociopathic behavior of those in corporate and government spheres who had plenty of advance warning but for decades minimized or denied the menace for the sake of profit or power.

It was in the year 1800 that the great German naturalist and geographer Alexander von Humboldt first sounded the alarm about the impact of human activity on the climate, having seen the environmental damage wreaked by colonial plantations in Venezuela. He prophesized that our interference with the ecology could have "unforeseeable impact on future generations."[16] Over two centuries later, more than eleven thousand leading scientists from 153 nations found it necessary to endorse an urgent warning. "We declare clearly and unequivocally that planet Earth is facing a climate emergency," they wrote. "To secure a sustainable future, we must change how we live. [This] entails major transformations in the ways our global society functions and interacts with natural ecosystems."[17] Four decades earlier the first international climate conference had been held in Geneva, and largely ignored. Ever since then, alarms have been sounded again and again by scientists, activists, and health professionals around the world. In 1992, long before the climate advocate Greta Thunberg called out the world's politicians on their failure to protect the climate—indeed, well before Thunberg was born—the Canadian activist Severn Cullis-Suzuki, aged twelve, addressed leaders gathered at the first U.N. Earth conference in Rio de Janeiro. "Coming up here today, I have no hidden agenda," she said. "I am fighting for my future. Losing my future is not like losing an election, or a few points on the stock market. I am here to speak for all generations to come." We know what has been done—or, more accurately, *not* done—in the face of a looming catastrophe that is now affecting people's well-being around the world and threatens the very basis of our existence.

"Health is inextricably tied to climate change," warned the *Journal of the American Medical Association* back in 2014. The health impacts are well documented. Four years later, the *Lancet* reported: "Vulnerability to extremes of heat has steadily risen since 1990 in every region, with 157 million more people exposed to heatwave events in 2017, as compared with 2000."[18] Yet more recently, in what the *Wall Street Journal* called "an unprecedented plea," editors of two hundred health journals internationally, including the *Lancet*, the *British Medical Journal*, and the *New England Journal of Medicine*, called the failure of political leaders to confront the climate crisis "the greatest threat to global public health."[19] The harms of climate change include acute and chronic physical illness such as cardiovascular disease and susceptibility to infections, along with mental health challenges. Especially at risk are people with heart or kidney conditions, diabetes, and respiratory ailments. I need hardly mention food and water insecurity, major stressors already affecting millions.

Underlying the active and callous disregard of our Earth's health is the sociopathology of the most powerful entities, whose planetary poison-pushing removes any hint of metaphor from this book's subtitular phrase "toxic culture." "The oil companies pumped billions of dollars into thwarting government action. They funded think tanks and paid retired scientists and fake grassroots organizations to pour doubt and scorn on climate science. They sponsored politicians, particularly in the U.S. Congress, to block international attempts to curtail greenhouse gas emissions. They invested heavily in greenwashing their public image." So reported the *Guardian* in 2019, a scenario also amply chronicled by the *New York Times* and many other publications. Nor are we talking only about the past: in 2020 the top one hundred or more American corporations channeled their political donations largely to lawmakers with a record of stalling climate legislation. No doubt, such openhanded generosity owed much to the certainty that these same politicians would also avidly support the interests of big business. Compared with financial gain the climate is, well, small change.

From a medical perspective Joel Bakan's comment about the pathology metastasizing could not be more apt. If in the body a cell begins to multiply at the expense of the entire organism, destroying tissues nearby and spreading to other organs, robbing the host of energy, disabling its defenses, and eventually threatening its very life, we call that unchecked growth a cancer. Such abnormal and malignant transformation is now besetting our world, run by a system that seems rigged against life. The abnormal has become the norm; the unnatural has become the inescapable.

In the logic of profit, greed is creed, and health nothing but collateral damage. "It's not that they want you to die," the endocrinologist Rob Lustig told me in a tone of mock reassurance. "They only want your money. They just don't care if it kills you."

Chapter 22

The Assaulted Sense of Self: How Race and Class Get Under the Skin

My brother raised his hand when Dad told us we were
Indians, and through the tears in his eyes he asked our father,
"But we're still part human, right?"

—Helen Knott, *In My Own Moccasins*

As a child in postwar Hungary, in the aftermath of the genocide that had claimed the lives of most of my extended family and community, I was often insulted for my ethnic identity. I'll never forget how a friend came to my defense once: "Leave him alone," he chided the bullies. "It's not his fault he's Jewish." I carried the corrosive shame of that blameless "fault" for a long time, having absorbed other people's view of me.

Despite such firsthand experience of having been "othered" early in life, my status since adolescence as a privileged member of a dominant culture—a white-presenting middle-class male in North America—has also seeped into how I see the world. I am still prone to having blind spots around what people from other backgrounds are carrying, what trials they must endure. It's all too easy for the privileged among us to assume we walk the same streets as everyone else. Though a satellite view of Earth may suggest we do, that's not how it plays out at ground level. Do

Indigenous people in Canada or Black people in America tread the same ground as their Caucasian counterparts, face the same daily obstacles, navigate the same sorts of adversity? Surely not.

Early in his posthumously published autobiography, the revolutionary Black leader Malcolm X recalls his self-abasement when he tried to remake himself according to the standards of a society that rejected who he was. As a young man he was "conking," searing his scalp to obliterate his hair's natural curliness. "This was my first really big step toward self-degradation," he writes, "literally burning my flesh to have it look like a white man's hair."[1] Many years later, as a leader in the Nation of Islam, Malcolm challenged his audience to confront their own self-loathing. "Who taught you to hate the texture of your hair?" he asked. "Who taught you to hate the color of your skin to such an extent that you bleach to get like the white man? Who taught you to hate the shape of your nose and lips? Who taught you to hate yourself from the top of your head to the soles of your feet?" I winced in recognition when I read those words, having been all too conscious of my own easily identifiable "ethnic" appearance in Eastern Europe.

Malcolm's withering questions probe far beyond mental or emotional self-concept. Self-rejection has powerful physiological dimensions that pertain to every aspect of well-being. From an early age it is one of racism's sharpest and most intimate harms.

Canadian physician Dr. Clyde Hertzman[†] minted the concept of "biological embedding," by which he meant precisely what we've been looking at in myriad ways in this book: that our social environments and experiences, in his words, "get under the skin early in life," shaping our biology and development. Hertzman

---

† Until his untimely death at age fifty-nine, Dr. Hertzman was professor of the Department of Health Care and Epidemiology at the University of British Columbia and Canada research chair in population health and human development. He was internationally renowned for his explorations of the social determinants of health.

meant "under the skin" literally, referring to what life events do to skin, nervous system, and viscera. It is no outcome of genetic destiny, for example, that in Canada Indigenous people suffer more illness and die earlier than others. Racism and poverty do get under the skin, in so many ways.

This chapter is a brief, trauma-informed look at a huge subject: how two major social determinants of health—race and economic status—become biologically embedded. I'll take up a third, gender, in the next chapter. But although I'm treating them separately here, it would be a fallacy to think of them as independent operators. For many individuals they intersect in ways that make it almost impossible to tease out what is a function of which—hence the term "intersectional." It is difficult to separate, for example, the health impacts of being a woman in a patriarchal system and at the same time a person of color in a racialized climate, of being poor in a culture that worships wealth, or living as a gay or lesbian person in a society where homophobia is still endemic.

An African Canadian-British friend of mine, the public speaker, mindfulness teacher, and author Valerie (Vimalasara) Mason-John, has intimately experienced the nexus of all four of these variables.‡ All contributed to their descent into bulimia and substance addiction, beginning with the racial torment they experienced as a young child in Britain at the Barnardo orphanage, Barkingside, Essex. "Daily I'd have this kid who would come up and say, 'Hey, woggamatter? Niggamind—go black home and eat your coon flakes, and you'll be all white in the morning.' That was relentless," Vimalasara told me. "People kept telling me my hands looked like a monkey's. By age four I was trying to bleach my skin." And now as an adult in Canada, they said, "It

---

‡   Vimalasara's preferred pronouns are "they/them." The racial pejoratives are cited above with their express permission.

is impossible to isolate my sexuality from my gender and/or my race—they can be all at play when someone is relating to me. The intersection of these determinants has impacted my whole life. Who knows which identity of mine will be oppressed when I walk out of my home in the morning. Sometimes it is all, and sometimes it's just one, but the identity that continually becomes a threat to others is my Black skin."

As the Black American writer Ta-Nehisi Coates tersely asserts, "Race is the child of racism, not the father." In other words, the very concept of race emerges from the distorted imagination of the racist. Though racism's impacts are real, in physiological or genetic terms race does not exist. Superficial differences in skin color, body morphology, or facial features do not create "races." Historically the idea of race arose from the impulse of European capitalism to enrich itself by subjugating, enslaving, and, if necessary, destroying Indigenous people on other continents, from Africa to Australia to North America. Indeed, the word "race" did not exist in any meaningful way until it was created in the late eighteenth century. Psychologically, on the individual level, the "othering" racism entails is an antidote to self-doubt: if I don't feel good about myself, at least I can feel superior to *somebody* and gain a sense of power and status by claiming privilege over them. "The anti-Semite," wrote the French philosopher Jean-Paul Sartre, "is a man who is afraid. Not of the Jews, to be sure, but of himself and his own consciousness, of his liberty, of his instincts, of his responsibilities, of solitariness, of change, of society, and of the world . . . The existence of the Jew merely permits the anti-Semite to stifle his anxieties."[2] The pernicious impact of racism flows from its very nature, which is to see and treat another, in essence no different from you, according to your self-serving, resentful, and twisted fantasy of who they are. The brilliant writer James Baldwin once said, "What white people have to do is try and find out in their own hearts why it was necessary to have a n—— in the first place. If you, the white people, invented him, then you've got to find out why."

Recalling the shame I felt as a child at being Jewish, I completely resonate with a powerful formulation by the Black American psychologist Kenneth Hardy:[†] the "assaulted sense of self." In this state, Dr. Hardy says, "the soul of one's being gets perpetually punctured . . . It's when one's definition of self is defined by someone else. It is when my sense of self is defined by what I am not, rather than by what I am." He adds, "Who I am thus becomes a response to how I am defined; it's always in response to something else."[3]

The author Helen Knott, who is of Dane-zaa, Nehiyaw, and European descent, knows well this experience of the assaulted self by virtue of being Indigenous in modern Canada. "I became 'the other' in my eighth-grade social studies class," she writes. "The outcast. The wild Indian. Merciless Indian savage."[4] The stain and the strain of being defined by outside prejudices could not but penetrate her core sense of who she was.

Knott and I met by Zoom one winter morning in 2019, shortly after I read *In My Own Moccasins*, her poetic memoir of trauma, addiction, and redemption. "Othering was socialized into me," she said. "It was present within my family and how they interacted with the outside world. With my mom, there was a lot of 'You're not brown enough, you're not white enough.' No matter where you go, you're always aware of your otherness within a room. You could be sitting somewhere and you're calculating, 'Is this a safe space for me to have the conversation that I want to have? Do I make myself less visible or more visible?' It's an almost unconscious calculation of safety, almost at all times."

---

†   Kenneth V. Hardy, Ph.D., is president of the Eikenberg Academy for Social Justice and a professor of marriage and family therapy at Drexel University, Philadelphia.

Knott had been reflecting on how the women in her life hold racism's marks in their very bearing—"even," she says, "how their bodies transform in public [white-dominated] spaces." She gave me a vivid example: "When my grandma goes into a grocery store, ever since I can remember, she will suddenly . . . her shoulders will hunch in, and her head will face the ground. She doesn't make eye contact with people; she will just shuffle along. This happens in any kind of larger public space. Her whole presence changes. Outside of that, she has been our matriarch where she *holds* space. She's the one telling stories and calling people and telling people to do this or that. In her old age, because now she's seventy-nine, it changed a bit in the last few years. She's taken a few more liberties because she's like, 'I don't care anymore.' "

When asked why he "keeps bringing up race all the time," Dr. Hardy offers a response as medically apt as it is candid: "If I don't bring it up, I have all these physiological things inside." Emotional suppression and its biological harms are, indeed, among the many wounds racism inflicts. In chapter 3 we mentioned that racism shortens lives. A study that examined the chromosome-protective telomeres of Black American men found that overt experiences of racism *and* the assaulted sense of self, including the internalization of racial bias, "operate jointly to accelerate biological aging."[5]

Socially entrenched bigotry, whether in its subtle or overt forms, takes an enormous and, until very recently, mostly unspoken toll on health. This silence—not in science or data but in public discourse—was finally breached following the May 2020 murder of George Floyd and the advent of the novel coronavirus. The former, one of a string of countless such killings of unarmed Black people, brought home to millions worldwide the venomous racial injustices structurally entrenched in Western societies, most egregiously in the United States; the second demonstrated all too clearly that police brutality is but one vector of lethal racism. Latino and Black Americans have been three times more likely to be infected by COVID-19 and twice more prone to dying of it. In Britain, too, communities of color were disproportionately affected, owing to deprived housing conditions, economic disadvantage, and preexistent health problems rooted in discrimination and inequity.

Behind the studies and dismal statistics are the tormented lives of real human beings, depicted with bitter eloquence by many great authors. No research paper, for example, could possibly convey the stress-inducing experience of confinement, deprivation, fear, and suppressed outrage with more force than the words of Ta-Nehisi Coates as he recalls his youth in inner-city Baltimore: "We could not get out. The ground we walked on was trip-wired. The air we breathed was toxic. The water stunted our growth. We could not get out... Not being violent enough could cost me my body. Being too violent could cost me my body. We could not get out."[6]

"In America, it is traditional to destroy the black body—*it is heritage*," Coates states. While that destruction has been most blatantly evident in the lynch-mob rampages of bygone eras and in officially sanctioned violence persisting to this day, it achieves more insidious and even more widespread effects through the direct imprint of racism on the body. Importantly, these effects show up in people's physiology as if programmed there from the start. "Heart disease, diabetes, obesity, depression, substance abuse, school success, premature mortality, disability at retirement, and accelerated aging and memory loss all have social determinants in early life," Clyde Hertzman pointed out.[7] Not surprisingly, Black people in the United States suffer more diabetes, obesity, and hypertension, along with life-threatening complications such as strokes, for which their risk is doubled.

For example, a forty-five-year-old African American man residing in the Southeast has the stroke propensity of a fifty-five-year-old white man in the same region and a sixty-five-year-old white man residing in the Midwest. Reviewing the literature, I found it most stunning that the race differentials in blood pressure rates are measurable already in children and adolescents.[8] Why? "Hyper" means "too much," "tension" means "tension," and racial discrimination induces it. For similar reasons, Black American children are six times more likely than non-Black kids to die of asthma.[9]

This is all of a piece with what we have seen throughout this book. For young children, being subordinated in their social milieu—whether family or classroom—leads to heightened cardiovascular, nervous system, and hormonal responses to stress and higher risks of chronic medical conditions. That remains true for adults as well. The suppression of individual authenticity plays havoc with biology, breeding illness; even greater mayhem will ensue for bodies belonging to groups whose self-suppression has been systemically imposed, often with great violence.

James Baldwin once said that "to be a Negro in this country and to be relatively conscious, is to be in a rage almost all the time." Baldwin uttered those words in 1961. They still ring true, decades of civil rights advances and a Black president later. Baldwin also understood that rage on its own, even if come by honestly, could not be the end of the story. In the very next sentence, he described "the first problem" as being "how to control that rage so that it won't destroy you."[10] I am convinced such anger, and moreover its obligatory suppression in a society that fears and punishes Black rage, contributes to the elevated risk Black American men face for dying of prostate cancer and Black American women do of succumbing to cancer of the breast.

The racial differences, independent of genetics, defy economic categories: for example, the abovementioned breast cancer risk for Black women cuts across class lines. Around birth, Black mothers are dying at three to four times the rate of non-Hispanic white mothers. And their infants are at least twice as likely to die as white babies—another trend that holds across education levels and socioeconomic status. "Put simply," warned a recent article in the magazine of Harvard's T. H. Chan School of Public Health, "for black women far more than for white women, *giving birth can amount to a death sentence.*"[11] And how not to be startled at the finding that having a non-Black doctor doubles a Black baby's risk of dying—the baby's "penalty," we might say, for the crime of being born while Black.[12] For white infants the race of the physician makes no difference. In short, it is "racism, not race itself, that threatens the lives of African American women and infants," a recent review of multiple studies concluded.[13]

We have seen how emotional stressors, among which racism ranks as a frontrunner, get "under the skin": the triggering of inflammation-promoting genes, the premature aging of chromosomes and cells, tissue damage, elevation of blood sugar, the narrowing of airways. Even *without* economic disadvantage, the stresses of racial prejudice mount over time, toxifying the body and undermining its capacity to maintain itself. That allostatic load, the wear and tear, just becomes too much. When so-called biomarkers such as blood pressure, stress hormones, blood sugar indicators, inflammatory proteins, and lipids were measured, they were significantly higher in Blacks than in whites, with Black women showing consistently higher scores than Black men. In both races poor people scored higher than their economically advantaged counterparts, but *non-poor* Blacks had a greater probability of high scores than *poor* whites. Differences were especially pronounced among non-poor Black women, compared with non-poor white women—once more illustrating the intersection of race and gender as they determine health in a racially stratified society.[14]

"When you have racism as a mechanism, there's generational trauma," the Tennessee psychotherapist Eboni Webb told me. The softness of her voice during our Zoom call could not mute the harsh realities of her family history. "All the women in my family are very fair," Webb said. "We didn't have Caucasians come into our story willingly, but forcibly. The women in my family have been subjected to brutalization through the generations. That assault itself is trauma, but the trauma is also how we have had to armor ourselves. I remember my parents telling me if something happens at school, you come home and cry. Don't cry there. Talk about emotions being traumatizing: What happens to a people that can't show the full range of their emotions? For people of color raising children, the lens is not just 'racism exists,' but 'racism can be life-threatening.' Our childhood experience is one of learning how to live out of our survival defenses, and that just hasn't changed. We don't have the luxury of raising our kids in any ideal manner." Living out of survival defenses is a formula for the lifelong activation of the body's stress apparatus, with myriad consequences.

I was thirteen in 1957 when, along with nearly thirty-eight thousand fellow Hungarians, refugees from a brutal Stalinist dictatorship, my family and I were welcomed with open arms by Canada. The North really seemed true and strong and free, in line with the words of this country's national anthem. What I didn't know and what no one was speaking of was that in the same year, even as we were adjusting to the advantages of life in British Columbia, a four-year-old First Nations child, Carlene, had a pin stuck in her tongue on her first day at a federally mandated, church-run residential school not far from where I lived. Her crime had been to speak her Native language in the classroom. For an hour this little girl could not put her tongue back in her mouth for fear of cutting her lips. Soon after, years of sexual abuse began. By age nine Carlene was an alcoholic and later became dependent on opiates to soothe her pain. We met at a healing ceremony not long ago and that was when, sobbing and trembling with emotion, she told me her story. I thought I had heard everything. I had not. Now a grandmother and years sober, she grieves to see her grandchildren suffer the throes of addiction. For her, our national anthem was a cruel hoax: there was no "true North strong and free!" Nor is there yet.

And so it is that in Canada, where looking down on Americans is something of a national indulgence, we have nothing to feel superior about. Police prejudice, including brutal violence, is notoriously inflicted on Indigenous peoples and on people of color. Nearly 30 percent of the jail population in this country is composed of Indigenous people, who make up no more than 5 percent of the general population.[†]

About the same proportion of my impoverished, addicted clients in Vancouver's Downtown Eastside were of Indigenous background, the inheritors and carriers of a toxic colonial legacy of extermination and expulsion; the genocidal destruction of communal existence; many decades of the involuntary placement of Indigenous children in state-enforced, rigidly Christian residential schools where Native languages and culture were outlawed on pain of punishment and a culture of appalling, entrenched sexual and physical abuse reigned; the period known as "the Sixties Scoop,"[‡] when the Canadian child-welfare (!)

[†]   Among women inmates, the ratio is 50 percent.

[‡]   In fact, the phenomenon lasted at least into the 1980s.

system abducted thousands of First Nations children from their homes and placed them with non-Indigenous families; atrocious living situations on reservations; ongoing multigenerational trauma; and the persisting encroachment on and pollution of Indigenous lands for economic projects that profit distant corporations. In 2021 the world was horrified at the discovery of thousands of small bodies at the former sites of residential schools across Canada. Many other thousands are known to have disappeared whose remains are yet to be found and whose deaths, deeply etched and grieved in the consciousness of their families and communities, have not until recently been formally acknowledged by the governmental and ecclesiastic institutions responsible. Nearly two thousand unmarked graves have been identified as of late 2021. Another five thousand to ten thousand such graves likely exist and await finding.

Health and living conditions among our First Nations populations are scandalous, matched only by the chronic failure of governments at all levels to remedy the social, economic, and cultural circumstances that foster them. The lifespan of Indigenous people is fifteen years shorter than that of other Canadians, infant mortality two to three times higher, and type 2 diabetes four times more widespread: this among a population that knew no diabetes a little over a century ago.[15] Elevated blood sugars are the least of it: diabetes is a leading cause of blindness, heart and kidney failure, and limb amputations. First Nations people are developing the disease in their forties, while among other sectors of the populace its onset is mostly in the eighth decade. The rates are rising. "By 2005," a 2010 study found, "almost 50% of First Nations women and more than 40% of First Nations men aged 60 or older had diabetes, [compared] with less than 25% of non–First Nations men and less than 20% of non–First Nations women aged 80 or older . . . First Nations adults are experiencing a diabetes epidemic that disproportionately affects women during their productive years."[16] Youth suicide rates in some Indigenous communities in Canada—First Nations, Inuit, Métis—were higher, according to a 1994 paper, than of any other culturally identifiable cohort in the world.[17] That continues to be the case.

Dr. Esther Tailfeathers is an Indigenous physician at the Blood Tribe Reserve in Alberta, a community that has had more than its share of severe substance dependence. She has invited me there twice to support their addiction programs, once in the wake of a three-month span when the community of 7,500 people lost 20 people to overdoses.[†] I asked Dr. Tailfeathers what it was like for her, now a successful professional, to grow up Indigenous in Canada. "At times horrific," she said. "We were one of the first Native families to move into the town of Cardston and rent a home. There was no school bus, so I had to walk a long way from the school on the other side of town. In grade one, I remember being followed by a group of children all the way home. The leader of this group picked up a big stone and threw it at me, and subsequently all the other children all threw stones. That was my first lesson on bullying and hatred." It wasn't her last. "When I was about nineteen, we had huge land-claim protests. I was beaten by the RCMP[‡] and thrown in jail.

"Sadly," she added, "you'd think things would have improved, because we know what had happened starting in residential

---

†   By contrast, the province of British Columbia, with a population of 5 million, had 170 overdose deaths in July 2020, its highest ever. Proportionately to this Blood Tribe tragedy, B.C. would have lost over 4,000 people in one month.

‡   RCMP: the Royal Canadian Mounted Police, the much-venerated national police organization among whose tasks, from its inception until today, has been to suppress the resistance of Indigenous people to the takeover of their lands and resources, and—during the residential school era—even their children.

schools and progressing forward. I don't think it has improved. It's gotten worse."

In 1848 a twenty-seven-year-old Berlin physician, Rudolf Virchow, was dispatched to Upper Silesia to investigate a deadly outbreak of typhus, a bacterial infestation then plaguing that impoverished, mostly Polish-speaking region of Germany. Along with his medical recommendations to counter the epidemic, Virchow caused an uproar by calling for social, political, and economic reforms. These included the introduction of Polish as an official language, separation of church and state, the creation of grassroots organizations, free education for both sexes, and, above all, *free and unlimited democracy."*

Virchow, these days honored as the father of modern pathology, disdained any separation of health from social conditions and culture. "Medicine has imperceptibly led us into the social field and placed us in a position of confronting directly the great problems of our time," he wrote. When challenged that his advice had more to do with politics than with medicine, Virchow issued his timeless retort: "Medicine is a social science, and politics nothing else but medicine on a large scale."

For all Virchow's renown, nearly two centuries later many doctors and scientists internationally are still striving in the face of political, professional, and social indifference to impart the broader lessons he derived from his investigations. When the contemporary epidemiologist Sir Michael Marmot[†] began his research into the impact of social stratification on health, he discovered that "inequality and health was completely off the agenda, bar a few trailblazers, writing about the evils of capitalism."[18] His

---

†   Sir Michael Marmot is professor of epidemiology and public health at University College London and in 2015 was president of the World Medical Association.

findings over the decades, published in numerous papers and books, have richly demonstrated the links between social and health disparities.

There's no need to repeat the science in detail. Both inequality and poverty stir the by now familiar brew of disturbed genetic function, inflammation, chromosomal and cellular aging, physiological wear and tear, hormonal disturbances, cardiovascular effects, and immune debility, all of which combine to bring illness, disability, and death. Biologically embedded in utero, in childhood, and throughout adolescence, all these are further exacerbated by adversity or threat at any stage of life. Stress hormone levels, for example, are much higher among children of low economic status—a biological hazard for future illness of many kinds.[19]

While we Canadians like to pride ourselves on our publicly funded health care system—and rightly so, especially as we peer over the 49th parallel at the law-of-the-jungle morass to our south—research shows that, at most, only about 25 percent of population health is attributable to health care. A full 50 percent is determined by social and economic environments.[20]

In my view there is plenty of reason to think that even this 50 percent is a serious underestimate. "Tell me your zip code," asserted a speaker at a 2014 Chicago health conference, "and I'll tell you how long you'll live." The life-expectancy gap between Chicago's poorest and most affluent neighborhoods is close to thirty years.[21] "Basically the difference between Iraq and Canada, within a few miles," a physician friend of mine commented. Canadians given to patriotic smugness might look at a similar study in our own country, done in 2006. In the city of Saskatoon, people in the poorest neighborhoods were two and a half times more likely to die in any one year. The infant mortality rate was triple in the city center than in its more affluent environs.[22]

In 1974 the anthropologist Ashley Montagu, cited earlier in this book, coined the phrase "sociogenic brain damage." Technologies since available to us confirm that stressed environments, including penury, do interfere with brain development. More recently, one scientist has called poverty a "neurotoxin." Brain scans of children and young people from deprived backgrounds have shown reduced surface area of the cerebral cortex, as well as smaller hippocampi and amygdalae—the subcortical regions involved in memory formation and emotional processing.[23] The brain's serotonin system in adolescents has been seen to be impaired by the stresses of poverty, increasing the risk for emotional turbulence.[24]

Toronto physician Gary Bloch, who serves an impoverished inner-city population, has been waging a campaign within the medical profession and beyond to raise awareness of how penury, race, and gender inequities intersect to promote disease. He wants doctors to recognize poverty as a risk factor for ill health, just as they would regard high blood pressure, smoking, or a poor diet. In practice, of course, these all tend to accompany one another. An affable forty-seven-year-old with an open smile and earnest demeanor, Gary—a long-time family friend of ours—writes prescriptions for diet supplements and refers people to financial aid workers to help with subsidies and tax problems: anything that could help ease their poverty. He shared a telling anecdote he heard from a social worker. "A physician says, 'Take this antibiotic three times . . . on a full stomach,' and I always laugh hysterically, and the women I know who are working poor laugh because they know that, 'Yeah, three meals, like what's he talking about three meals? A *full stomach*?' Another said, 'I had an old guy that needed diabetes medicine who lived in a shelter in Toronto . . . He was elderly and had mobility issues, and he didn't take any of his diabetic medication because the side effect it caused for him was diarrhea, and he was living in a shelter with sixty younger men and two toilets . . . He had no chance of getting to the toilet if he needed to quickly, so he wasn't going to take his pills.'"

"The missing piece I've been addressing is the link between knowing how social issues affect people's health and what to do about them," Gary told me—a Sisyphean task, given current social conditions. "Societal trauma is something I deal with all the time," he said. "I honestly cannot remember being taught that when I was in medical school. The traditional body of knowledge, medical culture, hasn't included interventions into social issues as a core part of what medicine is. Social trauma is a huge beast to come up against, and I can almost tangibly feel how strong and real an entity it is. It is daunting to try to confront it."

Were health professionals to take to heart information about social determinants, Canadian health expert Dennis Raphael mockingly suggests, they would stop issuing injunctions such as "Stop smoking," dispensing instead "Don't be poor" and related prescriptions: "Don't live in damp, low-quality housing"; "Don't work in a stressful, low-paying manual job"; "Don't live next to a busy major road or near a polluting factory"; "Be able to afford to go on a foreign holiday and sunbathe."[25] In other words, immigrate to a kinder, saner, more equitable parallel universe.

The beast of inequality has many tentacles with which to squeeze the life out of people's lives. For one thing, inequality's biological imprint doesn't affect only the very poor. In societies dominated by materialist principles, your relative position on the social ladder is a predictor of health across all strata. The linking of social rank with health is known as the *social gradient*, a slope that runs through all segments of society. It is easy to see why. Status grants people higher or lower degrees of control, the absence of which we already know to be a trigger for physiological stress and illness. This was shown in Michael Marmot's famous Whitehall studies, which found that people's rank in the British civil service correlated with their risks for heart disease, cancer, and mental health diagnoses.[26] The further down the position on the ladder, the higher the risks, independent of behavioral factors such as smoking or blood pressure. And this among a cohort of people with relative economic security and respectable, middle-class employment! "It is easier to vacate contaminated buildings than to change social structures," another leading chronicler of inequality, the British epidemiologist Richard Wilkinson, has commented. "We could speculate on how different the response would be if the slope of the social gradient in death and disease ran in the opposite direction, so that the highest-status people did the worst."[27]

Finally, amid a culture grounded in values of competition and materialism, we confront not only actual material conditions, pertinent as they are, but also how people are induced to *see* themselves. When people judge themselves or are judged by others according to financial achievement, being lower on the pyramid—even if in a relatively stable position—is itself a source of stress that undermines well-being. In the neuroscientist Robert Sapolsky's tart phrase, "Health is particularly corroded by your nose constantly being rubbed in what you do not have."[28]

Racism, poverty, inequality—in this society, people's faces are constantly rubbed in what they do not have and what the system daily reminds them they do not deserve.

Chapter 23

Society's Shock Absorbers: Why Women Have It Worse

Many of my female patients have no idea how to express
their anger in healthy ways. Their suppressed anger
contributes to their depression and, I believe, other
medical symptoms as well.

—Julie Holland, M.D., *Moody Bitches*

This chapter aims to pierce an apparent medical mystery: Why do women suffer chronic illness of the body far more often than men, and why are they far more likely to be diagnosed with mental health conditions? I say "apparent," because from all that is known about the *bodymind* unity and our biopsychosocial nature, the answers are staring us in the face and are entirely predictable. That we don't recognize them has everything to do with our taking for granted the "normal" way of things in a culture of patriarchy, which, despite centuries of female resistance and progress, is ruled as often by subliminal male concerns as by overt power dynamics.

By "we" I'm referring not only to my profession of medicine and to society at large but to my own membership in the dominant sex class and the conditioning that such an affiliation has instilled in me. The truth is, I talk a much better gender-equality game than I sometimes play. It has taken, and continues to take, a very strong and determined woman—my wife, Rae—to keep alerting me, far more frequently than she should have to, to such realities in our own personal relationship. Looking around me, I sense that Rae and I are far from unique in manifesting how unconscious transactions between men and women play out daily in our culture, to the detriment of both sexes but especially at the cost of women's physical and emotional well-being.

The gender gap in health is real, if underappreciated. Women are more subject to chronic disease even long before old age, and they have more years of poor health and disability. "Women have it worse," a leading U.S. physician wrote recently, pointing out that women are at much higher risk of suffering chronic pain, migraines, fibromyalgia, irritable bowel syndrome, and autoimmune conditions like rheumatoid arthritis.[1] As noted in chapter 4, rheumatoid arthritis strikes women three times more often than it does men, lupus afflicts women by a disproportionate factor of nine, and the female-to-male ratio of multiple sclerosis has been rising for decades. Women also have a higher incidence of non-smoking-related malignancies. Even when it comes to lung cancer, a woman who smokes has double the chance of developing the disease.[2] Women also have double men's incidence of anxiety, depression, and PTSD.[3] "We are creating a new normal that isn't normal at all," the New York psychiatrist and author Julie Holland said when I interviewed her. "Perhaps one out of four or more American women right now are taking psychiatric medications, but if you add in things like sleeping pills and antianxiety meds, it's even higher. At any given staff meeting or PTA meeting, you've got about a quarter of the people, maybe more, who are taking daily medicines to moderate the way they feel and the way they behave." Alzheimer's dementia, too, seems to affect women disproportionately, just as it does Black people in the United States.[4]

That last fact alone ought to give us pause, containing as it does a significant clue as to the sources of such conditions. This book has, after all, been tracing the physiological impacts of developmental needs not being met, of stress and trauma. A consistent theme, beyond scientific doubt, has been that such emotional disturbances frequently trigger inflammation and other forms of physiological and mental harm. We might ask ourselves what burdens, what stresses, could women of any color and class share with Black people as a group? To me the answer is clear: they are both especially targeted by a culture that does not honor but demeans, distorts, and even impels people to suppress who they are. If that is an accurate assessment, we would expect that as these pressures intersect and compound each other, so would the incidence of disease rise. And it does, hugely.[5]

In the previous chapter we examined the biological embedding of racism and inequality and the resulting health disparities. Here we take the logical step of looking at the stresses of being female in a patriarchal society. These, too, get under the skin, playing havoc with all systems of the body, including the immune system.

A feisty thirty-eight-year-old small-town Manitoba firefighter I will call Liz told me of her health calvary when we met at a health conference in Toronto. By then she had been off the job for nearly a year with Crohn's disease, the intestinal autoimmune condition we encountered with Glenda's story in chapter 2, with such symptoms as fatigue, bloody stools, and abdominal cramping. When that condition resolved, she came down with manifestations of post-traumatic stress: debilitating fear, horrendous fantasies, insomnia. "I had shaking every day," she told me. "I was terrified of things I had no reason to be afraid of. I developed a mistrust of myself, not knowing how I would react in a lot of situations. I would cry at the drop of a hat for reasons I couldn't explain . . . when I was in public or when I was doing things. I had suicidal thoughts. And I used a lot of alcohol to manage these symptoms; I started drinking every day."

By now, it will be no surprise for the reader to learn that there was early trauma in Liz's history. She had been sexually abused at age seven, a violation that recurred throughout her childhood and adolescence. We know that sexual trauma is a risk factor for all manner of conditions of mind and body, and that girls are more likely than boys to be subjected to it. It is no longer a secret that well beyond childhood, females in this culture face the constant menace of sexual harassment in both private and professional life. While the advent of #MeToo advocacy has thrown necessary light on this scourge, it has long been thus. When my wife was sixteen, working at an ice-cream store, she heard her boss, old enough to be her grandfather, snigger to his son as they walked behind her: "I wouldn't mind getting into her pants." "I was shocked and disgusted and weirded out," Rae recalls. "I had never heard that expression before, but it felt gross. It was total objectification. Naturally, I kept silent." Or unnaturally, as it were—but either way, an experience for women and girls so regular as to be entirely "normal." And that is the case worldwide.[6] In such a sexualized and threatening climate, how can many women avoid developing that "assaulted sense of self" Dr. Kenneth Hardy identified as one of the deep imprints of racism, along with the damage it does to physiological and psychological well-being?[†]

We are hearing more and more about the hazards women face in traditionally male fiefdoms such as policing and firefighting. Along with the risk of secondary trauma faced by all first responders, an atmosphere of toxic masculinity on the job also took a toll on Liz, helping to trigger her gut inflammation and mental distress. If she showed vulnerability, upset at the tragedies she often witnessed, she was treated with derision and contempt. "It was a very macho scene," she recalled. "If you have any issues, you're a

---

[†] For Dr. Hardy's concept of the assaulted sense of self, see chapter 22.

liability. Particularly if you are a woman, if you talk about it, you're considered a 'pussy.' They'll physically do stuff to you, sabotage you in some way. They threw tampons into my bed. I don't even know why. It was very much a symbol of femininity." Such bullying, too, assaults the body and the spirit. In a 2017 study of female firefighters, harassment and threats on the job were linked to suicidal ideation and more severe psychiatric symptoms,[7] findings that extend into other, less male-dominated professions as well. Not only mental but also physical health suffers.[8]

One healthy response to assault for any sentient creature is anger, a function of the evolutionary RAGE system in the brain whose purpose is to defend our boundaries, physical or emotional.[‡] My friend Dr. Julie Holland's comment in the epigraph to this chapter about women's anger being subdued to the detriment of their health tracks invariably with my observation among people with depression, autoimmune disease, and cancer. The ingrained abdication of the natural, spontaneous "no" is not restricted to women in this culture, but it is certainly imposed on them more widely and with greater force. The dynamic goes even deeper than deliberately holding in anger. As I distinguished earlier, repression (as opposed to suppression) occurs with no conscious awareness, as healthy feelings are banished beneath the level of consciousness: out of mind, out of sight. "Sugar and spice don't make space for anything that's not nice," Holland writes. "When we don't even know we're angry, we can't converse with the person responsible or otherwise tackle the problem. We cry; we eat; we soothe ourselves a thousand different ways."[9]

Early childhood mechanisms of self-suppression are reinforced by persistent, gendered social conditioning. Many women end up *self-silencing*, defined as "the tendency to silence one's thoughts

---

‡   The neuroscientist Jaak Panksepp's identification of the brain's emotional systems CARE, PANIC/GRIEF, FEAR, PLAY, LUST, SEEKING, and RAGE was introduced in chapter 9.

and feelings to maintain safe relationships, particularly intimate relationships." This chronic negation of one's authentic experience can be fatal. In a study that followed nearly two thousand women over ten years, those "who reported that, in conflict with their spouses, they usually or always kept their feelings to themselves, had over four times the risk of dying during the follow-up compared with women who always showed their feelings."[10] As at home, so on the job. Another study showed that for women with non-supportive bosses, the squashing of anger—a natural adaptation to an environment in which to self-express would be to risk the loss of employment—increased the risk of heart disease.[11]

Recall from chapters 5 and 7 this array of self-abnegating traits that predispose to disease: a compulsive and self-sacrificing doing for others, suppression of anger, and an excessive concern about social acceptability. These personality features, found across all autoimmune conditions, are precisely the ones inculcated into women in a patriarchal culture. "I was denying myself as a person, denying my own desires, my wants," the first responder Liz said. "I was not paying attention to what I needed. Everyone else was far more important. My job was way more important than any concern that I had. I wasn't listening to myself in any regard."†

That "not listening to self" in order to prioritize others' needs is a significant source of the health-impairing roles women assume. It is among the medically overlooked but pernicious ways in which our society's "normal" imposes a major health cost on women. More on that below.

The sexualization of women is another source of ill health. Being valued for the use another can make of you is an assault on the self.

---

† Typically, none of the physicians treating Liz for her Crohn's ever inquired about her childhood traumas or current stresses or about her relationship to herself.

Girls and women are much more likely to be subjected to it, even sold the seductive idea that there is empowerment in it. The famed Canadian singer-songwriter Alanis Morissette spoke to me of the "headiness of the power" she recalls feeling when the male attention she received as a young pop star and TV celebrity began to take on a carnal hue. On the one hand, she recalls, "My intellect or my being-ness was diminished almost everywhere I turned, if not obliterated entirely. At the same time, all of a sudden, I have this power that I can wield in terms of being objectified or sexualized. In some ways it was enticing to feel empowered in this way, of being found attractive or straight-up statutorily raped.‡ There was an element of it that felt like power to me. It was sort of a young perspective of 'Hey, I'll take the power wherever I can get it.' " Mind you, the era Morissette is describing came decades before the emergence of online platforms like OnlyFans, where young women provide explicit "content" of all sorts to (overwhelmingly male) subscribers. A *New York Times* headline—in the Business section, no less— said it all: "Jobless, Selling Nudes Online, and Still Struggling."[12]

Young people are increasingly getting their first round of sex education from all too easily accessed online pornography. This is not Victorian erotica we are talking about, or your stepdad's *Hustler* collection. According to sociologist and *Pornland* author Gail Dines, the most popular (read profitable) kind of internet porn today is known in the industry as "gonzo," a genre characterized by "hard-core, body-punishing sex in which women are demeaned and debased."[13] These physically violent, emotionally hostile depictions of sex are being accessed by children at younger and younger ages—most sources place the average age of first exposure around eleven years old.

---

‡　"It took me years in therapy to even admit there had been any kind of victimization on my part," Morissette says in the recent documentary *Jagged*. "I would always say I was consenting, and then I'd be reminded like, 'Hey, you were fifteen—you're not consenting at fifteen.' Now I'm like, 'Oh, yeah, they're all pedophiles. It's all statutory rape."

Girls must contend with a toxic conflation of sexuality with subservience. Dines notes that women's and teen magazines are featuring ever more content aimed at helping women make the most of the cultural shift by diversifying their skills at pleasing someone else, usually a male. Girls are encouraged to be sexual not as a natural or emergent self-expression, but as a means of attracting and keeping a partner, or a way of "empowering" themselves within an oppressive power structure. Where the normalization of abusive sex meets social media attention-seeking, the results can be gruesome: in summer 2020 a viral "TikTok challenge" came to light in which teenage girls share "post-coital videos of their bruised and cut limbs, in an attempt to emulate the recent Netflix kidnap-porn film, *365 Days*."[14] Meanwhile, pornography teaches many boys to associate pleasure with domination and a shutdown of tender feelings. The suppression of vulnerable emotions, of course, is one manifestation of male trauma, leading inexorably to a withering of compassion for others—especially when those others have something we want, as in every instance of date rape or nonconsensual sexual aggression.

The burdens placed on women in patriarchal cultures, and the ways these curtail and constrain women's prospects for authentic self-realization, have long been recognized—by women, that is. In 1792, thirty-three-year-old Mary Wollstonecraft published her astonishingly radical book *A Vindication of the Rights of Woman*, observing that women "*are made to assume an artificial character before their faculties have acquired any strength.*"[15] Almost exactly two hundred years later, the indomitable radical feminist thinker Andrea Dworkin captured the visceral dimensions of life in a female body under patriarchy: "That loss of self is a physical reality, not just a psychic vampirism; and as a physical reality it is chilling and extreme, *a literal erosion of the body's integrity and its ability to function and to survive.*"[16] I'm not sure if Dworkin knew the science buttressing her claim, but her use of the word "literal" was exactly right.

Such loss of self, in Dworkin's phrase, becomes women's portion in large part because, in addition to their role in providing for their families' economic and physical needs, they are the designated emotional caregivers, at their own expense. The task of caring, in fact, falls largely to women in this culture. The contemporary phrase *emotional labor* does a great job of conveying the joblike nature of this stress-inducing, externally imposed role. Arguably to an even greater degree than housework and childbirth, this is the proverbial "woman's work" that "is never done."

Women often serve as the emotional glue—the connective tissue, if you like—that keeps nuclear and extended families and communities together. It is no coincidence they suffer far more than men do from diseases of *actual* connective tissue, among which lupus, rheumatoid arthritis, scleroderma, fibromyalgia, and their multiple relatives are variants. Thus, these conditions, as most chronic maladies do, reflect social dynamics along the lines we have been investigating throughout, not simply individual physiology gone rogue.

It is no secret that the stress of caregiving enfeebles the immune system. The caretakers of Alzheimer patients, for example—the vast majority of whom are women—have significantly diminished immune function and poorer wound healing, suffer more respiratory illness, and experience much higher rates of depression than well-matched non-caregiving peers.[17] Immunity is not the only function impaired by caregiver stress. Mothers looking after emotionally challenged children were found to have abnormal cortisol indicators, poorer metabolic functioning as measured by blood testing, and less healthy distribution of body fat.[18] As mentioned in chapter 4, they also have shorter telomeres, indicating premature aging.

The self-stifling expectation of caregiving while ignoring one's own emotions and needs has only been reinforced by the COVID-19 pandemic. "Mothers Are the 'Shock Absorbers' of Our Society," a *New York Times* headline pronounced in October 2020. A survey of married women found that childcare was a major source of stress, with women largely internalizing their frustrations. Rather than ask their spouses to step up their domestic contributions, the researchers found, "mothers blame themselves for these conflicts and feel responsible for reducing them, including by leaving the workforce, beginning use of antidepressants, or ignoring their own concerns about COVID-19."[19]

"All this extra work is affecting women's health," the British author Caroline Criado Perez stated in *Invisible Women*, her award-winning book about the implicit male-oriented bias in virtually all aspects of social, economic, cultural, academic, and even medical life. She gives a fascinating example of the asymmetrical apportioning of chores between men and women: "We have long known that women (in particular women under fifty-five) have worse outcomes than men following heart surgery. But it wasn't until a Canadian study came out in 2016 that researchers were able to isolate women's care burden as one of the factors behind this discrepancy, noticing that women who have bypass surgery tend to go right back into their caregiving roles, while men were more likely to have someone to look after them."[20]

Our society reinforces men's sense of being entitled to women's care in a way that almost escapes being put into words. I refer here to the automatic mothering women provide their male partners, the emotional sustenance that forms the invisible mortar of many heterosexual relationships: a very conventional dynamic that speaks to how tenacious gendered social constructs are, how thoroughly steeped we are in them. Some men are aware of the care they receive only in its absence and experience intense resentment when it is withdrawn; for example, when their female partner is preoccupied elsewhere, as when children are born. Many a woman has complained to me that her spouse becomes distant and punishing when she so much as catches a cold. As I observed in family practice, the children may lose out on maternal attention when the husband demands mothering energy from his partner. (It goes without saying that the father's stable attunement with his kids is also compromised when he assumes an infantile role in the partnership.) Oftentimes the mother loses vitality or develops physical or emotional symptoms signaling her body's rebellion against being overtaxed, imposing further strain on both her and her dependents.

I confess that what I "observed in family practice" mirrored the scenario played out in our own home, especially when our children were small. Nor is it a dynamic I can honestly relegate to the past. I interviewed Rae, the world's leading authority on this subject. "It's as if your tension is my responsibility, which I have neglected," she said. "You see me through a negative lens, like it must be about me somehow. I begin to question myself. I get careful around you, as if I'm walking on eggshells. I start feeling depressed, alienated, lonely. I'm left with a lot of resentment, and that's really stressful and frustrating." And then came the expert diagnosis. "I think there is a mother rage that erupts with male frustration, and it's taken out on the woman," Rae concluded. "She has to keep him happy. He does not differentiate his anger and his frustration from her—she becomes just an object to him."

When I spoke with Dr. Julie Holland, she averred that the disproportionately high rate of anxiety and depression in women stems, in large part, from their absorption of male angst and their culturally directed responsibility for soothing it. In that sense, women are ingesting the antidepressants and anxiolytics (anti-anxiety meds) for both sexes. "Girls are given all sorts of overt and covert messages that the way to get along is to go along and seek consensus, make sure everybody else is happy," she said. "You know, they see their mothers. I definitely saw my mom doing this for my father—making dinner, doing the dishes, doing the laundry. He's reading the paper after dinner . . . You take on somebody else's pain. When I was first dating my partner, Jeremy, I remember saying to him things like 'If you're in a sad or scared place, I want to lead you out into the light.' " I nodded in recognition when Julie said this. Over half a century ago, Rae took on very much the same task, or should I say "burden." "I saw your light the first time we met," she recalls, "and I saw your shadow. I was going to heal you; I was going to dispel the darkness." An unenviable assignment, to say the least.

In *Down Girl: The Logic of Misogyny*, the contemporary feminist philosopher Kate Manne, associate philosophy professor at Cornell University, gives us a handy way of conceptualizing the expectations held of women and the demands made on them: *feminine-coded goods and services*—those which are "hers to give." They include "attention, affection, admiration, sympathy, sex, and children (i.e., social, domestic, reproductive, and emotional labor); . . . safe haven, nurture, security, soothing, and comfort." These are counterposed with the *masculine-coded perks and privileges* that are "his for the taking": for example, "power, prestige . . . rank, reputation, honor . . . hierarchical status, upward mobility, and the status conferred by having a high-ranking woman's loyalty, love, devotion, etc."[21] It is not hard to intuit which of these groupings would entail and engender (no pun intended) more self-suppression, sacrifice, and stress. Bear in mind, too, that Manne is depicting here women of relative privilege. So many others, in addition to assigned gender roles, struggle under the heavy freight of poverty, single parenthood, and racial discrimination. We have seen the cost in health these intersectional misfortunes exact.

When I speak of *patriarchy*, I mean not the conscious will nor, often, even the conscious awareness of individual men, but a system of power. Although patriarchy is ancient, having arisen with the dawn of civilization, capitalism has comfortably adapted it to its needs—we see that played out in economics, in politics, in all institutions of this society, as in the home. Men pay a price, too, even as they reap the dubious "benefits" of the system that privileges them. When I reduce my wife to an object whose purpose is to keep me satisfied, what role am I casting myself in? An impotent, dependent child whose emotional welfare hinges on Mommy's willingness to comply with my perceived needs. This child, in an adult body, struts, remonstrates, sulks, and makes demands on his caregiver. He is never sated, never satisfied. Both partners, in their own ways, are powerless.

Men's suffering, too, is part of the patriarchal cycle, in the mix as both effect and cause. The taboo against vulnerability, in particular, is deeply harmful to men as well as to women. Anger may be more permissible among men, but sadness, grief, or "weakness"—which really just means acknowledging one's limits—are not. Many combat veterans have had to overcome this patriarchal bylaw as they have struggled with anguish, depression, suicidality, and other manifestations of post-traumatic stress, from which there is no healing without a free flow of vulnerable emotion. Toxified masculinity, like the suppression of the feminine, is lethal. It claims its victims through many pathways, including alcoholism and other substance addictions, workaholism, violence, and suicidality†—all defenses against or escapes from vulnerability, grief, and fear.

"In our culture we 'turn boys into men,' through disconnection," says the therapist Terry Real. "To learn to disconnect from your feelings, from your vulnerabilities, and from others is what we call autonomy and independence. That's a traumatic wound, a hidden one because it's culturally normative. It's almost preverbal." In his book *I Don't Want to Talk About It: Overcoming the Secret Legacy of Male Depression*, Real speaks of male fragility and the denial of men's sensitivity. "To me, the fragility has to do with both the trauma and the injunction against being human," he told me. "The essence of [toxic] masculinity is invulnerability. The more vulnerable you are, the more 'girly' you are. The more invulnerable you are, the more 'manly' you are. So the fragility of being a human, the simple human vulnerability, is suppressed. Men are trying to live up to a standard which is inhuman, and they're dogged by a sense of falling short of that standard over and over and over again." As Real spoke, I was reminded of the male firefighters who threw tampons into Liz's bed and the vulnerability they were attempting to shame in her, as they were ashamed of their own.

"The guys that I treat are all captains of industry who've done beautifully in the world and are horror stories in their personal lives," Real confided. Male domination exacts a high price in both directions, and by all indicators, it costs more than it pays.

---

† Recent research shows that over thirty thousand U.S. veterans of the post-9/11 wars in Iraq and Afghanistan have committed suicide, over four times the number killed in combat. https://coloradonewsline.com/2021/07/08/report-veteran-suicides-far-outstrip-combat-deaths-in-post-9-11-wars/.

Chapter 24

We Feel Their Pain: Our Trauma-Infused Politics

In insider political circles, almost all politicians are seen as difficult and even damaged people, necessarily tolerated in some civics class inversion because they were elected.

—Michael Wolff, *Landslide: The Final Days of the Trump Presidency*

Having started our journey at the individual and cellular levels, we now arrive at the outermost layer of the biopsychosocial onion: the political. You may well be wondering, What does this have to do with this book's concerns—with illness and wellness, with trauma? Why does it matter? Why, as they say, "go there"?

Wherever one falls on (or off) the political spectrum, it's not hard to conclude that politics today, and the media culture around it, are more toxic than ever. It's true that current events, from village gossip to world affairs, have always been combustible fodder for conversation. These days, they are so incendiary that it often seems no conversation is possible, to the point where many people—as many as 60 percent of Americans, according to one poll—anticipate family holidays with dread.[1] The authors of a 2019 study of Americans out of the University of Nebraska–Lincoln found that "a large number of Americans believe their physical health has been harmed by their exposure to politics and even more report that politics has resulted in emotional costs and lost friendships."[2] They may be more correct than they realize. In an article titled "Stressed Out by Politics? It Could Be Making Your Body Age Faster, Too," telomere researcher Dr. Elissa Epel (see chapter 4) suggests that the allostatic wear and tear of politics may shorten those health-maintaining chromosomal structures.[3] A D.C.-area psychologist has even coined a name for this malaise of the governed: "headline stress disorder."[4]

The toxicity of political life might be of less concern if we could get even a momentary breather from it. Our phones have become handheld stress machines buzzing urgently with updates, from the banal to the grave, about matters of conflict and uncertainty—matters largely out of our control. Social media feeds "feed" us all we can eat, and more still. It never stops.

Not that we're entirely helpless: we probably all could, for example, adjust our news consumption habits to better filter out the rancor, spite, anxiety, and doom. We could practice better listening and exercise more empathy with those with whom we disagree. We could adopt a strict mindfulness regimen: five minutes of deep breathing before and after scrolling, no exceptions. These moves would all be salutary. They would also be not enough. In my view, there is something going on beyond and beneath the oft-lamented "hyperpartisanship," "polarization," and "radicalization" we're witnessing.

The closer I look at who populates the political landscape— the people at the top and we ourselves at its base (or somewhere in between, for the more privileged among us)—the more I see the wounded electing the wounded, the traumatized leading the traumatized and, inexorably, implementing policies that entrench traumatizing social conditions. Beneath all the posturing, punditry, and politicking, the pulse of unseen emotional undercurrents thumps insistently. I can't prove it, of course. Social psychology doesn't lend itself to the kind of firm conclusions achievable in the physical sciences. What I can do is point to it, offering my observations and citing examples and research where possible, and trust people to look for themselves. I do consider the issue of enormous importance—and not just because trauma adds flammable emotional fuel to already fiery family dinner-table debates.

For one thing, political culture is among the many avenues by which toxic myths become normalized truths. Politics are intimately linked with the social character as we have discussed it: the set of desired characteristics that most dispose people to function smoothly within a given system, even if those traits are literally sickening. The same holds for those who steer the ship. A society like ours demands of its leaders a certain set of dispositions and worldviews—call it the *political character*—without which their careers would never get off the ground, given the job requirements. The traits most amenable to stewarding a socioeconomic system that traumatizes populations as a matter of course will, naturally, be ones that inure their bearer to vital aspects of emotional life, if not disable the compassion circuitry outright. This always starts with the self, early in life. There may be exceptions, but I haven't seen many, especially not at the uppermost echelons of power.

When trauma manifests on the political stage, the consequences for people and the planet are massive. Politicians make policy, after all, and policy creates or cements the very cultural conditions we know are antithetical to our health. The level of trauma awareness or blindness they and we bring to the political conversation can't help playing itself out in the world we end up living in. If disease is the *individual* body's way of alerting us to something out of joint, something contrary to what our nature intends for us, then surely social maladies like addiction and global catastrophes like climate change are all signs of something amiss in the *body politic*. So, too, is the mood of resignation and cynicism that surrounds politics in general, and the sometimes ludicrous levels of suspicion and venom that infuse public discussions of everything from elections to abortion to how we should handle health pandemics.

Phantasmagorical vaccine paranoia, for example, is not the same as healthy skepticism. Nor is contemptuous, self-righteous scorn toward vaccine or lockdown dissenters equivalent to responsible citizenship. In my work on trauma, I have observed that it is not merely the ideas people hold but, even more, the emotional resonance of how they speak and act—of *who and how they are being*—that reveal their inner psychic life. When we try to address the content of their speech or their beliefs without attending to the energetic fuel, we miss the mark. The same is true in the sociopolitical sphere: if we want to understand why individuals and groups believe and behave as they do—and we should want to, if we truly care about the consequences—then we need to be willing to see the traumatic scars underneath the extreme emotional reactions. This can be difficult when we ourselves carry strong points of view about our rightness and their wrongness—which is yet more reason to take it on.

All this is more than speculative. Traumatic childhood experience has been shown to bear very directly on adult political orientations. Michael Milburn, emeritus professor of psychology at the University of Massachusetts, found that the harsher the parenting people were exposed to as young children, the more prone they become to support authoritarian or aggressive policies, such as foreign wars, punitive laws, and the death penalty. "We used physical punishment in childhood as a marker of a dysfunctional family environment," he told me. "There was significantly more opposition to abortion, and more support for capital punishment and the use of military force, particularly among males who had experienced high levels of physical punishment, *especially if they had never had psychotherapy.*" I was intrigued by that last finding. "Psychotherapy," Milburn explained, "speaks to a potential for self-examination, for self-reflection."

The confluence of politics and trauma is not a new concept. Decades ago, the great Polish Swiss psychotherapist Alice Miller pointed to how the harsh child-rearing practices long fashionable in Germany helped prepare the template for Nazi authoritarianism. She also argued persuasively that the intense suffering and oppression in childhood of the German fascist leaders, most especially monstrous psychopaths like Adolf Hitler and Hermann Göring, played a decisive role in shaping their mental-emotional lives and, necessarily, their political inclinations. "Among all the leading figures of the Third Reich," she wrote in *For Your Own Good: Hidden Cruelty in Child-Rearing and the Roots of Violence*, "I have not been able to find a single one who did not have a strict and rigid upbringing."[5] For "strict and rigid," we can substitute "traumatizing": Miller was not, after all, speaking about homes run by kindly parents with firm curfews but the sorts of environments that would imprint on a child a fear-tinged view of the world and/or require of him to go numb in the face of suffering, starting with his own.

The subliminal beliefs leaders hold about human nature, the world, and their position in it, and the unconscious impulses that motivate their actions, are of great consequence for their politics—which is to say, for our lives and our world. The worldview they developed early in life under the impact of misfortunes they did not choose and could not control imbues how they feel about, interact with, and act upon the universe and their fellow beings decades later. And yet, as the British psychotherapist Sue Gerhardt points out, "We rarely address the underlying psychological and emotional dynamics of our public figures, or our culture as a whole."[6]

Let's briefly examine two pairs of political nemeses—first in Canada, then the United States—all four of whom have convinced millions of people to entrust them with great power. What makes each of them so appealing and so appalling, depending on who's observing, owes much to personality traits forged in the crucible of early trauma.

In my own country, former prime minister Stephen Harper was much admired by conservatives for his icy, tough-on-crime, climate-science-is-irrelevant, addiction-is-a-criminal-choice views, and reviled by progressives for the same things. Harper has recalled an idyllic childhood, despite growing up under a stern "stickler" of a dad whose own father had disappeared mysteriously years earlier and was never located. I resonate completely with *Toronto Star* journalist Jim Coyle's aside that, contrary to Harper's recollections, it is "not difficult to imagine that life under such a patriarch might have been stifling."[7] This, after all, is a man characterized by his biographer as "autocratic, secretive, and cruel," and whose former chief of staff reported him to have been "suspicious, secretive, and vindictive, prone to sudden eruptions of white-hot rage over meaningless trivia." A Canadian columnist once wrote about Stephen Harper's "dead, sociopathic eyes," while another journalist described him as "chilly and inscrutable." No child is born with dead eyes: such a look bespeaks a recoiling from seeing what is dreadful to a young soul.

The man who succeeded Harper on Ottawa's Parliament Hill exudes a very different vibe, one of terminal likability. Justin Trudeau is known for speaking in warm tones and inclusive language. He has shed public tears of sorrow at more than one press conference, including when a Canadian rock music hero died of brain cancer in 2017.[8] There is nothing wrong with a politician showing their vulnerable side—would that it were more normalized—but, as many have noted, there is also something inauthentic, even unctuous, about Trudeau's nice-guy persona.

Recently, he has had to abjectly apologize for indulging in a private family excursion on a national day created to commemorate the trauma inflicted on our native peoples, a history about which he has waxed contrite in the past.[†] Such ethical and emotional obtuseness bears the imprint of a trauma-inflected childhood. Justin grew up in a home where the father—Pierre, the eminent and irascible prime minister of the 1960s and '70s—was consumed by work, status, and virility. As a boy, Justin was under the care of a mother three decades younger than her womanizing husband, with whom she was often in conflict, her gloom deepened by bipolar disorder. At times she was given to manic high spirits and embarrassingly public sexual hijinks with the likes of Mick Jagger. The current prime minister has recalled being "desperate . . . to inject a sense of magic into every moment we did have together as a family."[9] I am speculating, I'll admit—neither Trudeau nor any politician has ever sought me out for counseling—but I see it as no stretch to say that his fraught upbringing likely primed him to make cloying sweetness and shallow ingratiation his métier.

According to the popular narrative, there could have been no more diametrical opposites in American politics, whether gauged by demographic appeal, ethical values, or personality, than 2016 presidential opponents Donald J. Trump and Hillary Rodham Clinton. The differences are easy to spot, the similarities subtler but instructive. It may come as a surprise to supporters of both, for example, to read a *Scientific American* analysis published in 2016 that pointed out how many qualities that define psychopathy are routinely found in top politicians. One was "coldheartedness," a trait on which both Trump and his then opponent Clinton scored in the upper quintile.[10]

Donald Trump's cartoonishness, the havoc he wreaked

[†]   September 30, 2021: Canada's inaugural observation of National Day for Truth and Reconciliation.

on the U.S. political system, and the cultural tumult around his ascendancy can too easily obscure what a sad, thoroughly wounded person he is. It took one who knows him better than most, his psychologist niece, Mary Trump, to cut through both the hoopla and the opprobrium to the dark heart of the matter. We now know from Mary's revealing 2020 biography, *Too Much and Never Enough: How My Family Created the World's Most Dangerous Man,* that the young Donald had plenty of cause to push reality out of mind and sight; to become grandiose, narcissistic, combative, and utterly opportunistic. "Deep down I have no problem describing him as a sociopath," Mary has said of Donald's father, Fred, the paterfamilias. "He had no real human feeling, and he treated his children variously with contempt." Her own father, Fred Jr., Donald's older sibling, was driven by childhood trauma to alcoholism and an early death at age forty-one. The world has seen what Donald has been driven to. It oughtn't to have required Mary Trump's revelations to uncover the suffering behind the huckster-president's persona, but, in our trauma-blind world, it did. "He is a poster child for trauma," the psychiatrist Bessel van der Kolk told me.

The journalist Tony Schwartz got an up-close view when he ghostwrote Trump's bestselling *The Art of the Deal.* "Lying is second nature to him," Schwartz told the *New Yorker* years later. "More than anyone else I have ever met, Trump has the ability to convince himself that whatever he is saying at any given moment is true, or sort of true, or at least ought to be true."[11] "Second nature," as we noted before, is nobody's real nature. No one's original nature impels them to lie; there are plenty of *congenial* liars, but no *congenital* ones. Friedrich Nietzsche wrote somewhere that people lie their way out of reality when they have been hurt by reality, and this is eminently true of Donald Trump's origin story. Lying, automatic or deliberate, first insulated him from devastating rejection in childhood, and later served him in the realm of political power.

Hillary Clinton is still admired and pined for by many as a tenacious survivor and the rightful winner of the 2016 election. Compared with Trump, at least, she is a paragon of poise, grace, empathy, hard work, and reason. What almost never gets asked is, Where do such relentless ambition and "tenacity" come from, and at what cost? Ought we really to celebrate it, or is it in its own way also an unhealthy norm, even if not to the same degree as Trump's bloviating bluster? Such questions were completely bypassed in the hagiographic haze of Clinton's campaign, in ways I found literally incredible. One moment in particular stuck with me; it demonstrates how readily we normalize and lionize the "winning" personalities of our leaders.

On the evening of her nomination, a video celebrating Hillary's life and achievements was broadcast to an international audience, narrated by the actor Morgan Freeman. In it, the candidate quoted a life lesson imparted to her in childhood by her stern, exacting father: "Don't whine, don't complain, do what you are supposed to do, do it to the best of your ability." By all indications, this was a whitewash. As we know from biographical accounts, the father could be capricious and cruel. "He hurled biting sarcasm at his wife and his only daughter and spanked, at times excessively, his three children to keep them in line."[12] In the video Secretary Clinton also shared, "My mother wanted me to be resilient, she wanted me to be brave." She then related an instance of how this "resilience" was inculcated. "I was four, and there were lots of kids in the neighborhood. I would come out and have a bow in my hair, and the kids would all pick on me. It was my first experience of being bullied, and I was terrified. One day I ran into the house, and my mother met me and she said to me, 'There is no room for cowards in this house. You go back outside and figure out how you are going to deal with what those kids are doing.'" That isn't a call to resilience but to repression. The message a young child receives in such a circumstance is "Vulnerability is shameful in this house, there is no room for your fear. Do not feel or show your pain, suck up your feelings, you are on your own. Don't expect any empathy here." And yet no one in the arena seemed to find this blow to a small child's sensibility disturbing. No media commentator so much as registered that this handpicked example of supposedly inspiring parenting was, in fact, a public celebration of trauma. No observer suggested that a little girl seeking the safety of the parent's embrace is hardly a coward. She is a normal four-year-old.

In any case, the life lesson about pushing through the pain did its work. More than six decades later, a campaigning Clinton was ill and dehydrated with pneumonia but hid her "weakness" from everyone until she collapsed in the street. "I'm feeling great," she unconvincingly assured the public the same day. "It's a beautiful day in New York." No doubt, the same self-suppressing dynamic compelled her to tolerate her husband's philandering proclivities, described by the late writer Joan Didion as "the familiar predatory sexuality of the provincial adolescent." In stereotypical trauma-impact fashion, Hillary blamed herself for her spouse's infidelity. He was under great stress, and she had not sufficiently tended to his emotional needs, she told a friend, thus aligning with women's assigned role in the culture of patriarchy. "She thinks she was not smart enough, not sensitive enough, not free enough of her own concerns and struggles to realize the price he was paying," this close confidant summarized Hillary's views.[13]

The internalized lack of empathy showed itself during the election campaign when she carelessly—but all the more tellingly—dubbed half of Trump's base "a basket of deplorables," revealing to a wide swath of America what they already knew in their bones: that many urban elites view them with smug contempt as people whose economic, political, and moral grievances can be ignored. The deplorables' retort came that November, in the form of a stunning political upset.

"Hillary Clinton and Donald Trump," the conservative columnist David Brooks wrote discerningly in 2016, ". . . both ultimately hew to a distrustful, stark, combative, zero-sum view of life—the idea that making it in this world is an unforgiving slog and that, given other people's selfish natures, vulnerability is dangerous."[14] That sense of danger, I would only add, started long before their forays into political life. Although their respective supporters would likely shudder at the thought of them being remotely similar, Trump and Clinton were a match made in childhood suffering.

On reading the biographies of leaders from many countries across historical periods, one sees how each of them, in their own way, had emotionally starved childhoods; each "overcame" these adversities by dint of the very personality qualities that would land them in the history books as icons and change makers, no matter what great harms they perpetrated. In each case, these traits are seen by many people to this day as laudable and worthy of emulation. That's as normal as normal can get.

And that's where the rest of us come in. Abetted and amplified by the profit-driven media machine, political culture plays on our deepest longings for surety, security, and even supremacy, targeting our damaged "inner children" with force and precision. In fact, much of politics is a lot more coherent if we see how people, many millions of them at once, unconsciously look to their leaders to fulfill their own unmet childhood needs. As the cognitive scientist George Lakoff puts it, "We all think with a largely unconscious metaphor: the Nation as Family."[15]

I asked Daniel Siegel what draws people to follow leaders who exude hostility and an authoritarian streak, such as a Donald Trump. "People may actually feel excitement that someone in the public eye is expressing aggression or assertion, the opposite of impotence," the psychiatrist and mind researcher said, noting how such traits can feel empowering to those in whom a sense of real power is wanting. "It's like a child wanting to be with a parent that will protect them. There is a sense of 'I'm going to be safe and everything is going to be okay.'" What Dan describes is also a *sense memory*, an indelible and usually unexplored imprint from childhood, a longing stored in the bodymind and activated by present-day insecurities projected into the political realm.

On the liberal side, idealizing leaders as kind, supportive, caring, and inclusive can be another form of displaced longing for attuned parenting. One prominent Democratic-supporting celebrity, the song parodist known as Randy Rainbow, tweeted out a photo of a smiling Joe Biden with Kamala Harris the night she was announced as Biden's running mate. His caption read "G'night, Mom and Dad. See you in the morning."[16] People under the sway of such childlike idealizations, even in half jest, are liable to ignore discomfiting counterevidence.

Adjacent to politics—increasingly overlapping with it, in fact—is the vast expanse of entertainments, professional sports, fads, and obsessions that we call popular culture. Indeed, one social function of pop culture is to divert people's attention from things that really do matter; imagine if all the energy now expended on analyzing the private lives of celebrities or the detailed intricacies of sporting events were, instead, devoted to mobilizing populations to collectively tackle the great issues of our age.

The election of a former reality-TV game show host to his

country's highest office is but one example of the dissolving membrane between the two spheres. "Movie-star handsome" is one of the accolades Canada's own current prime minister was showered with as he shot to international fame. Thirty years ago Bill Clinton, then a novice presidential candidate, entered the national consciousness by playing the saxophone on *The Arsenio Hall Show*. These days, former president Barack Obama subjects himself to fawning interviews with late-night talk show hosts,[17] when he isn't trending for his celebrity-soaked shindigs on Martha's Vineyard. News is entertainment, and vice versa.

One may bemoan such fluff as a degradation of political life. Less appreciated is the way pop culture grooms us for a particular sort of passive, spectator-like engagement with politics. The hero worship and emotional projection driving modern showbiz run on superfuel distilled in large part from trauma. Think of how expected, how exceedingly *normal*, the following phenomena are: a bright young star, often among the vanguard of their craft, flames out in a blaze of addiction, mental instability, or self-harm; revelations emerge about this or that beloved mogul or star's longtime sexual predations; an athlete or entertainer reveals having endured sexual violations throughout their career, or longer; a former squeaky-clean child star turns objectified sex symbol, often with an unhappy ending.

At best, the pop culture machine treats these incidents as sobering interruptions: we briefly bow our heads in solemn silence to remember the fallen before getting back to gawking, gossiping, consuming. And what do we consume, exactly? Art, sometimes; harmless fun, often enough. But we also ingest the pain of wounded people, packaged as entertainment, to dull or perhaps validate our own distress. We venerate the "personalities" that cover up pathological suffering, then express surprise when things go awry.

For their part, many celebrities seek fame precisely because the love of a fan base is the closest they can come to filling a life-long void of homegrown esteem. Iconic figures such as Marilyn Monroe, Elvis Presley, Kurt Cobain, and Amy Winehouse are valedictorians of a sad class of superstars felled by the collision between their early torments and the public limelight. All four rose to superstardom on a charisma born of a blend of extraordinary ability and trauma-injected desperation, their talent idolized and exploited, their wounding ignored even when acted out on the public stage.

Many others suffer secretly over the course of long and illustrious careers, as in the case of Aretha Franklin, whose sister Erma once said, "Aretha is a woman who suffers mightily but doesn't like to show it." Of course, she *did* display it to anyone with eyes to notice. The revered singer of the self-assertive anthem "Respect" had been more than disrespected in childhood and continued to suffer abuse in her adult relationships. The disconnect is achingly apparent in the stunning concert documentary *Amazing Grace,* filmed at a Los Angeles church in 1972. With thrilling command and depth of feeling, a thirty-year-old Aretha rattles the rafters and electrifies the crowd. The confident mask only slips when her preacher father takes the pulpit to praise his daughter's gifts. In the presence of this emotionally cruel patriarch, she stiffens, her face a curious mix of practiced deference and involuntary dissociation, as if she's not quite in her body—the very same body that had been channeling the divine Word and the sweet ache of longing so transcendently just minutes before. In her music this magnificent artist conjured the power and force she could not wield in her personal life. Her lot was to be legendary in a business and a culture that would rather mythologize than empathize. We avert our gaze from the pain, lest real life intrude on the magic.

I will say that I am encouraged by the fact that celebrities such as Alanis Morissette, Dave Navarro, Lena Dunham, Ashley Judd, Russell Brand, and Jamie Lee Curtis, all interviewed for this book, and others like Oprah Winfrey and the singers Jewel, Sia, and Lady Gaga have opened up recently about their trauma and its impact on their lives and careers. In the political realm, Hunter Biden, son of the current U.S. president, has spoken publicly about some of the traumas underlying his addiction history; his father, though the owner of an infamously punitive policy record when it comes to drug-related "crime," has at least made some more compassionate statements of late with his son's troubles in the news.

All in all, the system works with cyclic elegance: a culture founded on mistaken beliefs regarding who and what we are creates conditions that frustrate our basic needs, breeding a populace in pain, disconnected from self, others, and meaning. A select few— especially those with the sorts of early coping mechanisms that prime them to deny reality, block out empathy, fear vulnerability, mute their own sense of right and wrong, and abjure looking at themselves too closely—will be elevated to power. There they govern over a majority who so crave comfort and stability, who are so ground down by cynicism and alienation, that they will trade authentic instincts and collective self-assertion for the pseudo-attachment of false promises and soothing charisma. Completing the cycle, our wounded leaders with their blinkered priorities enact social policies that keep conditions how they were, or worse.

When former Ohio state senator Nina Turner campaigned for Bernie Sanders in 2020, she was fond of paraphrasing Matthew 7:16: "And ye shall know the tree by the fruit it bears."

Judged by the current harvest, the tree of our social life and our politics is infused with trauma from the root to the fruit. If there is any hope for a different yield, a hope on which the future of the planet surely hinges, many of us—as many as are able, anyway—will have to do what so many of our leaders constitutionally (pun intended) cannot: look within bravely, the better to look out and around honestly.

Part V

Pathways to Wholeness

A change of worldview can change the world viewed.

—Joseph Chilton Pearce, *The Crack in the Cosmic Egg: New Constructs of Mind and Reality*

Chapter 25

Mind in the Lead: The Possibility of Healing

The mind cries out, explains, demonstrates, protests;
but inside me a voice rises and shouts at it,
"Be quiet, mind, let us hear the heart!"

—Nikos Kazantzakis, *Report to Greco*

Having navigated the concentric circles of human health and illness from the cellular to the social, and having traced the inextricable and reciprocal connections between them, we now delve into the "good news": the topic of healing. The news may be encouraging, but that's not to say it's easy. How to approach healing, after all, in these troubled times? How to move toward health in the context of a socioeconomic system staunchly uninterested in remedying any of its root maladies, and in the face of a pandemic that has both highlighted and deprived us of so much we take for granted? How to keep hope alive when the odds seem so prohibitive?

And what *is* healing, anyway?

When I speak of healing, I am referring to nothing more or less than a *natural movement toward wholeness*. Notice that I do not define it as the end state of being completely whole, or "enlightened," or any similar psychospiritual ideal. It is a direction, not a destination; a line on a map, not a dot.

Nor is healing synonymous with self-improvement. Closer to the mark would be to say it is *self-retrieval*. In fact, our modern self-improvement culture—which has to a large extent been co-opted by the same consumerist forces responsible for the conditions we have been chronicling—can too easily obscure or complicate the healing journey. When we heal, we are engaged in recovering our lost parts of self, not trying to change or "better" them. As the depth psychologist and wilderness guide Bill Plotkin[†] told me, the core question is "not so much looking at what's wrong, but where is the person's wholeness not fully realized or lived out?"

Healing is also distinct from being cured: the latter means the absence of disease; the former implies coming to wholeness. "It's possible to be *healed* but not *cured*, and it's possible to be cured but not healed," my colleague Dr. Lissa Rankin[‡] points out. "Ideally, healing and curing happen together, but this isn't always the case." We will see examples of that in the chapters to follow.

I have made a similar distinction when it comes to addiction: it is possible to be *abstinent* without being *sober*. One is the absence or avoidance of something harmful—itself a worthy objective—while the other is a new, positive capacity to live in the present, free to experience life as it is. Analogously, if cure is the banishment of life-impairing symptoms or conditions, healing is the process of reuniting ourselves with the inner qualities that still live within us as inherent possibilities, as I believe they always do, and that make life worth living. We do not heal "in order to" be cured, even if that understandable wish is present. Healing is best seen as an end in itself.

What follows is not an attempt to prescribe a one-size-fits-all solution—no size does—but to point to the possibility of healing

---

[†] Plotkin's Colorado-based Animas Valley Institute offers potent retreats, workshops, and "quests" that use Nature itself as a kind of template and teacher of human wholeness.

[‡] Rankin's own story of illness and healing was touched on in chapter 5.

on individual and societal levels, even in the context of our increasingly anxious and disordered culture. I intend also, to the best of my ability, to offer suggestions about what healing asks of us, the inner and outer conditions that are most hospitable to its flourishing.

Any movement toward wholeness begins with the acknowledgment of our own suffering, and of the suffering in the world. This doesn't mean getting caught in a never-ending vortex of pain, melancholy, and, especially, victimhood; a new and rigid identity founded on "trauma"—or, for that matter, "healing"—can be its own kind of trap. True healing simply means opening ourselves to the truth of our lives, past and present, as plainly and objectively as we can. We acknowledge where we were wounded and, as we are able, perform an honest audit of the impacts of those injuries as they have touched both our own lives and those of others around us.

This can be exceptionally difficult, for myriad understandable reasons. No matter what degree of discomfort our illusions cover over, the truth hurts, and we don't like hurting if we can help it—even if we sense that something better could lie on the far side of the pain. As Nadezhda Mandelstam wrote in her searing memoir of life under Stalinism, *Hope Against Hope*, "It is very difficult to look life in the face." Many of us will be ready to seek the truth only once we have concluded that the cost of *not* doing so is too high, or once we become sufficiently acquainted with our own ache of longing for the real. The Greek playwright Aeschylus was exquisitely on point when he had his chorus declare:

> *Zeus has led us on to know*
> *the Helmsman lays it down as law*
> *that we must suffer, suffer into truth.*[1]

There are exceptions, but I myself have never encountered anyone who was not spurred along their path of growth and change by some setback or loss, some illness, anguish, or alienation. Fortunately—or unfortunately, depending on how we choose to see it—life has a way of delivering the requisite suffering right to our doorstep.

"Truth" is a big little word, easily misconstrued. I am not speaking about some ultimate spiritual Truth; nor am I referring to purely intellectual verities or verifiable facts, as in "true or false." If that were all, then we could "study, study into truth" and every academic faculty would be staffed by modern-day Buddhas. Where, for all its merits, has our mighty intellectual capacity got us? Right to where we are: an unjust world, threatened self-extinction, untold and needless pain and privation in a universe of abundance, the spread of alienation and despair. In fact, our cerebral talents are all too readily recruited by the part of us that wants to *deny* how things are: there is a reason "rationality" and "rationalize" are linguistic siblings.

The truth I speak of is much more modest and down-to-earth: a clear look at how it is, how things actually happen to be at this moment. This is the kind of truth that ushers in healing. To access it, we will have to tap into something more resourceful than our smarts.

The intellect becomes a far more intelligent tool when it allows the heart to speak; when it opens itself to that within us that *resonates* with the truth, rather than trying to *reason* with it. "And now here is my secret, a very simple secret," the fox advises the Little Prince in Antoine de Saint-Exupéry's beloved tale: "It is only with the heart that one can see rightly; what is essential is invisible to the eye." The intellect can see verifiable *facts*—provided that denial doesn't obscure or distort them, as it often does to protect the wounded or pain-averse parts of us. It is possible to declaim,

declare, and insist on facts, all without a scintilla of what I'm calling truth. The kind of truth that heals is known by its felt sense,
not only by how much "sense" it makes.

If any of this strikes you as vague or unscientific, recall that
the heart is a living, beating organ before it is an abstract concept. Dr. Stephen Porges has brilliantly shown that the neural
circuitry of social engagement and love is intricately connected
with the heart and its functions. More than that, the heart also
has its own nervous system.[†] The verbal-thinking cerebrum has
arrogated to itself the honor of being the only brain, falsely so.
Actually, it shares the distinction with the gut and the heart. In
other words, the heart *knows* things, just as surely as a gut feeling
is also a kind of knowing. In fact, the gut's neural plexus has been
appropriately called a "second brain," as has the heart. Thus we
may speak of three brains, meant to function in concert, with the
autonomic nervous system connecting them all. Without that
heart- and gut-knowledge, we often function as "genius-level rep-
tiles," in someone's apt phrase.[‡]

And yet we can't ignore our minds, either, since that's where
so much of the action is. If the heart is our best compass on the
healing path, the mind—conscious and unconscious—is the territory to be navigated. Healing brings the two into alignment and
cooperation, often after a lifetime of one hiding behind or being
disregarded by the other.

"Everything has mind in the lead, has mind in the forefront, is
made by the mind," the Buddha said 2,500 years ago. I return to
this phrase of the great teacher Gautama because it is key to understanding our relationship to what we consider real. It is also

---

[†] The study of the neural net in the pericardium, the fibrous sheath encasing the heart, and
    its connections with the nervous system and brain is encompassed by the discipline of
    neurocardiology.

[‡] Joseph Chilton Pearce in *The Heart-Mind Matrix: How the Heart Can Teach the Mind New
    Ways to Think.*

the bedrock of the therapeutic approach I take to my work and, when I am conscious, to my personal path. With our minds we construct the world we live in: this is the core teaching. The contribution of modern psychology and neuroscience has been to show how, before our minds can create the world, the world creates our minds. We then generate our world from the mind the world instilled in us before we had any choice in the matter. The world into which we were born, of course, was partly the product of *other people's* minds, a causal daisy chain dating back forever.

This may sound grim. Yet the Buddha's dictum offers a way out, since we remain the ones creating the world we see, the world we think is real, in every moment. And here is where healing comes in. We can do nothing about the world that created our mind, that may have instilled in us limiting, harmful, untrue beliefs about ourselves and others. However—and here's the good news I alluded to—we can learn to be responsible for the mind with which we create our world moving forward. The capacity to heal is born of the willingness to do just that, to take on that responsibility. Such willingness is not a once-and-for-all declaration but a moment-by-moment commitment, one that can be regenerated when we lose touch with it. I, for one, have to keep reminding myself to do so. Nor is it an invitation to self-imposed naïveté or blithe so-called positive thinking. It is about the willingness to reconsider our entire view.

If the wounded mind can be tyrannical, it is a tyrant secretly longing to be deposed. I have seen this in my own life numerous times, experiencing the freedom that comes with relinquishing some unhappy belief or perception my mind had clung to just seconds prior. I have also been most fortunate, through my work, to encounter case after case of astounding turnarounds. In every instance, the essential shift transpired not in people's circumstances or histories but in how they related to them. This is evident in the following stories of two people who, in the most literal sense and in ways most of us will feel lucky to never have to experience, suffered into truth. If they can do it, any of us can.

One drizzly morning in 2019 I interviewed Sue Hanisch in her cozy cottage, located in Sedgwick, a village in England's verdant Lake District, about seventy-five miles north of Liverpool. Over a cup of tea, the soft-spoken sixty-two-year-old occupational therapist and trauma worker told me the story of her trek up Mount Kilimanjaro: a momentous feat for anyone, and all the more so for her, thirteen years after a bomb planted by the Irish Republican Army at London's Victoria Station blew off her right lower leg and severely damaged her left foot. "I remember a nurse crying and another one gagging at seeing my legs," she recalled. The explosion, from a ten-pound device left in a trash bin, occurred fifty years to the day Hanisch's grandfather lost his life in the 1940 bombing of Coventry by the Luftwaffe.

Multiple surgeries and years of despondence followed. Forty were injured that day; the man next to Hanisch had been killed instantly. Her mind carried enormous guilt about survival, and equally about her depression. "That man had been between me and the bomb. It's almost like, how dare I survive, and how dare I not take full advantage of life on planet Earth when he couldn't have that choice?"

By the time Hanisch set out to climb Kilimanjaro on her right below-the-knee prosthesis and surgically repaired, nearly insensate left foot, her psychic wounds had healed significantly. This liberation has grown with the integration of her experiences into the tapestry of her life, as she has divested energy from the limiting stories she once told herself about what it all meant. "It's a mixed blessing to be on planet Earth," she said to me softly. "It's a difficult experience. But I've also been given the opportunity to find out the gold in the wound. I've had some amazing experiences because of what's happened to me." For her, those experiences invariably involve others. "I've noticed how it's the connections that I make with people that are actually the thing worth living for, and nothing else, really. It's the connections that make me feel I am here and that also make me *want* to be here. How I can reach out to other people to help them feel connected? That's the only thing of any heartfelt importance to me."

Among the profound connections Sue made was with the last people you would have expected her to bond with. Ever the adventurous sort, some years after the explosion she found herself in South Africa's KwaZulu-Natal wilderness on a peacemaking mission with, among others, several participants from Northern Ireland, veterans of the very organization whose bomb had mangled her body and altered her life forever. "The idea," she said, "was to hear the other side of the story, to see each other's struggles, and to put us in a different environment where we would need to protect one another."

At some point the expedition had to ford a river. Sue's dilemma was that she could not expose her metallic prosthesis to water, and the anticipation made her quite agitated. She needn't have worried: plans had already been made for her safe and dry passage. Two men carried her across on their shoulders, one of them a former IRA militant. "The fact that it was an IRA guy, it made me absolutely overcome with emotion. I was crying and so was Don, the IRA man. The experience of working with these fellows made me realize just how damaged they had been by what had gone on in their lives before. Don himself was the youngest of seventeen. He had his first gun when he was eight, and he grew up in a children's home. He'd been in jail, he'd been bullied, and he'd been having a really tough time himself. He was carrying the burden of having killed people and not having a clear conscience. It was good for me to be with these people whose lives I had had no insight into before. I realized I could have easily been Don, had I grown up in those circumstances."

Hanisch's ascent of Mount Kilimanjaro came a few years later. There, too, she was accompanied by a man from Northern Ireland, someone who had heard her story and wanted to reach the mountaintop with her. Reach it they did, and then the two improbable co-climbers did something even more unlikely: they danced, giving new meaning to the term "peak experience." "I have had to be invited back into life," she reflected. "And it was love that invited me back."

Another illuminating conversation with a woman who had come through a personal hell ended up supporting my own unlikely reconciliation with the past. My interlocutor was Bettina Göring, grandniece of Hermann Göring, the Nazi Reichsmarschall whose Luftwaffe had killed Sue's grandfather, and one of the pillars of the criminal regime that murdered my grandparents. We had been brought together by the director of a documentary series that featured us both; the filmmaker intuited, correctly, that we might have something to offer each other. We spoke by Skype: I from Vancouver, Bettina from Thailand, where she now lives and does healing work with others part-time. That such an exchange actually happened, and that it was so heart-to-heart, requires a word that I don't often use: "miracle." She had initiated it, writing to express appreciation of my work. The magical quality of this meeting, for me, was the fact that two people who had begun life at such different poles—one the descendant of martyrs, the other the relative of a notorious perpetrator—would each be sent on a healing journey on which they would serendipitously encounter each other and find mutual understanding.

Born eleven years after the war, Bettina had carried a dark legacy her entire life. A hypersensitive child, she bore all the family burden of multigenerational trauma and absorbed guilt for her uncle's monstrous depravity. Having been abandoned by his mother at six weeks of age, Hermann Göring was brought up under the rigid and cruel child-rearing regimens Alice Miller identified in studying the lives of all the top Nazi leaders—what she had called the "poisonous pedagogy." Morphine addiction and compulsive eating were among his attempted escapes from his dreadful inner world, the monstrosities of which he did so much to inflict on others.

Bettina recounted how she had sought healing for herself. It was at an encounter group in Australia that she realized, she said, "how guilty I felt, even though it made no sense—I mean, from my brain, my mind, I knew it didn't make sense—but I felt it." She shuddered as she told me this. "It was very painful to face that shame and to face the horror and all that had been a part of it." A woman with acute empathic ability, she decided to use that inner resource and courageously opened herself to experience her great-uncle's psyche—that is, to its resonance and vibrations within herself. She did so not to forgive Göring, but to forgive *herself*, to let go of the darkness she had always identified with. "I faced it," she told me. "It was horrible. It was like going through the darkest night of the soul. I faced the worst of the worst, the monster. Very scary. Yet coming out of it again, I felt much freer."

That's exactly how I felt after we said our goodbyes. My own past had not changed one iota; my sense of the possible, though, had. I was reminded of something my colleague, the trauma expert Bessel van der Kolk, had said to me one balmy autumn day about ten years ago, over lunch at a conference we were both speaking at in upstate New York. I no longer recall what in the conversation or my demeanor prompted his comment, but suddenly from across the table Bessel peered over the rims of his glasses and said, "Gabor, you don't need to drag Auschwitz around with you everywhere you go." In that instant Bessel saw me. Despite all my positive engagements with life, despite the love and joy and immense good fortune that have also been my portion, that self-directed hopelessness was an ever-lurking shadow, ready to obliterate the light whenever I experienced a setback or a discouragement, and even in innocent, unguarded moments.

The mental prison camp Bessel identified was built and fenced in by *the meaning* my infant mind had forged from events that were painful and frightening and far beyond my control— *not just by the events themselves.* That meaning, the never-ending story whose moral is "I am a damaged being, beyond all hope of healing," has frequently colored my subjective experience of life, regardless of external factors and regardless of all I've witnessed and learned to the contrary, even in defiance of my core values and convictions about humanity. I have always believed—and "believed" is not a strong enough word here, because I'm speaking of a conviction more powerful than belief—that within everyone there is the potential for development and growth, no matter what they have experienced, believed, or done. And then there was me, the lone exception! Such is the power of the mind: it can rigidly maintain its convictions for a long time even when such views are self-defeating, contrary to experience, and even dissonant with other, neighboring beliefs.

The most inspiring journeys toward wholeness are the most improbable because they belie the notion that some traumas are beyond the pale. When writing this chapter, I had the pleasure of speaking with Dr. Edith Eger, a fellow Hungarian Jew, internationally beloved psychotherapist, and author, now in her nineties. The same filmmakers who had connected me with Bettina also introduced me to Edith.

Edith was sixteen years old in June 1944 when, five months after I was born, she and her family were transported to Auschwitz from Košice, the same Slovakian town where my mother grew up and from where my grandparents were deported. Very likely they traveled on the same train as the Egers. Her parents, along with my grandmother and grandfather, were sent to the gas chambers immediately on arrival. Edith's survival and, far beyond that, her transcendence of the horrors she endured are depicted in her book *The Choice*. What choice could she mean? Certainly not the choice of when and where she was born, or what befell those closest to her. Rather, she found a way to exercise the only agency she had, which lay in her own point of view and emotional attitude toward the unchangeable past. Here she explains how, decades later, she forgave Hitler himself. This happened at Berghof in the Bavarian Alps, the location of the Führer's residence from 1933 onward. "It is too easy to make a prison out of our pain, out of our past," she writes. "So I stood on the site of Hitler's former home and forgave him. This had nothing to do with Hitler. It was something I did for me. I was letting go, releasing that part of myself that had spent most of my life exerting mental and emotional energy to keep Hitler in chains. As long as I was holding on to that rage, I was in chains with him, locked in the damaging past, locked in my grief. To forgive is to grieve—for what happened, for what didn't happen—and to give up the need for a different past. To accept life as it was and as it is."[2] We could say that she came to "choose" her past, not in the sense of liking or condoning it, but by simply letting it be. "I do not of course mean," Edith adds, "that it was acceptable for Hitler to murder six million people. Just that it happened, and I do not want that fact to destroy the life that I had clung to and fought for against all odds."

When Bessel advised I could let go of Auschwitz, he meant precisely that I didn't need to keep clutching the pain and resentment of the past, nor the beliefs I developed at a time when I could not have known any better. It is a freedom worth seeking.

When I spoke with Edith Eger again in 2019, she was just completing *The Gift*, her second book of healing wisdom. I was moved, knowing I was unlikely ever again to encounter someone so intimately close to the story of my own beginnings. "Edie," I said, "I haven't got over it yet, and here I am, seventy-six years later." She laughed gently. "Gabor, perhaps you never will. You don't need to. You just need to allow yourself to be with it." Nothing needed to change, Edith was reminding me: only how I held my history in my mind.

None of us need be perfect, nor exercise saintly compassion, nor reach any emotional or spiritual benchmark before we can say we're on the healing path. All we need is readiness to participate in whatever process wants to unfold within us so that healing can happen naturally.

Anyone, no matter their history, can begin to hear wholeness beckoning, whether in a shout or whisper, and resolve to move in its direction. With the heart as a guide and the mind as a willing and curious partner, we follow whatever path most resonates with that call.

Chapter 26

Four *A*'s and Five Compassions: Some Healing Principles

Everything in nature grows and struggles in its own way,

establishing its own identity, insisting on it at all costs,

against all resistance.

—Rainer Maria Rilke, *Letters to a Young Poet*

No one can plot somebody else's course of healing, because that's not how healing works. There are no road maps for something that must find its own individual arc. We can, however, sketch out the territory, describe it, familiarize ourselves with it, prepare to meet its challenges. We can learn what natural laws seem to govern healing, specifically what attitudes and attributes it both awakens and responds to in us. Like natural childbirth, healing cannot be mandated or hastened, but it can certainly be helped along. As the poet and musician Jewel eloquently puts it, "You cannot force nature / only nurture it." That had been her personal experience of healing, she told me in an interview.

The following four *A*'s are not how-to steps or rigid injunctions. They represent healing principles that have proved useful guideposts for many people. I originally devised them while writing *When the Body Says No* and have since amended them, condensing them from seven to four. (In a later chapter I will propose two new *A*'s that harmonize individual and social healing, of which justice is a core tenet.) Each of these represents a healthy quality corresponding to a human need, often stunted or forced underground early in life by emotionally or physically inimical conditions or, in this confused and repressed culture of ours, just by environments that could not support its development. An essential aspect of healing is welcoming each of these qualities back into our life and letting it teach us its ways.

1. Authenticity

To put it bluntly, authenticity is a quality more often marketed than manifested in our culture. Even Coca-Cola is sold as "the real thing." We find ourselves surrounded by the rampant phenomenon of ersatz authenticity: someone is performing "realness" for the crowd or the camera, but it doesn't convince; maybe the words don't match the cadences, or there's too much defiance and bluster in the delivery.

Authenticity is hard to pin down. While synonyms like "genuineness," "truthfulness," "originality," and so on come to mind, authenticity itself eludes any precise definition that could fully capture its essence. Like its fellow natural state, love, authenticity is not a concept but something lived, experienced, basked in. Most of the time you know it when it's there. Have you ever tried explaining to anyone what love is in purely intellectual terms? As with love, so with authenticity.

The pursuit of authenticity is rife with pitfalls. For starters, we have the paradox that authenticity can't be pursued, only embodied. By definition, striving for some idealized self-image is incompatible with being authentically who one is. We have to begin with accepting ourselves fully, as Anita Moorjani discovered in her encounter with fatal illness.[†] "Even the slightest little resistance from the opposite person . . . like if I had displeased

---

[†]   See chapter 7.

someone even slightly—this was me *before*—I would be the one to back down," she told me. "Today, I'm not afraid of being disliked, of disappointing someone. I'm not afraid of what I used to think of as my negative qualities. I realized that they are just the other side of being who I am."

One of the most direct approaches to authenticity is noticing when it isn't there, then applying some curiosity and gentle skepticism to the limiting self-beliefs that stand in for it, or just stand in its way.

The lack of authenticity makes itself known through tension or anxiety, irritability or regret, depression or fatigue. When any of these disturbances surface, we can inquire of ourselves: Is there an inner guidance I am defying, resisting, ignoring, or avoiding? Are there truths I'm withholding from expression or even contemplation, out of fear of losing security or belonging? In a recent encounter with others, is there some way I abandoned myself, my needs, my values? What fears, rationalizations, or familiar narratives kept me from being myself? Do I even know what my own values are?

The growing capacity to admit to oneself, "Ouch, that hurts," or "You know, I didn't really mean what I just said," or "I'm really scared to be myself in this situation" is the impulse toward authenticity becoming stronger. After enough noticing, actual opportunities for choice begin to appear *before* we betray our true wants and needs. Whereas earlier, such awareness would have been clocked only after the fact, we might now find ourselves able to pause in the moment and say, "Hmm, I can tell I'm about to stuff down this feeling or thought—is that what I want to do? Is there another option?" The emergence of new choices in place of old, preprogrammed dynamics is a sure sign of our authentic selves coming back online.

2. Agency

Agency is the capacity to freely take responsibility for our existence, exercising "response ability" in all essential decisions that
affect our lives, to every extent possible. Being deprived of agency
is a source of stress. Such deprivation could arise from social or
political conditions: poverty, injustice, marginalization, or the
seeming collapse of the world around us. In the case of illness,
it's often due to internal constraints.

The exercise of agency is powerfully healing. The psychologist
Kelly Turner has studied many cases of so-called spontaneous
remission of what had been diagnosed as terminal malignancy.
"Having worked as a counselor at various hospitals and oncologists' offices," she reports, "I know firsthand that the patients
who listen and follow instructions are considered 'good' patients,
while the 'annoying' patients are those who ask a lot of questions,
bring in their own research, or—worst of all—challenge their
doctors' orders."[1] Yet these latter ones, she found, those who find
ways to take control of their own healing, are the ones likely to
do better in the long term. In hindsight, Dr. Turner notes, all her
radical remission survivors wished they'd started much earlier to
be active agents of their destinies rather than compliant patients
in the hands of physicians.

As with authenticity, capitalism sells a bogus version of
agency through personal-power mantras like "Be all you can
be" and "Have it your way." Personal choice becomes a brand,
with no attention paid to the contexts in which those choices are
made. Often the freedom being advertised is the dubious freedom to choose between this or that identity-burnishing product
or service that will not, cannot, satisfy us. Nor does agency mean
some sort of false omnipotence or ultimate dominion over all

happenings and circumstances. Life is so much bigger than us, and we do not forward our own healing by pretending to be in control where we're not.

Agency does mean having some choice around who and how we "be" in life, what parts of ourselves we identify with and act from. This often starts with renegotiating our relationship with the personality traits we have so long taken to be identical with who we really are, the ones that first arose in us to keep us safe but now keep us boxed in. There is no freedom in *having* to be "good" or the most talented or accomplished, or in the need to please or entertain or be "interesting." Nor can we wield agency when we react with automatic opposition to other people's demands: knee-jerk reactivity leaves no room for "response ability"—or what in our first chapter we called response flexibility, a capacity trauma greatly impairs.

Agency is neither attitude nor affect, neither blind acceptance nor a rejection of authority. It is a self-bestowal of the right to evaluate things freely and fully, and to choose based on authentic gut feelings, deferring to neither the world's expectations nor the dictates of ingrained personal conditioning.

3. Anger

People often ask me to define "healthy anger." Here's what it's not: blind rage, bluster, resentment, spite, venom, or bile. All of these stem from an unhealthy buildup of unexpressed or unintegrated emotions that need to be experienced and understood rather than acted out. Both anger suppressed and anger amplified out of proportion are toxic.

Anger in its natural, healthy form is a boundary defense, a dynamic activated when we perceive a threat to our lives or our physical or emotional integrity. Our brains being wired for it, we can hardly avoid it: this is the self-protective RAGE system identified by Jaak Panksepp. Its full functioning is a standard feature of our wholeness, essential for survival: think of an animal protecting its turf or its young. The movement toward wholeness often involves a reintegration of this oft-banished emotion into our repertoire of available feelings. This is not the same as stoking resentment or nurturing grievance—quite the opposite. Healthy anger is a response of the moment, not a beast we keep in the basement, feeding it with shame or self-justifying narratives. It is situational, its duration limited: flashing up when needed, it accomplishes its task of fending off the threat and then subsides. It becomes neither an experience to fear and loathe nor a chronic irritant.

The fact—and some people may need to actively remind themselves of this—is that we are talking about a valid, natural feeling that does not in itself intend anyone any harm. Anger in its pure form has no moral content, right or wrong—it just *is*, its only "desire" a noble one: to maintain integrity and equilibrium. If and when it does morph into a toxic version of itself, we can address the unhelpful stories and interpretations, the self-righteous or self-flagellating thought patterns that keep stoking it, without invalidating the emotion. We can also observe how our inability to say no fuels chronic resentment that leaves us prone to harmful combustions.

Many of us have learned to minimize our anger to the point that we don't even know what it looks like. In this case it's best not to idealize or exaggerate: picturing a bombastic eruption of ire or some righteous, curse-encrusted monologue will not help us. Like authenticity, genuine anger is not a performance. Anger's core message is a concise and potent no, said as forcefully as the moment demands. Wherever we find ourselves tolerating or explaining away situations that persistently stress us, insisting that "it's not so bad" or "I can handle it" or "I don't want to make a fuss about it," there is likely an opportunity to practice giving anger some space to emerge. Even the plainspoken admission that "I don't like this" or "I don't want this" can be a step forward.

Research suggests that anger expression could support physical health, for example in those with amyotrophic lateral sclerosis (ALS) or fibromyalgia, two conditions that baffle the conventional medical mind. We have already reported (in chapter 2) that ALS patients are perceived by their physicians as extraordinarily nice. Tellingly, in another ALS study, the most "agreeable" ones—the ones least likely to be in touch with anger, that is— also had the most rapid deterioration of their condition and of their quality of life.[2] The same is true with fibromyalgia, which many studies have linked to childhood trauma. A 2010 study in the *European Journal of Pain* concluded that "anger and a general tendency to inhibit anger predicts heightened pain in the everyday life of female patients with fibromyalgia. Psychological intervention could focus on healthy anger expression to try to mitigate the symptoms of fibromyalgia."[3]

The question for most of us is not whether to be angry but how to relate in a wholesome way to the feelings that naturally ebb and flow with life's tide, anger included.

4. Acceptance

Acceptance begins with allowing things to be as they are, however they are. It has nothing to do with complacency or resignation, though sometimes these can pose as acceptance—think of the shrugging expression "It is what it is"—just as stubborn egotism can moonlight as authenticity. Rather, acceptance is the recognition, ever accurate, that *in this moment* things cannot be other than how they are. We abstain from rejecting or condoning. Instead of resisting the truth or denying or fantasizing our way out of it, we endeavor to just *be with it*. In doing so, we foster an aligned relationship with the actual, present moment.

Acceptance also means accepting how downright difficult it can be to accept. It may seem paradoxical, but true acceptance denies or excludes no aspect of how it is, *not even our impulse to reject how it is*. Anger, sadness, trepidation, resistance, even hatred—within an accepting attitude, these all have room to say their piece. Sometimes accepting ourselves starts with facing that we don't know how we feel, or that our feelings are mixed. Rejection of *any* part of our experience is an unnatural self-rejection, one that nonetheless feels normal to many of us. You've made some serious mistakes? You find yourself filled with hatred, or resentment, or confusion? These, too, are candidates for acceptance; underneath them there is always pain. In fact, hatred, resentment, and even confusion can be the psyche's attempts *not* to feel pain or sadness. Healthy grief—the jewel so often hidden within ossified grievance—frequently waits on the other side of accepting how things are and have been. That, too, can be hard to embrace, but when we forestall the energy of mourning that wants to move through us, we only cause it to build up. As Gordon Neufeld puts it, "We shall be saved in an ocean of tears."

A distinction must be made between *accepting* and *tolerating*. Being with something and putting up with something have precious little to do with each other. Acceptance is vitalizing because it makes room for the other three *A*'s—it grants admission to *anger* if such is present, increases our sense of free *agency*, and makes room for whatever our *authentic* experience might be. Tolerating the intolerable, on the other hand, is deadening. For example, resigning oneself bleakly to conditions such as abuse or neglect involves *rejecting* crucial parts of one's self, needs, and values that deserve to be respected and integrity that needs to be safeguarded. That is far from true acceptance.

Darlene, a thirty-eight-year-old family therapist in San Jose, California, began to accept that the realities of her marriage were intolerable only when she developed an autoimmune disease. Based on her fundamentalist Christian upbringing, she had truly believed her God-given duty was to "accept"—read endure—the miseries her husband's own traumatic imprints visited upon her. "As the connection between my stress and my illness dawned on me," she related, "at one point I remember going, 'Holy shit—I've been in this kind of martyr-honoring-God position of staying in this abusive marriage, and there's just no way: this is going to kill me!'"

The same applies to injustice or oppression on the social level. To accept that whatever is currently happening is happening— the simple fact of the matter—does not mean conceding that it *should* happen. To deal with racism, poverty, or any other societal ill, we must first recognize that they are realities of life in this culture. They exist, and we must acknowledge our pain and grief that they do. Now we can ask ourselves how we might effectively work to eliminate not only their expressions but their root causes. We can move on to healthy anger, to agency, to autonomy in action.

The Five Compassions

The acclaimed neurosurgeon James Doty[†] heads Stanford University's Center for Compassion and Altruism Research and Education. "There is a subset of people who believe that compassion is soft, that it's not worthy of scientific study," he told me during a public conversation we held at the California retreat center 1440 Multiversity.[‡] "Yet, I assure you, the science we have today demonstrates these practices of mindfulness, self-compassion, and

---

[†] Author of the bestseller *Into the Magic Shop: A Neurosurgeon's Quest to Discover the Mysteries of the Brain and the Secrets of the Heart.*

[‡] A brief segment of this conversation can be viewed here: "A Neurosurgeon Talks of Vulnerability: Gabor Maté and James Doty" July 12, 2019 https://www.youtube.com /watch?v=WiAXbZmA2dU.

compassion are some of the most powerful that exist to change your physiology and to benefit you in your own health, mental and physical, and in terms of your longevity." Compassion, as both salve and salvation, is not limited to the realm of the individual. If we are to dream of a healthier, less fractured world, we will have to harness and amplify compassion's healing power.

In my work with clients and in training thousands of therapists, I have distinguished five levels of compassion that build on and reinforce one another nonhierarchically. Together, they encourage, guide, and orient us on the pathway to wholeness. As the playwright (and physician) Anton Chekhov wrote, "It is compassion that moves us beyond numbness toward healing."

1. Ordinary Human Compassion

The word "compassion" comes from the Latin, meaning "to suffer with." Whether or not we experience another's pain so vividly, entry-level compassion does mean the ability to *be with suffering*. It also means being *moved* by the awareness that someone is struggling; it does not register as a neutral fact.

Interpersonal compassion necessarily involves empathy, the ability to get and relate to the feelings of another. Our experience of it may fluctuate depending on who we are looking at and even on how we are feeling at any given moment. Certainly, it can be worn down or depleted, as anyone who has ever experienced work-related "compassion fatigue" can attest. For most of us it bounces back once we get the rest and replenishment we need. Its absence in anyone, glaring in sociopaths and psychopaths, is always a marker of a wound to the soul, or, in A. H. Almaas's words, "the suppression of hurt." When we notice such an empathy gap in ourselves, instead of self-judgment—itself a lack of compassion—we could well ask what pain *we* have not yet fully felt and metabolized. We can learn a lot about our own emotional-injury history by observing in what situations, and toward whom, our naturally open and supple hearts tend to harden and shut down.

Compassion is not the same as pity, which on some level always buys into a preexisting story about oneself or another. While compassion guides the best social policies, pity empowers no one. To take pity on you, I have to first cast us in unequal roles, looking down on your misfortune from some imagined perch. Even if there is an actual power gap between us in the world—say, one born of a racial or economic hierarchy—treating it as if it is a permanent, essential fact about us does neither one of us any favors. Self-compassion, equally necessary, also has its unhealthy analogue: "to wallow in self-pity" conveys the comfy but muddy trap of feeling perennially sorry for oneself. Self-pity takes a kind of solace in seeing oneself as an unfortunate character, beleaguered by fate. It undermines healing by reinforcing the stories that keep us ensconced in a world of hurt, and by discouraging responsibility for our own point of view. Self-compassion, by contrast, doesn't resist how things are, nor swaddle the pain in layers of narrative gauze; it just says, "I am hurting."

2. The Compassion of Curiosity and Understanding

The second compassion takes as its first principle that everything exists for a reason, and that the reason matters. We ask, without judgment, why a person or group—any person, any group—would end up being the way they are and act the way they do, even or especially when we are vexed or perplexed by it. We might also call this the compassion of context. However sincere our desire to help ourselves or someone else, we cannot do so without beholding the suffering being experienced, including knowing its source as best we can. It's not enough, for example, to feel bad for people caught in the coils of addiction without seeking to understand what pain in their lives they've been driven to escape and how that wound was sustained. Absent a clear view of the context, one is left, at best, harboring inert good wishes and engaged in well-meant but ultimately ineffective interventions. We see this limitation in the woefully inadequate addiction-treatment approaches currently in vogue.

The willingness to seek the why before leaping to the how is the compassion of curiosity and understanding in action. Though it is called for in every instance of chronic suffering, whether in the personal or social realm, it can be challenging in practice. In today's society we often default to easy explanations, quick judgments, and knee-jerk solutions. Questing with clear eyes to find the systemic roots of why things are the way they are takes patience, curiosity, and fortitude.

The Métis academic Jesse Thistle, cited in chapter 15, has authored a gripping memoir of his childhood, youth, spiral into addiction and crime, and ultimate recovery, a book suffused with precisely this kind of thoroughgoing compassion. "I wrote *From the Ashes*," Jesse told me, "mainly so that people could witness what happened to me and my brothers in our family . . . In a way, I was trying to vindicate my family and make people understand. So with my nation's history, I'm helping re-member. Not just remember, like a memory. Like re-member, reassemble this history that has been disembodied by the state and forgotten." In chronicling the events of his own life, Thistle, along with fellow writers and artists of Indigenous Canada, is reclaiming a compassionate context for his people—in both the familial and national senses of that word—to exist and be seen in the world's eyes, and their own.

3. The Compassion of Recognition

Remember Bruce from chapter 15—the Oregon vascular surgeon arrested at his hospital for forging drug prescriptions to feed his opiate habit? He views the experience, humiliating as it was, with gratitude for the life-changing awakening it sparked in him. "If it hadn't happened to me in the way it happened," he told me, "I would have gone on my merry way as the oblivious, technically proficient but emotionally retarded individual that characterizes so many of us in the surgical profession." In place of his old "self-centered" ways of relating, Bruce describes "a new attitude" characterized by seeing himself in others: "[I can say] 'I am a human being who has flaws, who struggled. You may be in that same category. Let's see how we can fix this problem together.' "

Bruce is embodying what I call *the compassion of recognition*, which allows us to perceive and appreciate that we are all in the same boat, roiled by similar tribulations and contradictions. Until we recognize our commonality, we create more woe for ourselves and others: for ourselves, because we increase our distance from our humanity and get caught up in the tense physiological states of judgment and resistance; for others, because we trigger their shame and further their isolation. If you are not sure what I mean, the next time you feel intense judgment toward anyone, check in with your body states—the sensations in your chest, belly, throat. Does it feel pleasant? Unlikely; nor is it healthy for you.

The lesson is not that you shouldn't judge, since it's not *you* that's doing it but rather your automatic mind. To judge yourself for judging is itself to keep the wheel of shame spinning. The opportunity is to inquire into your judgmental mind and body state with compassionate curiosity. Healing flows when we are able to view this hurting world as a mirror for our own pain, and to allow others to see themselves reflected in us as well—recognition paving the way for reconnection.

4. The Compassion of Truth
We may believe it an act of kindness to protect people from experiencing pain. While this is so when it comes to pain that is

unnecessary and preventable, there is nothing compassionate about shielding people from the inevitable hurts, disappointments, and setbacks life doles out to all of us, from childhood onward. Such a mission is not only futile, it is counterproductive—and may even be inauthentic, the seemingly altruistic impulse arising from our discomfort with our own woundedness.

Whatever our intentions, we do no one any favors by fearing their pain or colluding in their banishment of it. As people work to heal their traumas, hurt will inevitably arise. This is why all of us go into denial, suppression, repression, rationalization, justification, hazy memory, and varying grades of dissociation in the presence of hurt. When we face all the ways we have numbed ourselves, pain will inevitably emerge—in fact, it has been waiting a long time to do so. Of course, the fear of these exiled parts is also natural. "When you have a lifetime of emotions that you have been running from," writes Helen Knott, "it seems like once they catch up they will gang-beat you and leave you crippled in an alleyway."[4] That need not happen. The compassion of truth recognizes that pain is not the enemy. In fact, pain is inherently compassionate, as it tries to alert us to what is amiss. Healing, in a sense, is about unlearning the notion that we need to protect ourselves from our own pain. In this way, compassion is a gateway to another essential quality: courage.

The compassion of truth also recognizes that truth may lead, in the short term, to further pain. Darlene, the San Jose family therapist, found this out once she left her dysfunctional marriage. "My childhood community doesn't understand me, can't see me, doesn't get it," she said. "It breaks my heart because I want to be loved and connected, but I suspect they will never be able to see me or connect with me." That some attachments may not survive the choice for authenticity is one of the most agonizing realizations one can come to; and yet, in that pain, there is freedom. It reverses and vindicates the tragic, mandatory choices we had to make in the opposite direction as we started in life. "It's a journey of ditching people-pleasing and not caring what people think," Darlene told me. "There are times when I go, 'I want that person's approval.' I can't say I've arrived, but it's an onion process: I've gotten lots of the layers off, and more and more freedom in my authenticity. I've had to find my own pockets of community where I am seen and understood. It's been a painful process, but I know it's the right thing."

Truth and compassion have to be reciprocal partners. We are not being compassionate by dumping unwelcome truths in someone's lap, perhaps justifying it on the grounds that "I'm just being honest!" "Only when compassion is present," writes A. H. Almaas, "do people allow themselves to see the truth." And without safety, the truth cannot do its healing work.

5. The Compassion of Possibility

There is more to each of us than the conditioned personalities we present to the world, the suppressed or untrammeled emotions we act out, and the behaviors we exhibit. Understanding this allows for what I call *the compassion of possibility*. I don't mean possibility in the hypothetical, future-dwelling sense, as in "maybe someday," but as a present, alive, ever-available inherent quality. Possibility is connected to many of humanity's greatest gifts: wonder, awe, mystery, and imagination—the qualities that allow us to remain connected to that which we can't necessarily prove. It's up to us to nurture this connection, because the day-to-day world will not always provide us with reassuring evidence. This deepest aspect of compassion recognizes that the seemingly impossible only *seems* so, and that whatever we most need and long for can actualize at any moment.

Staying open to possibility doesn't require instant results. It means knowing that there is more to all of us, in the most positive sense, than meets the eye. The same applies to whatever seems the most real, solid, or intractable in us or others. In a famous story, the Buddha saw the universal potential for the humane self to emerge in a notorious criminal who accosted him with murderous intent; the man became his humblest and most gentle follower.

"In order to gain possession of ourselves, we have to have some confidence, some hope of victory," wrote the Catholic mystic Thomas Merton. "And in order to keep that hope alive we must usually have some taste of victory."[5] The compassion of possibility, I would say, is a door we keep open so we can see that victory coming. If we didn't mistake ourselves or one another for whatever personality features and behavioral traits appear on the surface, "good" or "bad," if in each person we could sense the potential for wholeness that can never be lost, that would be, for us all, a victory worth savoring.

Chapter 27

A Dreadful Gift:
Disease as Teacher

Surviving breast cancer redefined who and how I am . . .
Until then, I'd spent a lifetime being a caretaker for everyone
around me. From then, I started to put myself first. I had
voices at the back of my head telling me whatever I did wasn't
good enough. Now, finally, I've silenced them.

—Sheryl Crow[†]

"I have beautiful conversations with my rheumatoid arthritis these days—it makes me want to cry," we heard forty-two-year-old Julia say in chapter 5. On its face, it's an odd and improbable statement. Wouldn't it be more natural to see a potentially crippling disease as a dire threat to be avoided, suppressed, or combated than as an intimate, life-affirming companion? And yet, as in the stories I will relate in this chapter, and as in so many others I have encountered in my work, Julia found value and meaning in her encounter with illness. Some people, more than a few, go beyond that to call their disease a cherished gift. *Blessed with a Brain Tumor* is the title of a book by a young man I interviewed, Will Pye. "This was a gift from spirit, for my soul to facilitate healing transformation and awakening," he told me. What Julia and Will had arrived at is a profound pivot away from conventional thinking: seeing disease itself as

---

†   From an interview the singer-songwriter gave the *Guardian*, July 10, 2021.

an agent of healing, or at least as an opportunity for learning and growth. Rather than merely healing *from* disease, they have somehow learned to heal *through* it.

To be clear: disease is not a "gift" I would wish on anyone. It is not a path of transformation I would direct anyone to if there were any way to avoid it. For the brave women and men whose stories follow, it was just the route their lives took. Nor do I take for granted that I, in their place, would be able to find the inner strength, courage, trust, and sagacity to approach my ailment as they have. Nonetheless, their travails can teach us much about healing, if we are willing to learn from their example.

Let's keep in mind the distinction we made in chapter 25 between healing and cure. Although I have witnessed people reversing and outliving the direst of prognoses, and have seen such cases documented elsewhere, it is not getting better but getting *whole* that we are exploring. Healing, not cure, is the blessing that disease bestowed on these people. Cure can never be guaranteed. Healing is another matter, and it is available until we draw our last breath. It is the movement toward experiencing oneself as a vital whole, whatever may be happening corporeally. Healing is not an endpoint: it is as much a process as disease is. In the following histories, illness happened to be the teacher that initiated people into their healing journey.

None of us, sick or not, need to wait for it to get that dire before we embark on our own journey.

"What happens in these conversations with your rheumatoid arthritis?" I asked Julia, who, since adding therapy, meditation, and other forms of self-work to her low dose of a single drug, has experienced few flare-ups, with no progress of her disease for over a decade and significant improvement in her blood work.

"When it speaks to me," she replied, "rather than seeing it as something I've got to push through or go into a big drama about, I literally just feel it. I sit with it, get curious about what's been happening in my life, what I might be suppressing."

We saw how, in her abusive family of origin, Julia had become a hyper-responsible "nice" person who repressed her feelings to protect everyone else's. "I do my own self-inquiry," she continued. " 'What are you trying to tell me?' I wonder. This happened to me just two weeks ago, when my jaw blew up. I knew it was just there to remind me to allow some difficult feelings to arise, so I listened. I lay on my bed and breathed for an hour. I did some mindful contemplation. I didn't get upset about it, just stayed curious. Literally the next day it was gone. I didn't have to adjust my medication. I never do."

In contravention of all cultural mores, Julia expressed gratitude for her rheumatoid arthritis. "It saved me," she said. "It was my body's way of saying, 'Wake up, wake up. You're not helping yourself holding this much anger and rage deep down inside.' Anger and rage are not feelings I want to hold on to, but I do see them as guides that let me know that something in my life is out of balance. I get [rheumatoid] flare-ups maybe once a year now. When one shows up, I just accept that it's here and there is something I can do about it, something more to learn from it." This is a profound testament to the twin power of acceptance and agency—two of the core universal principles of healing we looked at in the last chapter.

I would never suggest that Julia's practice of compassionate inquiry toward herself is solely responsible for her well-being or that her medication was not beneficial. What we are witnessing is the self-transformation the disease has guided her to, along with the ensuing increase in awareness, equanimity, joy, health, and satisfaction in her life. What she learned from her condition also impelled her to grow professionally. It has revealed her true calling and fostered skills and capacities with which to support others. "It has given me so much," she said. "It led me to my doing my master's and becoming a psychologist. And now my whole field—my specialty is chronic pain in illness." That conversation took place three years ago. She recently sent me an email reporting that for the past twelve months she has "been medication-free for the first time in 16 years with zero symptoms."

To my friend the psychologist Richard Schwartz, nothing about Julia's journey is surprising. Dick is the originator of a widely practiced form of therapy called Internal Family Systems. IFS imagines the personality as an amalgam of independent "parts," each of which comes along as a response to life events. The "internal family" is a constellation of all these different aspects, some at odds with one another, some collaborating. In Julia's case, the anger and rage her childhood emotional and sexual abuse evoked would be seen as "exiled" parts: facets of herself she could not afford to experience as a child, and therefore repressed. The "nice," overachieving, hyper-responsible persona represents "protector" parts, adapted to keep the love and approval of others coming her way. Somewhere in there, and yearning to assert its leadership, is what IFS terms the Self, or what in chapter 7 I described as the "sense of self arising from one's own unique and genuine essence."

That's what the body is calling us back to, through indicators emotional or physical. Symptoms and illness are the body's way of letting us know when we have strayed from that core.

"My experience is that when parts of us can't get through to us otherwise, they don't have a lot of options, but they do have the body," Dick told me. "There are many, many different kinds of medical symptoms. As we have the client focus on the symptom itself and get curious about it, and ask questions of it, they will usually encounter the part that's using the symptom to get a message through, to try and express itself somehow, because the client has refused to listen to it otherwise. As they begin to actually listen to the part, a lot of times the symptoms go away, or they get a lot better." That was the precise finding of a study in which IFS was applied to a group of rheumatoid arthritis patients. As people listened to their "parts" and to their bodies, similarly to how Julia taught herself to do, the subjective aspects of their experience, such as pain and self-compassion, improved, as did objective physical parameters like blood markers of disease and joint inflammation.[1]

The Romanian medical doctor Bianca, also introduced in chapter 5, continues to have her own intimate conversations with her illness. As you may recall, she had flare-ups of her multiple sclerosis when stressed on the job or in her personal life—that is, when she took on too much or ignored her own needs in either realm. Her condition is stable, despite having given up the drug regimen she had been told she'd have to rely on for the rest of her life. Although her MRI findings still show signs of inflammation in her central nervous system, they have not progressed after many years and she has no symptoms, unless she neglects herself in some way. At such times, she has numbness of the skin, which she sees as a perfect metaphor for some emotion she may not be permitting herself to feel. "This is that red light," she said, "telling me, 'Okay, stop. Go back to yourself.' And that's exactly what I do. At that moment I stop, because in the last years I've learned, when I feel it, even a little bit, I stop. I relax. I meditate. I go to see how I feel, what it's telling me. And the moment I discover what it is—maybe it's some emotional pain, maybe I'm sad about something, maybe it was some trigger that took me somewhere and suddenly I'm not here—then I come back to myself. The moment I discover it, that moment the symptom disappears."

Bianca now mostly works with MS patients, most of whom suffer from post-traumatic stress and all of whom exhibit the same overcompensating tendency that used to drive her, with a focus, she said, "on overperformance and success."

In 2003 Donna Zmenak, a speech-language pathologist in Ontario, Canada, was diagnosed with cancer of the cervix. It happened in the aftermath of high stress in her life, including a bitter three-year custody battle for her three young children. The oncological gynecologist suggested that Zmenak immediately undergo a radical hysterectomy, involving removal of the uterus and some ligaments, as well as excision of multiple nodes in her pelvis and of the upper part of the vagina, all to be followed by radiation. She declined. "I told the surgeon I didn't want to live like that, my insides gutted. He said I was making a stupid decision and that he could make decisions, too. Then and there he discharged me."

That the surgeon would part with a patient unwilling to follow his professional opinion is understandable. That he should demean the patient for it is unacceptable. I was reminded of the angry outburst of the recalcitrant patient Kostoglotov in Aleksandr Solzhenitsyn's novel *Cancer Ward*: "Why do you assume you have the right to decide for someone else? Don't you agree it's a terrifying right, one that rarely leads to good? You should be careful. No one is entitled to it, not even doctors."[2]

For a year Donna did it her way, following a cleansing diet, taking supplements, and working with a medical doctor who specialized in nutrition. At the end of that period, she was devastated to be told the cancer had spread and that, without surgery, she had no more than six months to live. Once more, she declined. As I interviewed her, even in retrospect and even knowing the story's happy ending, I had trouble grasping the source of her confidence and determination. "There was just something inside of my heart saying, 'You can do this,' " she replied by way of explanation. "I thought that my inner voice had more value than the people in the world around me who were giving me their best advice. I knew they were. But I didn't feel it was the best advice for me. As a young woman, as much as I wanted to live, I did not want to live in that body. I knew enough at that point in my life that quality of life was more important to me than longevity."

Zmenak embarked on a further six-month inner and outer pilgrimage that took her to healers who taught her practices such as yoga and meditation. She also consulted former cancer patients who had forged their own paths. Along the way, she read a book, *Profound Healing* by Cheryl Canfield, another cancer survivor who had declined conventional treatment and has long outlived a prognosis of a grisly death. She met Canfield, now a hypnotherapist and wellness consultant in California, staying with her for a while and learning from her, in Zmenak's summation, the values of "acceptance, autonomy, and authenticity. She taught me all that, and she taught me how to *die well*. I went home in such a different space that I never really went back to my old ways of being."

Above all, Donna made a fundamental decision about how to live whatever lifespan remained to her: true to herself, even if her intuitions defied the opinions of doctors, family, and friends. "If I only have six months to live, my children are going to know me, the real me, who I am," she recalled telling herself. "This always makes me cry. I remember that moment. And I said, 'You know what? No more. I accept this. I'm going to be me, and I'm going to go forward being happy' . . . And I meant it. I just drew this line, and I never went back." Catching her own hyperbole, she quickly corrected herself: "I'm human, and I fall into that trap all the time. But I get out quick."

Six months into her psycho-emotional-spiritual odyssey, Zmenak heard the same prognosis from another gynecologist, stated in even more alarming terms. Without surgery, this doctor said, her death was inevitable, imminent, and would be "a smelly mess." "This time I *knew* the cancer was gone," she recalled. "I told him I don't think I have cancer anymore; as a matter of fact, I think I'd like to have another baby . . . And he looked at my partner, telling him, 'Not only will she never have a baby, but she will also never live through a baby, and she won't even live long enough to have a baby. You as her partner need to convince her to get this surgery right away, because it's not pleasant.' Then he turned back to me. 'You've got to think of the people around you. Think of your children. You've got to think of your partner.'" The irony of this doctor urging her to "think of the people around you" after years of the people-pleasing self-suppression that had helped precipitate her disease was not lost on Donna.

A short while later, repeat biopsies and scans showed no trace of cancer in Zmenak's uterus, abdomen, or lymph nodes—tests she had submitted to in full confidence she had overcome the malignancy, but also having agreed to have the surgery if she was proved wrong. She returned to see the surgeon to discuss the results. "I get into the room, and I'm sitting there on the chair, smiling, and he goes, 'Why aren't you up in the stirrups?' He was angry. I said, 'Didn't you hear the news? There's nothing there.' He said, 'You're not healed. You have cancer, you'll always have cancer. Cancer comes back, and we need to do the surgery now. You can't heal yourself. This is not possible. Don't delude yourself. You are not healed.' I just stood up and said, 'What's not coming back is me.' And that was it. I left, and I never saw him again."

From time to time since, Donna has sent this surgeon Christmas cards, including after the vaginal full-term delivery of her fifth child, now twelve years old—another feat she had been assured was impossible, given the instability of her uterine opening following the cone biopsy. "In my first Christmas card I said, 'Please don't tell anyone it can't be done. Because I'm still alive, and I'm here, and this is what I have done.' " She has never heard back.

I contacted Nancy Abrams, Zmenak's family physician, who verified every detail of the medical history. "I witnessed the whole thing. I have the records," Dr. Abrams said. "She did all that, and all of a sudden she didn't have cancer. What I really find odd is why do these oncologists not want to know how these people cure themselves? She did it. And she went on to have another child, number five, vaginally, when she had a super-big contraindication, the cone biopsy. She probably shouldn't have even had a competent cervix to carry on her pregnancy, but she did all of that and nobody says, 'Wow, how come that happened to her?' "

Such lack of curiosity is the norm. When I spoke with the oncological psychologist Kelly Turner, whose book *Radical Remission* reported on many cancer patients who recovered despite the direst of prognoses, I wondered whether the people she had studied, those whose courses eluded the grim predictions of health professionals, had found their medical caregivers open to hearing their histories of healing. "For the most part the answer is, sadly, no," Turner replied. "The vast majority of people that I researched said to me in gratitude, 'You are the first doctor ... the first person with some kind of a health-related degree who has taken any interest in why I got well ... I tried to tell my oncologist all the things I was doing, and the oncologist didn't want to know it.' I hear that all the time, and it really breaks my heart." The same indifference was noted by Dr. Jeffrey Rediger,[†] who, in researching his book *Cured: The Life-Changing Science of Spontaneous Healing*, documented over one hundred cases of

---

[†]   An instructor in psychiatry at Harvard Medical School and medical director for the McLean SouthEast Adult Psychiatric Programs.

"spontaneous remission." "The best the doctors will say is, 'Keep it up, it's working,'" he remarked. "But they are never curious about how their patients did it."

I can understand something of these doctors' reticence. Even for someone like me, well versed in the science of mind-body unity and with a great appreciation for the power of the human spirit—the only grounds on which histories such as Donna Zmenak's make sense[‡]—it is a challenge to fathom a saga so out of line with customary medical expectation and experience. Her example is one few could emulate; indeed no one ought to without the inner resources and a genuine inclination to do so. The teaching from her trajectory is not that anyone should follow her radical choices, but that it's possible to gain the capacity to accept life as it actually is, the authenticity to search for our own truth in all situations, and the agency to choose our response to whatever occurs. Rounding out the four *A*'s, there is healthy anger, which flashed in Donna's declaration, "What's not coming back is me." Her journey into self is not over. "I work daily at maintaining my authenticity," she says.

Another uniquely determined—and self-determined—person I met, Dr. Erica Harris, has undergone more medical treatments in a decade than most of us could imagine for several lifetimes, including aggressive chemotherapy, whole body radiation, a bone marrow transplant, a double lung transplant, prolonged hospitalization for a chronic infection, and repeated excisions for skin cancer—to list only the most salient ones. She would have died long ago without astute medical intervention, nor could she stay alive without it now. The potent medications that ensure her

---

‡   The only secular grounds, that is.

survival exact a high cost. "I've lost the vision in my right eye," she wrote to me recently, "have endless skin cancers, lost half of my lower lip, am osteoporotic, have chronic kidney damage, am on lifelong immunosuppression, have lost my monthly cycle at the age of 35 [now 44], had three strokes, require ongoing immunoglobulin infusions, blood transfusions. I have even lost my once happy marriage as a result of what cancer brought, and yet, I'm the happiest I have ever been or could ever imagine being! Truly so blessed!" For all that she has had to surrender in terms of physical health, she has given up nothing in exuberance and joie de vivre. In fact, for her those qualities have become fuller, more deeply felt, and far less conditional.

A skilled and much sought-after sports chiropractor, once a pillar of health, Dr. Harris never spared herself when it came to work. "I was passionate about my athlete clients," she told me. "I loved helping people. Let's say they had trained forever, and they endured an injury a few months before a race. My inner reward would come from seeing their joy crossing the finish line. I was a bit of a workaholic, one might say—"

"You could probably take out the 'a bit,'" I interjected.

"Yes," she concurred, "my clinic grew really, really fast. When the regular hours were fully booked, I found it really hard to leave somebody in pain. I started coming in very early and staying very, very late. People began to notice I was getting sick all the time. I had strep throat at least every month. I had a terrible disk herniation in my low back that impacted my right leg, and I would still go into the clinic. I was hobbling, trying to help others succeed through their pain, ignoring my own. I loved being busy. I loved everything about it."

If her personality loved the overwork, her body did not. At age thirty-five, on an outing with her two children, Harris got the shocking news. "There I am," she recalled, "I'm a mom of two babies, still nursing my youngest, and I'm standing at the aquarium. I had done a very routine blood test that day, and now it's the lab calling, with this tone of urgency and panic. 'Is this Erica Harris? You need to go the nearest emergency ward right now.' I ended up being diagnosed with a very aggressive form of AML, acute myeloid leukemia, a rare version of it that usually only older men get." Encouraged by the high rate of expected good results, she received two courses of chemotherapy. Neither proved effective.

In 2012 Harris was advised to enter a palliative care facility, where she was told that daily transfusions might keep her alive for no more than two months. Unwilling to yield to that grim diagnosis, she fought to stay home with her small children, going to the hospital daily to receive her transfusions. She also continued to pursue her emotional healing and spiritual path until, just before the ominous two months were up, an unlikely remission surprised both her and her physicians. "It was really hard," she told me. "I'm not sure why I'm here today, but I truly believe it was because I transformed myself from within, allowing myself to be real about everything that was going on now in the present, but also in the past. And allowing myself just the space to express it all."

Like Donna Zmenak, Harris did yoga and meditation and pursued nutritional healing. But the biggest change was that, for the first time in her life, she allowed herself to feel the entire range of her emotions, releasing a lifelong pattern of repression. She fully gave herself over to her grief and shed tears of despair. "One time during my first hospitalization, I watched my kids going home with the nanny," she recalled. "*I* wanted to be the one driving home with those babies. *I* wanted to be making them dinner. *I* wanted to be putting them to bed. I turned around from that window, and I slumped down to the floor with my back against the wall. I grabbed my knees and I wept. I wept and I wept. I didn't stop for days." As a telling sign of the reigning medical culture, the ward psychiatrist was consulted to see her. "She came in," Erica said, smiling in recounting this, "and she literally had this Hawaiian floral-print gown, and she's like, 'I'm off to Hawaii, but I can prescribe something for you to treat this depression, whatever you need. I heard you have been crying.' What I really needed was just the space to experience all of my emotions, with no pretense—no pretense, for the first time. I needed to feel the hurt of it all."

For all her recurrent health challenges, nearly ten years after her terminal prognosis of a mere sixty days' survival, Harris is vibrant, brimming with energy, raising her two children, whom she has triumphantly shepherded into adolescence, and actively inspiring and helping others on their healing path. We have plans, she and I, to work together someday. I see in her case the miracles of modern medicine joining with the power of self-transformation to achieve results neither could have achieved without the other.

The Harvard psychiatrist Dr. Jeffrey Rediger, who has explored many cases of "miraculous" recovery from terminal malignancy and other fatal diseases, told me that a transformation of identity, such as Zmenak and Harris underwent, seemed to him to be the key. "It's a nebulous concept," he conceded, "but ultimately that's where the healing is to be found. These people who get better really change their beliefs about themselves or their beliefs about the universe." This has been my observation as well, no matter with what illness: cancer, autoimmune disease, or neurological disorders like MS or ALS.[†] Some, like Donna Zmenak, refused medical treatment; others, like Will Pye and Erica Harris, wouldn't have

---

†   Even with the usually fatal diagnosis of ALS, there are dozens of medically documented and peer-reviewed published cases of partial or complete reversals in the neurological literature, or decades of survival after terminal prognoses, even after long years of people having been wheelchair-dependent and on respiratory assistance. The physicist Stephen Hawking famously outlived his two-year prognosis by over fifty years.

survived without it. In all cases, people voluntarily and with relentless courage underwent a painful but ultimately exhilarating shedding of a second skin, the blend of adaptive, self-abnegating traits I cataloged in chapter 7, on attachment versus authenticity, and grouped also under Erich Fromm's term "social character." Disease's role as teacher rests in how it leads people to question everything they had thought and felt about themselves, and to retain only what serves their wholeness.

In her own documentation of "miraculous" healing, Dr. Kelly Turner unearthed similar themes. The centrality of reorienting identity in the direction of the authentic is among her essential findings. "Everyone that I've interviewed said that they actually wouldn't trade this experience for the world," she told me. "Because the person they are now is so much more complete. They feel whole, they feel happier, they feel more grateful, that they wouldn't want to go back to who they were before that hardship. Many of them, I would dare say nearly all of them, tell me that they're a completely different person now than they were at the beginning of their journey." As I related earlier, Turner also said that many of her interviewees wished they had learned these same lessons decades before their illness. The challenge we all face is: Can we acquire that learning before life forces it upon us? Do we have to wait to "suffer into truth"?

"Every moment was precious," Erica recalled. "I needed to go deeply inward at that time and reflect on all of the layers, like I hadn't done all my life. I finally realized how my body had been screaming no all my while as a sports chiropractor, and how I had ignored it. The disease has been my greatest teacher."

Intrigued by her advice to Donna Zmenak, I contacted Cheryl Canfield, now decades past the uterine cancer she had been assured was terminal. I was surprised to learn that she had accepted the possibility of succumbing to the disease. "When I started writing *Profound Healing*," she told me, "the working title was 'Dying Well,' because I assumed that what the doctors were telling me was not necessarily true, but likely to be true. The probability, if not for sure the inevitability, was that I would die of this cancer. I began the book because, at forty-one years old, I had no idea how to face this totally unexpected journey that meant leaving my body early, my family, and my loved ones. I wanted to create my last project, writing something that would help me figure out how to take this path and might also help others coming along behind me. It turned out that the title had to be changed. What we need to die well is also what we need to live well. That's what the disease taught me."

I also talked with Will Pye about the experience that caused him to write *Blessed with a Brain Tumor*. This tall, athletic man had been diagnosed at age thirty-one with a malignant growth at the precise spot where, as a depressed twenty-year-old, he used to imagine pointing a gun to his head in a visual fantasy of suicide. Heeding his inner guidance and with the agreement of his neurosurgeon, he delayed surgery for two years. He pursued what medical parlance calls "watchful waiting" while engaging in intense self-healing practices, until the onset of seizures signaled an increase in the size of the malignancy. The tumor was then excised, followed by radiation. By now Pye is just beyond the outer limit of the anticipated survival period for his type of brain cancer.[†] For seven years he has been off his antiseizure medications, despite having been told he'd need them for the rest of his life. He cannot know how it will go for him, and yet, as the title of his

---

[†] As this book goes to its final editing stage, December 2021, Will Pye reports he is now in rehab/recovery from a repeated bout of surgery this past October, owing to the recurrence of his tumor, first diagnosed in 2011. The average survival rate of his original diagnosis is five to ten years.

book asserts, he insists the disease has been a blessing. The diagnosis, he told me, served as a wake-up call.

"What did it wake you up to?" I asked.

"The finite nature of this life, for one thing. It brought the truth of my mortality into a more felt, easier-to-grasp dimension. While we all know it intellectually, psychologically we function with an avoidance or disregard for the reality of death. After the diagnosis, I'd be having conversations with people in the awareness that this might be the last conversation I ever had with that person. And that creates an extraordinary degree of shared presence, listening, care. So yes, total transformation. Day to day when I get out of bed, there is a practice of fully recognizing the gift of this moment, of this day, of this body, of this breathing happening now."

Ours is a culture wholly averse to death and even aging; think of how many products are geared toward erasing or "reversing" the signs of oncoming infirmity, the physical reminders of life's finitude. Here, then, is another sense in which healing is an upstream journey: it necessarily involves the full-hearted acceptance of the inevitability of our passing and the determination to experience all the days and moments that lead us to our earthly exit.

Some years ago, I led a retreat for people with all manner of health challenges, from mental distress such as depression through addictions to physical illness. One attendee was a sixty-four-year-old I will call Sam, with advanced ALS, that mysterious, paralyzing, and fatal degeneration of the nervous system. His form of the condition was the so-named bulbar onset type, meaning that it was not his limbs, but the muscles of speaking, chewing, and swallowing that were first affected. "I . . . came . . . here," he told the group in a voice hoarse, attenuated, and halting, "because . . . I want . . . to live." As he described himself, his pre-disease personality lined up with what I have seen in everyone with his condition: what we have earlier called superautonomous self-sufficiency, the shutdown of feelings and the almost phobic refusal to seek help or emotional support from anyone.

After a week of intense self-exploration, intimate sharing with fellow participants such as he had never been capable of, and some revelatory psychedelic sessions, Sam said he had an announcement to make. "When I first said I wanted to live," he said, his voice notably stronger and more resonant, "I meant I wanted to live longer. I don't see it that way anymore. I still want to *live*, but I now know that 'living' means not chronology but quality. I really want to be in my life every moment, experience what is ahead of me to the fullest, as I have never done before." He died a year and a half later, in keeping with his prognosis. In the months following the retreat, Sam—and after his death, his family—sent messages of gratitude and celebration for the vitality, love, and joy he was able to manifest in himself and with his close ones in the final phase of his life.

The manner of Sam's dying, measured not in numbers on a calendar but in the aspects of himself he was able to reclaim, came as close as I have ever seen to what has been called a "good death." He had not been cured of his illness, but he had healed. He had brought into harmony parts of his essence that might have remained fragmented and discordant without the unasked-for invitation his disease presented him with. He also found a way to make life-affirming meaning of what he could just as easily have viewed as cruel, destructive, or senseless—as many do view death from "untimely" illness. As his family's later communications made clear, the meaning he made has endured well beyond his bodily existence, radiating into their own lives.

"The journey," Will Pye said to me, "is to find the gift in the challenge. It impelled me to practice and cultivate the capacity to consciously choose the meaning of all that was happening."

That challenge, and the gifts of self that can ensue from engaging with it, is waiting patiently for each of us in the "what's happening" of our lives right now. The choice we have is whether to take it up now or to wait for a more urgent occasion for the learning.

Chapter 28

Before the Body Says No: First Steps on the Return to Self

Healing has no choice but to ripple out when we are
real with ourselves and with others.

—Helen Knott, *In My Own Moccasins*

I'll say it again: disease is not the authenticity instructor I would wish for any of us. Major calamities of body and mind are only the latest and loudest summons from essential parts of ourselves we have lost touch with. To make such drastic signals less necessary, we can get better at hearing and heeding the more subtle alerts our lives unfailingly send our way, before they become a clamor. This chapter offers some simple but potent practices, distilled from my work with thousands of people, that can retrain mind and body to become more sensitive and responsive to these calls from within.

It may be helpful, in doing these exercises, to bear in mind some fundamental and by now familiar principles discussed throughout this book:

a. *Your personality is not you; you are not your personality.* The mystery of who we truly are lies somewhere beyond the veil of personality. This does not make the personality "false," any more than clothing is true or false. Unlike clothing, though, "taking off" the personality, or perhaps just some parts of it, appears to be out of the question because *it seems like who we are.* The point is not that we should (or can) suddenly strip it all away in the name of authenticity. It helps, however, to remind ourselves that it does not define us. We were not, to channel a popular song, born this way.[†]

b. *The personality is an adaptation.* What we call the personality is often a jumble of genuine traits and conditioned coping styles, including some that do not reflect our true self at all but rather the loss of it. Each personality takes shape according to how one's particular temperament reciprocally interacts with family, community, and culture. It may not express our real needs, deepest longings, and truest nature, but rather our attempt to compensate for our estrangement from them. "We suffer from a case of mistaken identity. Our culture has sold us a bill of goods about who we really are," writes marital/family therapist Dick Schwartz.[1]

The aim of healing work is not to shed the personality entirely but to free ourselves from its automatic programming, granting us access to what's underneath, to reconnect with what's essential about us. "Liberation," A. H. Almaas says, "is really nothing but the personality becoming free in the moment; the personality loses its grip, lets itself just relax."[2] Our genuine strengths remain, with more room than ever before to stretch out and make themselves known.

c. *Our bodies do keep the score.*[‡] If the authentic self can be covered by many layers of limiting self-belief and conditioned behavior, it is never obliterated. It continues to speak to us through the body. We can learn to heed the messages the body sends by learning its language.

d. *The personality, and the loss of our essential nature, is not personal.* The disconnect from self is endemic in our materialist

[†]   Lady Gaga, "Born This Way," 2011.

[‡]   A nod here to the title of Bessel van der Kolk's contemporary classic work on trauma, *The Body Keeps the Score.*

culture, encouraged and then exploited in many spheres, from economic to cultural and political. Historically speaking, of course, the search for the true self under the limiting layers of mind long predates modern society. Each of us, then, while responsible for our own healing journey, and bound to grapple with our own personality's particularities, can also take heart in knowing that we are engaging with a universal dynamic—a tale as old as time, to quote the theme song to *Beauty and the Beast*, the beloved Disney musical about unlikely transformations and recovering one's essence.

What matters in applying the practices below is not so much the letter of the law as the spirit of the endeavor. That spirit is captured in the name of a methodology I have developed: Compassionate Inquiry (CI). Compassionate Inquiry is both a professional training I have taught to thousands of therapists in over eighty countries and a practice of individual self-reflection, as outlined below. To their edification (and sometimes dismay), the professional participants in the CI course spend the first three months working on their own issues, not those of others. *Therapist, heal thyself.*

Taking the latter half of the name first, what does it mean to *inquire*? If genuine, an inquiry is an open-ended exploration. It requires, first and foremost, humility: allowing, with Socrates, that we do not already know the answer or, better yet, the very real possibility that we haven't yet happened upon the right questions. Accordingly, in what follows I recommend you do your best to suspend, at least for the moment, whatever you believe you know about yourself. In this heyday of superficial pop psychology, self-knowledge is most often a case of the personality being an expert on the subject of itself, rather than the deeper, more intimate kind of knowing that can illuminate darkened corners of our histories, the better to see our present predicaments clearly. This is what we are inquiring into here. We are out to know ourselves, not merely to know *about* ourselves.

The other piece is *compassion*. To inquire compassionately takes openness, patience, and generosity. Think of how you would treat a struggling friend or loved one in their time of need, the leeway you would grant them to be confused, perplexed, frustrated. Being compassionate to yourself is no different, except that it's often harder to practice. In compassion there is no exhortation that we should be other than the way we are, only an invitation to inquire into the what, how, and why of the beliefs and behaviors that do not serve us. I would never tell anyone that they *should* be compassionate with themselves. Compassion brooks no "should." In any case, our defended, walled-off parts do not respond positively to such demands—why would they? It is far kinder and more effective to bring attention to the *lack* of self-compassion, to notice it and be curious about how it presents in one's life. Once seen, it softens, allowing one to investigate its long-ago origins and present-day impacts.

There is nothing touchy-feely here. Compassion is distinct from conjuring up warm feelings toward anyone, including the self. It is an attitude, not a feeling. Unlike feelings, which come and go of their own accord, attitudes can be invited, generated, and nurtured in the face of *any* emotional state. The attitude here is one of inexhaustible non-judgment toward whatever one notices. When self-judgments arise—as they inevitably do—we can stay curious about their origin without believing their content.

Everything is a candidate for inquiry, even intensely negative experiences like self-loathing.† Rather than admonishing ourselves

---

† More on the adaptive sources of self-loathing in chapter 30.

for hating ourselves, we can be curious as to why self-hatred arrived on the scene in the first place. A question posed in that spirit often illuminates. When the beauty in us can compassionately accept the beast—allow it to "be our guest," if you will—the latter may transform into a handsome and loving companion; at the very least, it can relax and stop hounding us so ravenously.

Before the Body Says No: A Self-Inquiry Exercise

Here's an exercise, to be done daily or weekly, or at whatever frequency seems right to you. It does require commitment over time—which, if I'm any example, can be hard to muster. If committing even a few minutes a day for such self-inquiry seems beyond the doable, it's worth noticing that, too, without judgment, and asking whence the reluctance.

Without judgment doesn't mean without vigilance. Our personalities are adept at throwing up roadblocks of rationalization when they sense we may be trying to unfasten or even question their hold. A commitment to healing means being hip to their tricks, as it were. The standard excuse is also the lamest: "I don't have the time." Most of us, even the busy ones, have more time than we know what to do with; what we lack is a strong sense of *intention* for its use. Default pursuits, whether noble or frivolous, quickly fill the void, and suddenly there's "no time." We don't help matters by protesting, "Oh, but I really *do* want to work on myself, it's just . . . ," and then listing all the reasons that make it impossible. If that sounds like you, ask yourself, empowered by compassionate curiosity, what discomfort it may evoke in the present to even engage in self-work. It may be that setting a strong intention opens you up to the vulnerable fact that you could be disappointed, or confronted, or pushed beyond well-worn zones of comfort. These risks are real. Whatever the case, it will not help to coerce, cajole, or shame yourself into any practice, not even ones meant to help you.

This exercise is best done in written form, in a quiet room where you can be with yourself and your experience, free from distractions. You will want to write out your answers, because doing so will engage the mind more actively and profoundly than observing your mental ideas or insights; also, because you may want a record of your progress. Writing by hand rather than typing helps create a sense of connection with yourself, while keeping the digital distractions at bay.

This exercise, I've often been told, has helped to change people's lives. The key is to do it regularly, at intervals of your choosing but at minimum once a week.

Question #1:

In my life's important areas, what am I not saying no to?
In other words, where did I, today or this week, sense a "no" within me that wanted to be expressed, but I stifled it, conveying a "yes" (or a silence) where a "no" wanted to be heard?

Get current and stay specific. Really look, and remember that we are speaking here not of occasional lapses but of chronic patterns. We all make mindful and heartfelt decisions to support others at the cost of our own convenience. Parents, necessarily, act this way all the time: most children will never know how many sleep-deprived nights a mom or a dad spent watching over them when they were ill. Or, if a friend is in serious distress, opting to meet them rather than following our desire to stay home and rest might be an authentic choice. In no way does compassionate inquiry seek to stigmatize genuine altruism. It is the *habitual, unwilled* selflessness ingrained in many people's personalities, the kind that takes a heavy toll, that we are gently bringing to the fore.

People tend to find this dynamic present in two major realms: work and personal relationships. On the job, for example, you may have accepted an additional task that you sensed would overburden you; or you took work home for the weekend, giving up time for yourself or for your family. You might not have said no to a colleague who was impinging on your personal space; or maybe someone asked your opinion, and you gave them what you thought they wanted to hear, not what was true for you.

In your personal life, you may have accepted a friend's invitation for drinks when you really needed to rest. You may have engaged in sex with a partner when physical intimacy was the last thing on your mind, or when some issue needed to be resolved before resuming erotic contact; or you may have overridden a "no" feeling that cropped up in you midway through. You may have assented when, on short notice, neighbors asked for help with moving, even though you had other pressing matters to attend to. Perhaps you needed to take space for yourself but opted against asking your partner to mind the kids for a while. Or you assumed your perennial role of family caregiver to your aging parents, rather than requesting that your siblings pitch in and lighten your load.

More generally, ask yourself: With whom and in what situations do I find it most difficult to say no? Even if I say it, do I do so reluctantly, apologetically, or with guilt? Do I beat myself up about it afterward?

There is a world of difference between a considered, conscious "yes" and a compulsive suppression of a "no." Admittedly, the realities of modern-day work can blur the distinction: we may rationally decide that holding on to a job requires saying yes to demands that tax us, demands that we would rather rebuff. All too many people find themselves in such situations for the sake of sheer economic survival. In such cases, we can ask ourselves whether the price we pay is worth the stress thereby incurred. That millions lack the freedom to even raise that question is a social problem of vast proportions. But for many among us, the absence of the "no" does not serve either our personal or economic well-being. Only you can know which denial of "no" characterizes your own situation. Even so, just getting clear that we are consciously and purposefully accepting a situation that incurs chronic stress is already a step up from doing so automatically.

Question #2:

How does my inability to say no impact my life?
You will find this impact lands in three main spheres: the physical, the emotional, and the interpersonal.

On the physical level, we are talking about bodily warning signs such as insomnia, back pain, muscle spasms, dry mouth, frequent colds, abdominal pains, digestive problems, fatigue, headaches, skin rashes, loss of appetite, or the urge to overeat.

On the emotional plane, this inquiry yields answers such as sadness, alienation, anxiety, or boredom. The impact can also manifest as emotional deficits: for example, the loss of pleasure in things that used to bring joy, a dulling of one's sense of humor, etc.

In the interpersonal realm, the most frequent impact is resentment toward the people or situations where the authentic answer was stifled. That, on close examination, is an ironic outcome. Let's say you suppress the "no" in order to maintain closeness with someone you care about. In practice, resentment drives you further away because it will contaminate your love for that person. They, too, will sense the emotional withdrawal fueled by resentment. It will show up in your facial expressions, tone, body language. You will have achieved the opposite of what you had wished for. And if you pay attention, you will know that resentment is more than an abstract emotional quality: it literally feels corrosive in your belly or chest, or tight in the muscles of your jaw, neck, or forehead. Resentment can be seen as the residue of things unsaid, feelings not honored. The word "resent" comes, after all, from the French *ressentir,* meaning "to feel again." And again, and again, and again, in our minds and bodies, until we get the memo.

For a fuller accounting, one additional place to look for impacts is slightly further out, in the material, everyday world. The question here would be "What do I miss out on in life as a result of my inability to assert myself?" Possible answers include fun, joy, spontaneity, self-respect, libido, opportunities for growth and adventure, and on and on.

Question #3:
What bodily signals have I been overlooking? What symptoms have I been ignoring that could be warning signs, were I to pay conscious attention?
The third question reverses the direction of the previous one: here we *start* with the physical impacts, trusting them to reveal where authenticity has been missing. It requires you to take an inventory of your body—a regular and deliberate scan—for the day or the week. For some people, this question is an essential backup measure, because their self-denial has become so normal that they might not be able to identify an unsaid "no"—the word doesn't even dare form itself in the mind, much less on the tongue.

The idea is to take a regular survey of ongoing symptoms— say, fatigue or a persistent headache or upset stomach or low back pain—and then ask what unsaid "no" these might be signaling. Of course, this requires pausing long enough to spot the signs. In our culture of mind-body bifurcation, many of us have become accustomed to ignoring the body's messages. The brain's reward mechanisms may even revel, in a manner very much like addiction, in the elevated levels of dopamine and endorphins that flow when others appreciate or benefit from our self-denial. There's a reason for the term "adrenaline junkies." The drive to be good to others, a genuine impulse when not compulsive, can thus overwhelm the equally authentic imperative to be good to ourselves.

Likewise, in people who are completely identified with their roles in the world, the "no" has a hard time breaking through the soundproof armor of identity to make itself heard. We confuse ourselves with our worldly job descriptions—doctor, therapist, teacher, lawyer, CEO, man of the house, supermom. Hence this third question, inviting us to proactively consider what the body has been telling us all along, how it is trying to draw our attention away from our conditioned identity and toward what we really need. This may very well prevent the body from having to shout at us more loudly or to initiate a more disastrous crash.

Question #4:

What is the hidden story behind my inability to say no?

What feeds our habitual pattern of denying our "no" is what I call *the story*. By this I mean the narrative, the explanation, the justification, the rationalization that makes these habits seem normal and even necessary. In truth they sprout from limiting core beliefs about ourselves. Most often we are not aware that they *are* stories. We think and act as if they're true.

When I pose this question in workshops, it can take people some time to identify the underlying narrative, the story beneath the story. When we get past the minutiae of the particular situation (e.g., "Well, you know how my mom is—it's just easier to say yes than to go through the hassle"), we find the deeper tale, whose internal logic determines our interpretations and reactions. This subtextual layer is always about the self, not the current circumstances.

If you have a hard time spotting the story underlying your behavior, try asking, "What must I believe about myself to deny my own needs this way?" The answer, even a speculative one, will likely be very close to the mark. Our stories, though neither objective nor accurate, are always *internally consistent* with our behavior and our experience.

Some examples of familiar stories:

- Saying no means I can't handle something. It's a sign of weakness. I have to be strong.
- I have to be "good" to deserve being loved. If I say no, I'm not lovable.
- I'm responsible for how other people feel and what they experience. I mustn't disappoint anyone.
- I'm not worthy unless I'm doing something useful.
- If people knew how I really felt, they wouldn't like me.
- If I turned down my friend/spouse/colleague/parent/neighbor, I would feel deservedly guilty.[†]
- It's selfish to say no.
- It's not loving to have anger.

Notable in these answers is the implied double standard. We usually think of double standards as differential rules of the road from which we exempt ourselves while holding others to unsparing scrutiny—as parodied in the phrase "Do as I say, not as I do." In practice, such unconscious duplicity is just as often employed *against* the self: call it reverse hypocrisy. I often ask people, "If your friend said no to some request because that's what felt true to them, would you condemn them as 'weak'?" The answer is, predictably, "Of course not." Check in with yourself: Would

---

†   Befriending our compulsive guilt feelings is covered in chapter 30.

you burden anyone else with the responsibility never to disappoint others' expectations? If a neighbor had to turn down a request because they had something to attend to, would you charge them with selfishness? Would you say to your child that she is worthless unless she makes herself "useful"? I'm confident that you, like everyone to whom I put these questions, will answer in the negative.

Some people balk at saying no, out of an ingrained sense of being "the strong one" whom others respect for their uncomplaining reliability. This kind of "strength" comes at the expense of real power, a quality that involves having a say in which burdens we do or don't pick up. Most of us, given a choice, would rather live a life of conscious power and cultivated fortitude than one of unwilled strength.

Question #5:
Where did I learn these stories?
No one is imbued at birth with a sense of worthlessness. It is through our interactions with nurturing caregivers that we develop our view of ourselves. If, because of their own trauma, they treat us badly, we take it personally. If, for whatever reason, they are stressed or unhappy, we take that personally, too. Awareness of our parents' distress, which as young children we could not have alleviated, can lead us to question our own value, even if we were assured verbally that we were loved. That certainly happened to me, as came to my awareness most forcefully on a therapist's couch—an incident I will describe in chapter 30.

The intention in looking at the past is not to dwell on it but to let go of it. "The moment you know how your suffering came to be, you are already on the path of release from it," the Buddha said.[3] Hence this fifth question calls for a frank look at our childhood experiences—not as we would have liked them to be, but as they were.

Question #6:
Where have I ignored or denied the "yes" that wanted to be said?
If stifling a "no" can make us ill, so can withholding an authentic "yes." What have you wanted to do, manifest, create, or say that you have forsaken in the name of perceived duty or out of fear? What desire to play or explore have you ignored? What joys have you denied yourself out of a belief that you don't deserve them, or out of a conditioned fear that they'll be snatched away?

As with the unspoken "no," ask yourself: What is the belief keeping me from affirming my creative impulses? For me, it was the imperative to keep working at the expense of ignoring my intuition. As I wrote in *When the Body Says No*:

> For many years after becoming a doctor, I was too caught up in my workaholism to pay attention to myself or to my deepest urges. In the rare moments I permitted any stillness, I noted a small fluttering at the pit of my belly, a barely perceptible disturbance. The faint whisper of a word would sound in my head: writing. At first I could not say whether it was heartburn or inspiration. The more I listened, the louder the message became: I needed to write, to express myself through written language not only so that others might hear me but so that I could hear myself.

"Music saved my life," the Nashville songwriter and former alcoholic Mary Gauthier told me.† "The self-expression that I'm

---

†   In fact, Gauthier expressed as much in the title of her recent book, *Saved by a Song: The Art and Healing Power of Songwriting.*

able to articulate through song, and then of course the resonance when it connects with other people, has been literally a lifesaver for me. And it has kept me sober as well. It's a reason to get up in the morning that continues to move me." The creative force within, whichever way it calls us, is a powerful support to healing.

"What is in us must out; otherwise we may explode at the wrong places or become hopelessly hemmed in by frustrations," wrote that wise medical scientist János Selye in *The Stress of Life*.[4] I've learned this lesson well. Whenever something in me demanded to be uttered and I gave it no expression, I suffocated in the silence. The books I have written, including the one now in your hands, came from heeding the call of what in me needed out.

Chapter 29

Seeing Is Disbelieving: Undoing Self-Limiting Beliefs

Healing cannot occur if we do not accept our worthiness—that
we are worth healing, even if doing so might shake up our
view of the world and how we interact with others.
—Mario Martinez, Psy.D., *The MindBody Code*

In a society that capitalizes on people's sense of inadequacy, the most prevalent self-limiting story is bound to be "I am not worth it." It underlies all the others bullet-listed in the previous chapter. Unaddressed, it sabotages our best efforts to inquire compassionately into ourselves. I felt its sting even while writing this book. It was touchingly acknowledged by one of my friends and mentors in the therapeutic field, Peter Levine. "I have answered the question 'Have I *done* enough?' positively," Peter said during a recent conversation. "I *have* done enough. But '*Am* I enough?' I'm still wrestling with that one." I smiled in recognition.

There are many ways of working with the tall tale of unworthiness. Some teachers suggest positive affirmations. Personally, I have found that such messages seem to evaporate precisely when I most need them.

We should not underestimate how entrenched and insidious this conviction of unworthiness is, or how difficult it is to dislodge with words. We were almost literally hypnotized into it. In a neural framework, as the biologist Bruce Lipton explains, it's a matter of brainwaves. Delta waves, the brain's lowest frequency, predominate in our first two years, then theta waves ramp up until we are about six. "A child under seven is predominantly in theta," he told me. "Theta is a hypnotic state, and it's how you absorb all this stuff for seven years. Just as under the spell of a hypnotist, you believe whatever messages you get." Only afterward does the state of conscious awareness and logical thinking associated with alpha and beta wave activity come on line. "We download our perceptions and beliefs about life years before we acquire the capacity for critical thinking," Dr. Lipton writes. "Those perceptions or misperceptions become our truths."[1] From such truths, we will henceforth generate our concepts about ourselves in the world. More precisely, from such untruths.

We strike a powerful blow for authentic autonomy when we notice where the self-deceptions reside and bring fresh perception, fueled by compassionate inquiry, to them.

———

You have pinpointed the unspoken "no" or "yes," started to identify the various impacts, looked at the stories underpinning such patterned self-denials, and inquired into their sources. Now what? While there is inherent value in knowing our stories *as* stories, what we ultimately want is to unfasten their hold on us.

The following exercise will suggest some first steps to liberating ourselves, to waking up from the hypnotic reverie of unworthiness.

For the healing section in my book on addiction, I adapted— with permission—a series of steps formulated by Jeffrey M. Schwartz, a psychiatry professor at the University of California, Los Angeles, in his book *The Mind and the Brain*.[2] Here I take the adaptation one step further, applying the method to self-limiting beliefs of all stripes.

While Dr. Schwartz originally developed these steps for healing obsessive-compulsive disorder, they readily lend themselves to reprogramming other kinds of thought loops as well. After all, negative thinking has a more-than-obsessive quality: we are compelled to it, over and over, despite deriving no pleasure from it. The idea is to retrain the brain, to strengthen through conscious effort the prefrontal cortex's capacity to break out of a past-based trance and repatriate us to the present. Any repetitively self-deprecating thought pattern can be worked with in this way.

The method is an *experiential* one, requiring commitment and mindfulness. It needs to be not only done but fully experienced. Only when attention is present can the mind rewire the brain. "*Conscious attention must be paid*," Jeffrey Schwartz insists. "Therein lies the key. Physical changes in the brain depend for their creation on a mental state in the mind—the state called attention. Paying attention matters."

To Dr. Schwartz's original four steps, I add one more. These five steps are most effective when practiced regularly, but also whenever a self-undermining belief pulls you so strongly that you fear becoming mired in it. Find a place to sit and write, preferably a quiet place. With this exercise, too, you'll want to keep a handwritten journal.

Step 1: Relabel

The first step is to call the self-limiting thought what it is: a thought, a belief, not the truth. For example, "I *seem to believe* that I'm responsible for everyone's feelings." Or, "I'm *having the thought* that I have to be strong." Or, "I'm *acting as if I think* I'm only worthy when I'm being helpful." Bringing conscious awareness to this step in particular is vital: we are awakening the part of ourselves that can observe mental content without identifying with it—acting as our own interested but impartial observer.

The point of relabeling is not to make the self-negating thought disappear: a longtime occupant of your brain, it will resist eviction with everything it has. In fact, it is strengthened by efforts to suppress or expel it, just as surely as by giving in to it. Remember: you're not trying to debunk the story or make it wrong. Arguing with it would be like telling a two-year-old screaming, "I hate you!" over a plate of vegetables: "No, you don't. That's just a thought you're having." Nor do you try to replace it with some sort of cheerful opposite—for example, "I'm a good person," or "I am a channel of pure light." Rather, you are divesting from the *certainty* that the implicit belief is true. In doing so, you put the story in its place, gently taking it off the nonfiction shelf. It is no longer an ironclad law to be resisted or an accusation to be refuted: just a thought, painful or dysfunctional though it may be. Odds are, the thought will come back—at which point you'll relabel it again, with calm determination and mindful, vigilant awareness.

Step 2: Reattribute

In this step you learn to assign the relabeled belief to its proper source: "This is my brain sending me an old, familiar message." Rather than blaming yourself or anyone else, you are ascribing cause to its proper place: neural circuits programmed into your brain when you were a child. It represents a time, early in life, when you lacked the necessary conditions for your emotional circuitry's healthy development. You're not pushing the thought away, but you're also making clear that you didn't ask for it, nor have you ever deserved it.

Reattribution is directly linked with compassionate curiosity toward the self. The presence of a negative belief says nothing about you as a person; it is not a moral failure or a character weakness, just the effect of circumstances over which you had no control. What you do have now is some say over how you respond to the negative belief. The quality of your present-moment experience is far more tied to that choice of responses than to anything fixed or preordained by the past.

Step 3: Refocus

This one is all about buying yourself a little time. Being mind phantoms, your negative self-beliefs will pass—if you give them time. The key principle, Jeffrey Schwartz points out, is this: "It's not how you feel; it's what you do that counts." That doesn't mean you suppress your feelings or beliefs, only that you don't let them pull you under or derail your inquiry. You stay in relationship with them even as you consciously take a detour.

So here's the game plan: if you manage to catch a negative self-belief striving to seize control, *find something else to do*. This takes awareness, and it's best not to beat yourself up if you miss it at first. Sometimes these belief patterns just take over before we can swing into action.

Your initial goal is modest: buy yourself a quarter of an hour. Choose something that you enjoy and will keep you active, preferably something healthy and creative, but really anything that will please you without causing greater harm. Instead of helplessly sinking into the familiar despair of negative self-belief, go for a walk, turn on some music, do a crossword puzzle—whatever can get you through the next fifteen little minutes. "Physical activity seems to be especially helpful," Schwartz suggests. "But the important thing is that whatever activity you choose, it must be something you enjoy doing." Or, if you don't immediately have the energy for that, you might refocus on what is loving and alive in your life: on possibilities you have fulfilled or glimpsed, on what you have contributed to yourself or others, on people you have loved or who have offered you love.

The purpose of refocusing is to teach your brain that it doesn't have to succumb to the old, tired story. It can learn to choose something else, even if—to begin with—it's only for a while.

Step 4: Revalue

Here's where you take stock and get real. Up until now, the self-rejecting belief has ruled the roost, overshadowing whatever else you may consciously believe about yourself. Let's say you've told yourself, "I deserve love in my life," but all the while your mind is assigning greater value to the currency of "I'm worthless." It's that second one that tips the scales at least nine times out of ten. You can think of this step, then, as a kind of audit, an investigation into the objective costs of the beliefs your mind has invested so much time and energy in.

What has this belief actually done for me? you ask. Possible answers: *It has left me feeling ashamed and isolated. It has produced bitterness. It has stopped me from pursuing dreams, from taking risks, from experiencing intimate love. It has incurred physical illness or symptoms.* To recognize its impact, allow your answers to go beyond the conceptual. Feel your own body state as you consider the space the belief has occupied in your mind. The impacts live right there, in your physiology, as surely as they do in your actions and relationships.

Be specific: What has been the net value of the unworthiness story—or whichever identified story you are working on—in your relationship with your partner, wife, husband? Your best friend, your children, your boss, your employees, your co-workers? What happened yesterday when you allowed the belief to rule you? What happened last week? What will happen today? Pay close attention to what you feel when you recall these events and when you foresee what's predictably ahead.

A complete revaluation also takes into account any *payoffs* or *dividends* you have derived from this belief. Has it kept you safe from harm, even in the short term? Has it protected you from criticism or rejection? Include these, too: the more thorough the audit, the better.

Above all, do this exercise without judging yourself. You didn't come into life asking to be programmed in this way, and you will not be punished for what gets uncovered—on the contrary, you are trying to commute the sentence you've been living out. Remember, too, that it's not personal to you. Millions of others with similar experiences have developed the same mechanisms. What *is* personal to you is how you choose to respond to it in the present.

Step 5: Re-create

What has determined your identity up until now? You've been acting out mechanisms wired into your brain before you had a choice in the matter, and from those automatic mechanisms and long-ago programmed beliefs you have fashioned a life. It is time to re-create: to imagine a different life, one truly worth choosing.

You have values. You have passions. You have intention, talent, capability, a desire to contribute, perhaps a latent sense of purpose or calling. In your heart there is love, and you want to connect that with the love in the universe. As you relabel, reattribute, refocus, and revalue, you are releasing patterns that have held you and that you have held on to. In place of a life blighted by your compulsive obsession with acquisition, self-soothing, self-justification, admiration, oblivion, and meaningless activity, what is the life you really want? What do you choose to create? Write down your values and intentions and, once again, do so with conscious awareness. Envision yourself living with integrity, being able to look people in the eye with compassion for them—and for yourself.

The road to hell is not paved with good intentions; it is paved with lack of intention. The more you relabel, reattribute, refocus, and revalue, the freer you will be to re-create. Are you afraid you will stumble? Guess what: you will. That's called being a human being.

———————

To conclude, a word to the wise—or those who wish to be. If we remove the hyphen from "re-create," we are left with the verb form of "recreation," as in "play." An excellent reminder that we do ourselves no favors by taking ourselves, or the process of inquiry, so seriously that we lose a sense of spontaneity and vitality. These steps may not be much fun, but they still work best when infused with some lightness. I have seen more than a few people surprise themselves, mid-process, with a smile.

Chapter 30

Foes to Friends: Working with the Obstacles to Healing

My life has not been about fixing what is broken.
It has been about engaging in a loving and tender
archaeological dig back to my true self.

—Jewel, *Never Broken: Songs Are Only Half the Story*

I wish I could tell you that healing is as straightforward as applying a particular mental exercise a certain number of times a week. Alas, the quest for wholeness is not reducible to any one or two (or three, or twenty, or fifty) practices, modalities, or approaches. Far from a one-and-done proposition, returning to ourselves is a road we choose, with all the twists and turns and seeming cul-de-sacs that come with following—or indeed, forging—an uncertain path. In my experience we are never as close as we hope, and never as far as we fear.

This chapter will offer a way of working with some of the most universal obstacles to healing: crippling guilt; self-loathing and its close cousins, self-rejection, self-sabotage, and self-destructive impulses; and blocks in our emotional memory, or what we may call denial of pain. Again, we're not referring here to abstract concepts. "I'm unworthy" and "I am defective" are much more than thoughts; they live in our neurophysiology and mind as "discrete clusters of related mental processes," in the words of Dick Schwartz. "For efficiency's sake, the brain is designed to form

these clusters—connections among certain memories, emotions, ways of perceiving the world, and behaviors—which stay
together as internal units that can be activated when needed."[1]

Seeking to understand the genesis and, especially, the original function of vexatious brain-mind clusters leads us to the first
principle of compassionate self-inquiry. Everything within us, no
matter how distressing, exists for a purpose; there is nothing that
shouldn't be there, troublesome and even debilitating though it
may be. The question thus shifts from "How do I get rid of this?"
to "What is this for? Why is this here?" In other words, we endeavor first to get to know these irksome aspects of ourselves and
then, as best we can, to turn them from foes to friends.

The truth is, these disturbers of our peace have always been
friends, strange though it may sound. Their origins were protective and beneficent and that remains their current aim, even
when they seem to go about it in a misguided way.

We need not fear, avoid, reject, or suppress these "undesir-
ables"; in fact, we merely delay our emancipation from them
when we do. It isn't them but rather our desperate efforts to keep
them at bay that levy the heaviest toll on our mental or physical
well-being. Once we see these seeming inner antagonists for
what they are and let them be, they tend to respond in kind and
begin to let us be. Agency is gained not through resistance to ourselves but by way of acceptance and understanding.

Somewhat playfully, I call these apparent foes "stupid
friends." If the adjective strikes you as harsh, feel free to substitute something with less pejorative charge, like "obtuse" or
"stubborn." The wilderness guide and depth psychologist Bill
Plotkin even honors them with the term "loyal soldiers," after the
Japanese military men who, as late as the 1970s, were found hiding in the Philippine jungle, unaware that World War II had long
ago ended. All I mean by "stupid" is that these parts cannot learn

new tricks: they refuse to get the memo that the circumstances under which they first came along no longer exist, and we are no longer helpless children in peril.

Their reason for being, mind you, is anything but stupid. Although they cause us pain now, they first came along to save us. Their presence is in fact an unmistakable sign of the deep intelligence of the human bodymind. And fortunately, healing does not require their disappearance, only their realignment—or perhaps their reassignment. What matters is that we, rather than they, are in the lead.

———————

Over the years I have performed many acts of commission or omission for which healthy remorse was—or would have been—an appropriate response. I have lied, neglected duties, and been harsh to people. In the wake of such behaviors, I would hope for myself that I'd feel a proportionate degree of regret that would prompt me to be accountable: to rectify matters as much as possible, to restore trust, and to think twice before conducting myself that way again. This kind of healthy remorse goes hand in hand with self-knowledge, having a moral compass, and prosocial values; we might even call it Nature's way of bringing us back to our interconnected nature. I doubt any of us would want to live in a world where people were incapable of it.

But there is an unhealthy kind of guilt: a chronic conviction that we are innately blameworthy and should expect, or even deserve, punishment or reproach. In this dim light our faults and failings become evidence of our irredeemable lowliness rather than invitations to grow and to do better. This type of guilt, or the fear of it, often strangles a robust "no," smothering self-assertion: the prospect of others' disapproval or disappointment triggers the intolerable conviction that we are bad, wrong, inexcusable.

Left unchecked, it augurs physical or mental distress, as we have witnessed in stories throughout this book. Many people suffer a corrosive, automatic guilt and shame if they so much as contemplate letting others down, treating their own needs as valuable, or acting on their own behalf.

At its worst, there is a bone-deep guilt that makes a person feel culpable for even being here. Such existential guilt predates language and conscious awareness. I touched on this feeling in myself not long ago during a therapeutic psilocybin session.† Lying on the couch, I experienced what a patient of mine once described as "double-mindedness." On the one hand, I knew exactly who and where and when I was, and whom I was with; on the other, the dominant experience as I gazed up at the counselor's kind face was that she was my mother and I a one-year-old infant. I heard myself say, sobbing, "I'm so very sorry I've made your life so hard." I was being shown myself at my life's inception: a baby already bearing responsibility for the suffering around him and flooded with shame and guilt at being the source of it.

Chronic guilt, like the rest of the mind's "stupid friends," is just a guardian past its prime. How so? What possible role could this debilitating, self-shaming stance have played in preserving our safety? Think of it as harm reduction. When the adult world requires, even if inadvertently, that an infant or child suppress parts of her true self—her own desires, feelings, and preferences—she cannot risk noncompliance lest the indispensable attachment relationship be compromised or threatened. She must develop within herself some sturdy enforcement mechanisms to preempt the anxiety of disappointing, or being cut off from, the caregiver. Guilt is one of the most reliable of these inner invigilators. The child's self-expression is curtailed, yes, but above all the

---

†   Psilocybin, a.k.a. "magic mushrooms." I'll have more to say about psychedelic modalities in chapter 31.

relationship with the parent is preserved. For survival, attachment trumps authenticity, as at that age it must.

Most chronic guilt is obsessively single-minded, knowing only one stimulus and exactly one response. The stimulus is that you, child or adult, wish to do something for yourself that may disappoint someone else. This could be a true misdeed, such as stealing or behaving in a way that violates a moral principle; far more often, however, it's nothing more than a desire to act in accordance with an innate impulse, from asserting your boundaries to expressing a negative feeling to even *having* that feeling. Making no distinction, guilt hurls at you the same epithet for all of them: *selfish.* Caught in a time warp, this overstaying friend cannot discern between then and now: it interprets every present-day interaction—be it with a spouse, child, parent, friend, doctor, neighbor, stranger—through the filter of your earliest relationships.

Guilt speaks in the voice of tightly coiled implicit memory circuits, making it incapable of and impervious to reason. It can't help being there, and we cannot get rid of it by force. Even by obeying its dictates we shake it off only temporarily—it is sure to raise its clamor again soon. Our acquiescence, and our trap, derives from the fact that we fear guilt, loathe it, are eager to be rid of it. *Yes, I'll comply,* we plead. *Anything to make you go away.*

Recognizing guilt for the well-meaning friend it is—doggedly faithful to a fault—we can make room for it. Engaging it in cordial conversation without believing its self-devaluing message, we realize we are talking to a very young and innocent creature. Understanding this opens space for compassion toward the inner blame-monger. One might even, with time, feel gratitude for its devotion: we can now listen to the one-note song of warning, *Don't be selfish,* but consciously decide for ourselves whether or not we want to dance to its tune. *Yes, thank you, I hear what you're saying, and thanks for sharing. You're welcome to stick around, but I will let my adult intelligence judge whether I am really hurting someone else or merely respecting my authentic self. This is my show, not yours.* When we give guilt a seat at the table, it no longer needs to ransack the entire house.

———————————

Guilt's ornery downstairs neighbor is self-accusation. The internationally celebrated photographer Nan Goldin had long berated herself for her years of addiction, having been dependent on many substances, particularly opiates. "Every morning I wake up in hell," she told me, "waking up to self-condemnation. And then I'm taking two hours to get up because it's so awful." Our conversation took place during a Compassionate Inquiry session she had requested.

"If this were a trial," I asked, "and you were the defendant, what would the prosecution have to say about you?"

Nan didn't miss a beat. "That I've missed years of my life—I don't have many more years to go. That I've spent most of my adult life addicted to drugs, and I, as a result, know nothing. My knowledge is very limited. I didn't look in the mirror and deal with myself. So much has been lost." This from a creative dynamo who had never stopped producing fierce and distinctive art, exhibiting internationally to great acclaim.

"What's the verdict here?" I asked. "Because you've done all those things, that makes you what?"

"Worthless, defective." Nan had moved seamlessly from the roles of plaintiff, prosecutor, and accused to that of hanging judge.

She also said that when she accuses herself of being worthless and defective, she notices a tightness in her throat and a pressure in her torso. At this point in the process I generally ask whether such physical sensations are new phenomena. "No, deeply familiar," Nan replied. "The choked voice and this pressure here, they're familiar feelings." This is a prototypical response: there is nothing new under the sun, or in the shadows, as it were.

"What about the sense you have of yourself as worthless and defective. How familiar is that?"

"Very, very, very."

"And how far does it go back?"

"At least to when I was nine. Or maybe even before—I was told my mother had panic attacks when I was little." In other words, the core beliefs that Nan used to label herself, and their physiological embodiment, well predated her "wasted decades" spent in addiction. They were conceived long before the period about which the self-slandering voice castigated her each morning.

Unless their emotional distress can be shared with and validated by attuned adults, children's necessary developmental narcissism disposes them to take everything personally. It is natural that they should believe that when bad things happen— when life hurts them, when the environment is stressed, the parents unhappy or ill—it is because *they* are culpable, unworthy, defective.

Less obvious is that this belief, too, has a protective function. When a young person's universe is in turmoil—when things fall apart and the center cannot hold, to channel Yeats[†]—there are two working theories the child could adopt. One is that her little world is terribly awry and misshapen, her parents incapable or unwilling to love and care. In other words, she is unsafe. The other, which wins out virtually every time, is that she—the child—is flawed. Helen Knott depicts this process in her eloquent account of intergenerational trauma, sexual violence, and

---

†   W. B. Yeats's 1919 poem "The Second Coming."

addiction:‡ "I was so convinced that I was to blame, and because of that, I remained silent." She could not have been convinced otherwise: acknowledging that those on whom one depends are incapable of meeting one's needs would be a devastating blow to a young person. Thus self-blame, like guilt, is an unflagging protector. Believing that the deficiency is ours gives us at least a modicum of agency and hope: maybe, if we just work hard enough, we can earn the love and care we need.

Self-accusation is the relentless whip that spurs so many perfectionists and high achievers to buckle down, do more, be better. As with guilt, there is no bargaining, reasoning, or arguing with this booming but callow voice. It needs to be acknowledged, seen for what it is, and gently put in its place.

Once, at a group workshop in Budapest, I worked with a young German woman who carried inside her an entity she called her "inner Adolf Hitler," full of world-destructive rage. She hated and feared this part of her, as if it were literally the Führer's ghost haunting her. She experienced herself as being personally, devastatingly connected with and even guilty for the genocide that had annihilated millions decades before she was born. When she allowed herself to sink into the full-body memory of it, her "Adolf" was revealed to be a distraught and scared two-year-old, enraged at being left alone for long periods in her crib. That rage protected her from feeling the terror and pain of abandonment that she had long ago buried and that kept her from situations in which she could again be vulnerable and wounded. Of course, it also kept her in miserable isolation from which she sought relief in addiction.

"We are not all descendants of Nazis," Edith Eger, the Auschwitz survivor and therapist author, writes, "but we each have a Nazi in us."[2] The inner fascist, which can seem so fearsome,

‡ I have cited Knott's book throughout this volume: *In My Own Moccasins: A Memoir of Resilience.*

turns out to be a frightened part of ourselves that we have long ago banished from awareness.

Realizing that vicious self-loathing, like guilt, first showed up to defend us from greater harm, and realizing, too, just how young this inner dictator is, gives us the chance to now receive it with curiosity, compassion, and even, possibly, with appreciation. Allowing it to exist, neither condoning nor condemning its lectern-pounding invective, relaxes its totalitarian hold.

When it comes to guilt, self-loathing, and so on, we can easily hear the voices: after all, they never stop talking. But there are other, more insidious ways that our inner exiles and protectors can manifest. These ways are more visible than audible: they show up in our behaviors, mood states, and mental processes. I am speaking of compensatory afflictions we covered earlier in the book, such as addiction and so-called mental illness. These dynamics, too—and recall, they are dynamic processes rather than solid "things"—can be worked with in a way that turns them from adversary to ally, instructor, or, at worst, an annoying acquaintance.

Nan Goldin, regretful as she is for the "wasted" decades, readily acknowledges that her escape into substance use rescued her when she first resorted to it at eighteen, during an extraordinarily painful time for her, the details of which she asked me not to divulge. "Literally, addiction saved my life," she told me. Without that solace, she acknowledged, she might have been driven to suicidal despair. She wishes only, as all do, that the consequences could have been less harsh. But what if we focused not on the harm but on the harm reduction?

"What if I came to you at age eighteen," I suggested, "and said, 'Okay, let's make a deal. I'm going to save your life. You need not kill yourself. I'm going to give you a way to escape pain that will allow you to live and create and still be alive in your sixties and have new vistas open to you, but you're going to have to pay a price.' Would I have your attention at least?" Nan nodded in assent. "If you make this deal," I continued, "you'll be able to do a lot of great creative work in the world. You'll be able to express truth and beauty and suffering—the genuine artist's life. But it's going to exact a price—a heavy price—in isolation, loss of relationships, of self-esteem, and physical health even if you do live to be sixty. You're going to surrender some possibilities, miss out on experiences. Is that a 'bargain' you, having endured abuse and other traumas, might have struck?" She nodded again without hesitation. Such are the unconscious "bargains" we all strike with these obtuse friends of ours, and rightly so: at the time, it may be the best deal we're going to get.

Jesse Thistle was embittered about his years as a drug addict and outlaw, until one of his elders set him right. "I went to her kitchen and I was bitching about being on the streets and all the horrible stuff that happened," he recalled. "Just horrible. I knew that she had a similar past as a heroin addict when she lived in Vancouver back in the sixties. I thought she would relate to me, and we could, like, bond over griping . . . And she scolded me. She said, 'How dare you. How dare you talk about your elders that way.'" Before Jesse could apologize, the woman continued. "She said, 'I'm not your elder, Jesse; those addictions were your elders. They were teaching you the importance of family. They were teaching you the importance of good health. The importance of human connection. The importance of perseverance. All those things are taught through addiction. All of them.' And so for me it was the great test, the great tribulation of my life. Almost like a rite of passage into a wisdom. It's given me such wisdom where I can see things that other people can't see. I have a different perspective. I'm not condoning addiction. I would have rather started twenty years ago having a family and potentially owning a house like all my other friends are now. But I have a vision and a way of seeing the world that they'll never get."

The conditions we group under the umbrella of mental and personality disorders can be seen as having their helpful dimensions, too. We alluded to this in chapter 18 with respect to finding meaning in these disturbances; now we can take it one step further and glimpse the possibility of an amicable coexistence, even a productive alliance. My son and co-author, Daniel, describes an example of that from his own life:

> Being diagnosed in 2019 with cyclothymia, basically a mild form of bipolar disorder, was huge for me. Something about my life became coherent when I realized that the crazily productive streaks and depressive crashes aren't really opposites—more like conjoined twins—and that both have been trying to help me get through the world since childhood. The can't-stop-won't-stop mode is a little boy's brain in overdrive, trying to keep up and cut through the noise around him, while the emotional collapse is like a breaker switch installed to prevent my fuse box from exploding.
>
> Thanks in part to the mood stabilizers I take, there's now someone home in between them, observing the ups and downs, knowing they're not me. Now, anytime I find myself in hypomanic turbo mode, all insomniac inspiration, or when I wake up feeling heavy and reluctant, I don't fight it or sweat it. Both states come bearing gifts: on the one hand, exhilaration and creative flow; on the other, the

gift of rest, of embracing my limitations. Neither one ever takes over for long.

It's a big deal, I'm finding, to know that your mind is not your enemy.

––––––––––––

"I don't remember my childhood," I've heard people say. "All these folks with their childhood horror stories . . . nothing I can recall explains why I behave the way I do." You, too, may have found yourself drawing a blank in the face of tale after tale of adverse upbringings presented throughout this book.

Many people, stymied by what they believe is a failure to remember, often wonder if this memory gap inhibits their healing. There are a couple of good reasons why the answer is an encouraging no. As we have said, the trauma is not what happened *to* us, but what happened *inside* us as a result. Peter Levine reminds us that "trauma is about broken connection. Broken connection to the body, broken connection to our vitality, to reality, and to others." That being the case, it's impossible to overstate that so long as we are alive and of sound mind, reconnection remains possible. We do not require the past for that, only the present. That's the first reason we need not despair of healing even if we can't connect the historical dots. We can always work with the here and now, even if the long ago is locked away.

But there is a second, more practical reason: *it isn't true* that we don't remember. Our memories show up every day in our relationship to ourselves and others, if we only know how to recognize them. Every time we are triggered—which is to say, caught up suddenly in an unwanted, puzzlingly overwrought emotional reaction—that is the past showing up: an echo of our childhood as we actually experienced it, if not how we consciously recall it. There are ways to retrieve such encoded memories by using present-moment emotions and body experiences to find their origins.[†]

The word "trigger" is itself a major clue. It has become something of a rhetorical cannonball, hurled back and forth by opposite sides in many a debate or confrontation, rarely deepening conversations and often ending them. Yet, on closer examination, it has much to teach us about ourselves. Consider: How big a part of a weapon is the trigger? Minuscule, really; perhaps the smallest visible component. The weapon also bears ammunition, explosive material, often a guidance system, and mechanisms for delivering the payload to its target with the desired force. If, when triggered, we focus our ire only on the external stimuli that set us off, we miss a golden opportunity to examine what ammunition and explosive charges we ourselves have been packing since childhood.

Let's briefly revisit the issue of the "happy childhood," which is so often professed regardless of later challenges with illness, addiction, or emotional afflictions. The point in accessing a more well-rounded history is not to engender self-pity, nor to wipe the genuinely good times from the record. It's this: to make peace with our inner tormentors, we have to first understand them against the backdrop of their origin stories. This is the compassion of context.

I was once asked to provide expert testimony in a murder case where the accused, a chronic alcoholic, having been interviewed by three psychiatrists, was reported to have grown up in a happy environment. Ten minutes into our jail-cell conversation he told me that his father had been a heavy drinker, his mother depressed. When he was four, his arm was broken and his hair

---

[†]   Illustrated in practice with the forthright participation of the podcaster Tim Ferriss here: "Dr. Gabor Maté on How to Reframe a Challenging Moment and Feel Empowered, *The Tim Ferriss Show*, November 4, 2019, YouTube, https://www.youtube.com /watch?v=__JLFw2FtEQ.

set on fire by his brother; later he was bullied in school. It had never occurred to him—nor to the forensic specialists who had accepted his "happy" story without further inquiry—that the actual history might contradict, even debunk, his whitewashed recollections. Nor was he being insincere: it was all he knew. He was probably holding tight to certain genuinely pleasant moments, a curated slide show of memories that he had titled "My Happy Childhood."

The myth of the happy childhood doesn't require such obvious extremes for its cracks to show. Recall Dr. Erica Harris, self-confessed workaholic and a survivor of leukemia, a double lung transplant, and a life-threatening, drug-resistant, blood-borne infection. At one point in our conversation, she remarked: "I was blessed with what most people call a very happy, blessed childhood. We were well off financially, I had a ton of friends, and so I wasn't bullied—I didn't have any of those big life circumstances. But at age twelve I had a really hard time." A family conflict left her sad, confused, and bewildered. This, she believed, was when her traumatic wound was sustained.

Actually, the self-disconnect had occurred long before then, in her "very happy, blessed childhood," as revealed by my next question. It's one I regularly pose to clients and participants, and I'll now put it to you, the reader. Anyone whose conscious recall is of a happy childhood—a category that may range from innocuous to idyllic—and yet is confronting chronic illness, emotional distress, addiction, or struggles to be authentic, is particularly invited to engage with it:

When I felt sad, unhappy, angry, confused, bewildered, lonely, bullied, who did I speak to? Who did I tell? Who could I confide in?

Notice your answer, and also your feelings around it. If, as in Erica's case, the answer is "No one" or indicates anything other than the presence of a consistently available adult "someone," an early disconnect was surely at play. (A loving older sibling can in some ways stand in for a parent, but it is unlikely they can fully replace a parent. And even then it signals a disconnect from the adult caregiver.) No infant refrains from emoting to the parents precisely what he feels or from signaling when she requires help. The failure to do so later in childhood is a developmentally abnormal adaptation—for some a truly devastating one, which undergirds the woundings that follow.

Thus, the suppression of early sorrow is not limited to overt trauma or abuse. I have never treated or interviewed anyone with chronic physical illness or mental affliction who could recall sharing unhappy feelings openly and freely, without restraint, with their caregivers or any trusted adult. This is a feature of life that most happy-childhood memories filter out, for the simple reason that we have an easier time recalling what happened than remembering what did *not* happen but should have. The pleasant memories we do recall, though genuine, are two-dimensional, missing the depth and the fullness of the child's actual experience. Until we can reestablish a link to that inner third dimension, we lack the depth perception to see ourselves in our totality, and healing and wholeness are blocked.

For those still unmoved by this notion of "nobody to talk to" being traumatic, I'll illustrate the point via my conversation with Dr. Harris, who was not subjected to maltreatment, nor ever came close to it. I offered my customary thought experiment, encouraging her to step outside herself and imagine another child, namely her own, in a similar position. Our conversation, prototypical in my experience, went like this:

> "If you, as a parent, found out that your kid had an emotional shock at age twelve such as you experienced, but didn't talk to you, how would you explain that?"

"That they didn't trust me."

"What does it feel like for a kid not to trust their parents?"

"That would be really terrible. It wouldn't feel safe and secure.
Like you were on your own, very alone."

There, then, was Erica's "very happy, blessed childhood," as
actually lived. And none of it means that her parents didn't love
her or wouldn't have done anything in their power for her well-
being. It means only that some essential disconnect had happened earlier in that relationship. It didn't begin all of a sudden
when she was twelve, even if that's when it hit home for her.

Finally, people often make comparisons that unfairly deni-
grate their own experience. Though you may be justifiably
grateful for your lot, the fact that others have suffered "more
than" you does not diminish by one iota your own pain, nor
erase its traces in your psyche. Levels of trauma are not to be
evaluated, much less graded on a bell curve. You may, for example, have reassured yourself along the same lines as Erica
did: "We were well off financially, I had a ton of friends, and
so I wasn't bullied—I didn't have any of those big life circumstances." "And fortunate you were," I customarily interject. "But
just imagine for a moment your little niece or nephew sobbing
to you, 'I feel so sad and alone and confused and I'm afraid to
tell Mommy or Daddy about it.' Would you, if you wished to
be supportive, dismiss this little one with 'Come on, what's the
problem here? Think of all the children who are having big life
circumstances, like hunger or abuse or bullying. By contrast,
you have nothing to complain about.' Is that what you'd say to
them if you wanted them to know their feelings were safe to
feel, that they were lovable no matter what?" I have yet to hear
anyone respond in the affirmative: when I put it to them that

plainly, they're finally able to hear in it the absurd double standard enforced against the self.

———————

As we wrap up, a bedtime story:

> Once upon a time, our wholeness was lost to us when our all-star team of inner friends—Guilt, Self-Hatred, Suppression, Denial, and the rest—came aboard to keep us safe. We were barely involved in the hiring process, and mostly we didn't notice them as they went about their business. Like a cadre of reality-TV design experts, they set about remodeling our personalities so that we'd make it out of childhood in one piece: beautifying certain rooms and boarding up others, installing alarms, locking the cellar door. But their success at keeping us intact required that we emerge into adulthood with core parts of ourselves walled off. They were good at their jobs.
>
> After many years of living in this stuffy, segmented home, we came to long for a more spacious, better-ventilated existence. So we thanked the experts for their service, and sent them out for a well-deserved sandwich. And we devoted ourselves gently but diligently to a new task, the literal antidote to the psychic dismemberment required of us long, long ago: the task of remembering ourselves.

Chapter 31

Jesus in the Tipi:
Psychedelics and Healing

The only cure I know is a good ceremony.

—Leslie Marmon Silko, *Ceremony*

One morning, not long ago, I was fired from my own retreat by a group of Shipibo shamans. The night before, in the steamy heat of the jungle, these men and women had known nothing about me; by dawn, they understood everything they needed to draw up my walking papers. They did so for the well-being of the health professionals who had flown from many parts of the world to work with me, and to my eternal benefit.

To get to the Temple of the Way of Light, you transfer in Lima for a ninety-minute flight to Iquitos in northeastern Peru. From there you travel down the surging Nanay River, an Amazon tributary, through the lush rain forest, intermittently floating past small villages on the bank's edge. Occasionally the river branches narrowly enough that you can touch the verdant tropical vegetation.

The day we arrive, it has been raining heavily. We don Wellingtons to trudge through the forest paths, where the reddish muck is deep in spots. More than once the footwear I've been given, several sizes too large, gets stuck, leaving me to rely on our Shipibo helpers to lift me, extract my captive boots, and ease me back into them again. After a forty-five-minute hike through the dense, drenched woodland, the track narrows as we climb a hill to reach our destination.

I have been invited to this place to lead a healing retreat for health care providers from four continents, from countries such as Romania, Britain, Australia, Brazil, Canada, and the United States. The attendees are psychotherapists, psychologists, psychiatrists, counselors, family doctors, and internists. There are twenty-four of us in all, that being the maximum occupancy of the maloca, the thatched communal hut where the ayahuasca ceremonies will take place. Many facilities in Peru and other countries in the Amazon basin offer such ceremonies, some in full good faith and integrity, others more interested in the dollars the tourist trade provides.[†] The Temple of the Way of Light is widely known as one of the better ones. It is run by an Englishman, Matthew, whose personal salvation owes much to the plant and the traditional practices around it. The shamans are Shipibo people native to Peru, as are the staff who assist in the ceremonial buildings and the dining and meeting halls. The temple staff work closely with the Aboriginal healers, taking care to honor their traditional ways while trying to provide a meaningful and digestible experience for their mostly neophyte Western clientele. There are usually some international volunteers as well.

I have been facilitating retreats that use the bitter drink brewed from the mystic ayahuasca plant for over a decade. These events combine the Amazonian tradition of *vegetalismo*, an ancient and highly sophisticated system of plant healing, with my Compassionate Inquiry therapeutic approach. The plant sessions are conducted by shamans at night; usually I attend, ingesting *la medicina* along with the participants. My work begins earlier in the

---

[†]   Generally, the latter kind are the places you hear about in sometimes sensationalistic but regrettably factual news stories about the dangers of psychedelics. Really, though, these headlines are about what happens when potent medicine traditions are co-opted by the profit motive—which, needless to say, is not particularly indigenous to the Amazon.

day, helping people formulate their intentions for the ceremony. An intention might take the form of a thorny personal issue they want to illuminate, a difficult emotion they hope to explore, or an inner quality they wish to nurture with the medicine's help. The following day, I help them process and integrate whatever revelations, thoughts, emotions, visions, nightmarish apparitions or dreamlike wonders, sensations, physical discomforts, or sheer ennui they had experienced as the shamans chanted to the circle and performed their energetic healing.

Over the years I have become adept at this work of facilitation, helping people overcome depressions and addictions and to heal from physical conditions. For whatever reason, as others pass through ayahuasca's portal, I find myself highly attuned to the nature of their stumbling blocks and the nuances of their breakthroughs, intuitively able to guide them as they carry their new, fledgling insights back to their ordinary plane of consciousness. I am inspired and moved by the transformations to which I regularly bear witness, transformations that gratifyingly ripple outward into people's lives, far beyond a weeklong retreat.

When it comes to my own transformation, it's a different story. All my life, no matter what breakthroughs I've beheld or helped potentiate, a glum certainty has dominated my outlook on my own healing prospects. I have participated in many dozens of ayahuasca ceremonies without believing that much could happen for me, and usually find my pessimism rewarded: nary a vision or visitation, no ancestors or spirit animals, not even one deep thought, just some mild nausea and the wish that more were happening. To be sure, a handful of moving experiences have left me with deepened gratitude or appreciation for my life's many blessings, but for all that, even these positive encounters with the plant have not shifted my mind's wondrously stubborn Eeyore setting.

We enter the first ceremony, the twenty-four of us, joined by six Indigenous shamans—three *maestras* and three *maestros*—all five feet tall at the most, dressed in white, with belts and sashes of vivid colors. Each of us will be visited by each of them in turn: six personalized chants for each participant. Interspersed with periods of silence in the dark maloca—not counting the night creatures that chirp, ribbit, and hoot all around us—are hypnotic incantations in the Shipibo language's ancient cadences, at once gentle and powerful. Under the influence of the acrid brew, these chants can take on synesthetic qualities: some people see images, while others experience the syllables as body sensations or travel in their minds to long-buried memories. A few are like me, and experience the disconcerting absence of these things.

Each time a shaman sits in front of my mat, I steel myself, silently daring them to do their worst. Go ahead, I think, try to break through the barricades of *this* psyche. Knowing full well this is an unhelpful attitude doesn't deter that inner voice from speaking first and loudest. Predictably, nothing happens except the usual frustration and disappointment. (Which, I would point out if I were coaching someone else, is hardly "nothing." Any experience at all in such a ceremony can be rich with teachings if approached with compassion and curiosity: easier preached than practiced, evidently.) Much of the time I'm almost dissociated, barely conscious of the chants or the goodwill being directed at me. The next day, after the appropriate sleep and food, the group gathers and I do my usual laser-guided counseling. As people describe their experiences of agony or joy or confusion, I guide them to make sense of their visions and help them connect the plant's teachings to their own life histories. In my role as healer and teacher, I can easily leave behind all cynicism: the retreat is not about me. All is going well.

At lunch Matthew pulls me aside. The shamans want to meet with me, he says; the group of them has delegated two spokesmen to deliver a communal decision. Through an interpreter, they give me the news. "You have a dense, dark energy our *icaros*[†] cannot penetrate," they say. "That energy pervades the room, so it impairs our work with the others. We cannot have you there." Before I can respond, they add that I may not work with the group even in the daytime.

To say that I'm taken aback is an understatement. My ego is not liking this at all—haven't these people rearranged their lives to come from all over the world to the rain forest specifically to work with *me*? Surely there must be some workaround, some compromise. The shamans are unmoved. "Even during the day," they explain, "your energy would have a disturbing effect on the others, and more importantly, you would be absorbing their griefs and traumas. As a *médico*,[‡] you have obviously done that for so long, working with troubled people, and you have done nothing to clear that out of yourself. And, long before that, we all sense you must have suffered a big, big scare very early in your life; you haven't gotten over it yet. That is why your energy is so dense."

Until last night these shamans had never heard of me. Apart from knowing me to be a doctor, they are familiar neither with my origin story nor with the work I do in the world. And yet they have read me with absolute accuracy. Even through my dismay, I immediately feel and understand that they are right. "We can help you," they promise. Despite their assurances, I have strong doubts they will succeed. And yet it is not deference alone, nor blind faith, that impels me to follow their lead. Something in me, it seems, is relieved to be relieved of duty.

[†]   A Quechua term for the healing chants performed in ayahuasca ceremonies.

[‡]   Spanish for "doctor."

For the next ten days I am socially distanced, as it were, from the retreat. I remain isolated in my cabin, except for mealtimes in the hall, when I do not interact with the participants; they are, luckily, in the able hands of an American colleague of mine. Throughout my psychic quarantine, I meditate, read spiritual books, do yoga, walk the rain forest paths, and contemplate. Assorted mental and emotional reactions to my strange situation come and go. And every second night, in a ceremonial hut all to myself, one of the shamans pours me the medicine, then chants to me and only me in Shipibo for more than three hours. He blows smoke, waves his arms above me, lays hands on my chest or back. Mostly he chants in his native language, but at times he incants Catholic hymns in Spanish, invoking Espíritu Santo, Santa María, and Jesús over my Hebraic head. His voice, now plumbing low baritone depths, now an insistent nasal tenor or keening falsetto, is indescribably supple and beautiful. In the murky dark of the maloca, this small man looms like a giant. Each day I feel myself lighter, my mind less preoccupied. Still, for the first four of those ceremony nights, no visions come, no deep experiences, only a growing sense of ease and gratitude.

The fifth and final ceremony over—so I think—with the anticipated non-results, I nevertheless feel cleansed and thankful. Via the interpreter Publio, I converse jovially with the maestro. Abruptly, mid-sentence, I throw myself on the mat—or rather, I should say, I am thrown facedown with sudden, involuntary force. At long last, the medicine is driving the bus and I am its helpless passenger. I am finally, indisputably, blessedly not in control.

Later they tell me I remained prone for nearly two hours. To me it might have been two days; in the vision's vortex, there was no sense of time. All the while, cross-legged, still, and silent, Publio and the shaman sat vigil next to me. I need not, indeed cannot, describe what I experienced, but I remember the transcendent joy of it.

What I can articulate is what I saw at the very end. On a sky-screen of deep blue, outlined in giant cloudlike wisps of letters, was spelled *B O L D O G*: the Hungarian word for "happy." The vision and the inner peace evoked with it came from beyond thought—even, I'd venture, beyond my subconscious mind.† It was both beyond me and deeply a part of me, connecting whatever I'd previously thought of as "I" to something mysterious, transcendent, awesome. That same state—spacious and aware, unfragmented, free from self-concern—infuses my awareness now as I revisit the experience and ponder its lessons (which I will return to in the next chapter).

The reader might wonder what happened with the health professionals who had traveled so far to engage in the plant work under my guidance. I'm pleased to report that most of them did famously well. My co-leader acquitted himself admirably. And for all their understandable disappointment, and contrary to my fears of a mutiny, people appreciated that I was modeling for them a willingness to care for myself. This may have been the teaching these overworked, compassion-fatigued, wounded healers most needed; certainly the shamans thought so. The temple had hosted many Europeans and North Americans, but never a group of medical workers, and the Shipibo healers reported afterward that, to their own surprise, they had never worked with such a "heavy bunch." "As healers ourselves," they said, "we must face all the pains and traumas people bring to us, but we take care of ourselves: we regularly clear those energies out of our bodies and souls, so they do not accumulate and burden us. We expected you *médicos* to have done the same for yourselves. But no, we found, you came here weighed down by the griefs and heavy energies you have all been absorbing for years and years."

---

† I usually think, even dream, in English.

I spoke recently with a physician who was at the retreat, a specialist in his late fifties who holds a high medical position in the Canadian Armed Forces. Often his patients suffer from a combination of physical injuries and PTSD. "I'm finding so much joy in my work now," he told me. "I had been tired, cynical. After thirty-two years I couldn't wait to retire. Now I look forward to connecting with people at a real level, rather than in a shallow, artificial medical way." I have heard similar reports from many of the others of how much they had gained from the shamans giving "Dr. Gabor" the pink slip.

The morning after I read the Hungarian word for "happy" in the azure sky, Publio asked the shaman how he saw my journey. The *maestro* smiled. "Oh," he said, "Dr. Gabor was communing with God."

Sometime after the 2009 publication of my book on addiction, *In the Realm of Hungry Ghosts*, I began to receive inquiries about what I knew regarding the therapeutic use of ayahuasca. At the time, the answer was "Nothing," just as I knew nothing about the potential of psychedelics in general to promote well-being. Though I'd always been keen to investigate ways of healing outside the Western medical model, I initially found these inquiries bothersome. I didn't want to learn about anything so strange and new, so "out there." Nor could I imagine how a psychedelic substance could help anyone overcome addiction, or help heal PTSD, or decondition the ingrained patterns of self-suppression that so often contribute to illness.

Since then I have developed deep respect for the synergistic power of psychedelics allied with the insights and practice of modern psychology. "Respect" may be too mild a word—"reverence" hits closer to the mark. Over the years I have worked with people struggling with drug use and sex addiction, people facing cancer, degenerative neurological illness, depression, PTSD, anxiety, and chronic fatigue, as well as those seeking wholeness, meaning, and an experience of their true selves. In all cases, people have sought liberation from ingrained, habitual, constrictive patterns. I have witnessed people looking for their vulnerable and fully alive child selves, for their parents, for love, for God, for truth, for community, for Nature. I can't say that everyone found everything they were seeking. What I can say is that most people took major steps forward on their way to authenticity and found significant liberation from their limiting or even deadening mind patterns and behaviors.

One man in his thirties, a first responder in British Columbia, wrote to me, "Since my first ayahuasca experience several months ago, I have been experiencing that shift in my consciousness daily. My presence within myself and with others, including animals, is different. I see everything I've done from a completely new perspective and live it. I am able to see the difference I make to ease pain in others, and to help them see themselves in a different light." A real estate broker from New York who attended one of our retreats struck a similar chord: "In my day-to-day capitalistic pursuits, I often meditate now on ways that I might help other people in a deeper way." And a woman whose life had been blighted by chronic pain and addiction, the template for which had been a history of childhood sexual abuse, wrote, "Today I stand in awe of life's blessings and the sacred and precious nature of life. I never understood it until now."

To be sure, before spiritual transcendence, the psychedelic experience may first penetrate to the most hidden recesses of torment in the psyche. "Tonight I experienced my fetal pain, and then I gave it up to the heavens," a young man reported after a plant ceremony. "I had been asking the medicine to take me there, to my deepest, most fundamental suffering, but it hadn't.

All of a sudden tonight I was there, feeling myself in the womb, and feeling the harshest pain I think I've ever felt. It was awful. It consumed me fully. I stayed with it for as long as I could because I knew this is what I needed to experience. Then I came out of it, and without hesitation, I released that pain to the heavens. From the worst feeling I can recall, I was now experiencing one of the most joyful."

Michael Pollan's book *How to Change Your Mind: What the New Science of Psychedelics Teaches Us About Consciousness, Dying, Addiction, Depression, and Transcendence* has opened many eyes to the healing possibilities of psychedelics. "People are hungry for something," the bestselling author told me. "It's very hard to say what it is, but people are certainly looking for a spiritual dimension to their lives, it seems to me. Also, we have very high levels of mental illness: people are suffering in all sorts of ways, and the mental health treatments available are completely inadequate, not up to the job."

Pollan acknowledged that he had been startled by the reception that greeted his book—named as one of the ten best of the year by the *New York Times*—from within the medical world. "I thought there would be a lot of resistance from psychiatry, from people who work in mental health care," he said. "But they know how empty the cupboard is, how empty the medicine cabinet is, of effective drugs, effective healing modalities. This renaissance of psychedelic medicine is coming along at a time when it's much more urgently needed than I ever imagined when I wrote the book." His survey covered traditional ceremonial plants such as ayahuasca, peyote, tobacco, and mushrooms; it also included modern human-made substances such as the psychedelic LSD (or acid) and MDMA (the psychoactive drug popularly known as ecstasy, E, or Molly), both of which are increasingly studied in therapeutic settings, with encouraging results.

We often equate the word "psychedelic" with terms like "mind-altering," but a glance at its etymology gets us closer to the mark. The British psychiatrist Humphry Osmond, who coined the word from the Greek words *psyche*, for "soul," and *deloun*, "to reveal, to make visible," meant it to indicate "mind-manifesting." In other words, not altering or even "expanding" the mind, but revealing consciousness to itself.[†] The therapeutic use of psychedelics requires the proper setting and the right intention and guidance. This is absolutely crucial: absent these conditions, the use of psychedelics can too often lead to a *Sorcerer's Apprentice* nightmare scenario. Conversely, in adeptly led sessions and in safe circumstances, psychedelics can uncover and bring acceptance to pain and sorrows people have tried desperately to escape all their lives and, too, reveal the peace, joy, and love at the core of being alive, qualities often buried under the edifice of the conditioned personality.

Readers interested in the research and science behind the resurgence of psychedelic therapies in our time can consult Pollan's comprehensive volume or the many scientific studies continually being published internationally.[1] I'll say here only that after over a decade of experience as participant, physician, and healer, I have been more than impressed with the possibilities, which are rooted in the mind-body unity we have explored. I have seen people recover from addictions of all kinds, including pornography, cigarettes, alcohol, and drugs; from mental health challenges such as depression and anxiety; and from physical conditions such as multiple sclerosis and rheumatic diseases.

Recall Mee Ok, from chapter 5—the traumatized, sexually abused Korean adoptee in Boston with the diagnosis of advanced

---

[†]   Another word—coined more recently and applicable to plant medicines only—is "entheogenic," which literally means "becoming divine with."

scleroderma, unable without assistance to move her painfully "mummified" body, as she called it. Moribund, beyond the help of Western medicine, she at one point longed for death as the only conceivable release from suffering. One evening, on her own, Mee Ok took some ayahuasca she had somehow obtained. That night, for the first time in months, she was able to rise from her bed, stand, and walk on her own. The experience was transformative. "Instead of seeing myself as Mandy[†] and as identifying with my physical body," she told me, "meaning my demographics, my race, my gender, and all of that, the plant helped me to see a deeper core to myself that would still be there after you stripped away all of those elements."[‡]

Mee Ok has since attended one of my retreats and has received other forms of therapy and physical treatment. As I mentioned in chapter 5, she is now independently mobile, physically active, and currently writing her autobiography. "Before, when I was very sick," she recalled, "I saw everything, as all of life just having happened to me. 'This is my fate; I'm going to die. I have no voice in this.' And I've never had a voice . . . When I saw that there was a reason behind all of that, then I could search for meaning. That was a big conceptual shift for me. I realized that all of those traumas I've experienced in my life could be meaningful and that I could choose the life I am meant to live. And so these traumas were also manageable, whereas before, I couldn't even access them. I couldn't remember a lot of my childhood. The ayahuasca did slowly open up a lot of those memories and

---

† Mandy was Mee Ok's Anglicized name. Part of her reclaiming of herself has been reclaiming her original Korean name. She has now taken on the surname Icaro to honor her connection to the medicine.

‡ Desperate as Mee Ok was and helpful as her experience proved to be, *I never recommend anyone ingesting the plant on their own.* Ayahuasca, more even than most psychedelic plants, is best experienced in a ceremonial context with trusted practitioners. This is for safety, and also for the integrity of the tradition itself, in which the plant is seen as one part of a rich body of practices, not to be consumed ad hoc, especially by newcomers to its ways.

all those things I had forgotten about: who I was as a child, and who I really am."

I spoke with Mee Ok's Boston family doctor, who confirmed the medical history and the recovery, which she herself, the physician, was at a loss to explain. Yet from the perspective of body-mind science, there is nothing miraculous or even perplexing about it. Once Mee Ok reconnected with her authentic self—in her case with the aid of a plant, but the principle generalizes—she was able to divest from the trauma-confined personality. She began to free herself from the conditioned set of beliefs, behaviors, and emotions, and hence from the physiological responses these dictated. Her body—nervous system, immune system, and tissues—followed her lead, along pathways we have described.

Beyond the realm of healing, many have found psychedelics to be transformational teachers. Certainly, in their original contexts, plant medicines were and are consulted for far more than cures and pain relief: shamans consulted the spirits of these plants for community guidance, for divination of hunting and weather patterns, to commune with ancestors and help make peace between warring factions, and, most elementally, simply to know and learn their ways. Each plant—including many flowers, bushes, and trees that wouldn't be considered psychedelic by our standards—is thought to have its own wisdoms to impart, with its own curriculum that can take years of dedicated practice to absorb. The anthropologist Wade Davis is fulsome in his appreciation. "I always tell young people that our parents were so frightened of these substances, you know, that they'd scream at us, 'Don't take this. You'll never come back the same!' But that was the whole blessed point. In that sense, I am very open about how catalytic these substances have been in my life and how valuable they are. One thing I know is that these medicines allowed me to understand our connection to the natural world in a way that never in a million years could have happened just by reading books."

How can psychedelics exert such potent transformative effects? Through the mind-body unity we have been exploring and through their power to access the unconscious, where, hidden from awareness, many of the emotions and motivations driving our lives reside. Sigmund Freud once said that dreams are the royal road to the unconscious. Psychedelics may be said to be an even more direct route. Dr. Rick Doblin, founder and executive director of the Multidisciplinary Association for Psychedelic Studies, has spearheaded the drive for the investigation of psychedelic treatment modalities. "There is a membrane between conscious mind and unconscious mind," Doblin told me when we spoke recently, "between what we are paying attention to and what we are thinking and feeling on deeper levels. Psychedelics open up that membrane so that more emerges. Each substance does it in a different way. It both connects you to parts of yourself that have been suppressed or ignored, but also you can see the wider world beyond yourself, beyond your ego self." He drew an analogy to the Copernican revolution of the 1600s. "We tend to believe with our ego that we are the center of the universe," he explained. "Psychedelics displace that and we see that we are part of something enormously bigger than any individual and that this unity goes back in time and forward in time. They can take us out of our habitual patterns. When you are no longer looking at things from the perspective of the 'I,' you feel a newly released potential and sense of connection."

Plant substances and synthetic psychedelics are not "drugs" in the medical sense of the word. A pill like the antidepressant Prozac, or the easily accessible aspirin or codeine, is meant to change your biological state—your physiology—so long as you are taking it. Depending on circumstances, that may or may not be a good thing, but such pharmaceutical treatments are not designed to get at root causes and unconscious dynamics. Psychedelic medicines are not intended to be taken daily to keep you in a state of altered physiology. Ideally, they can help facilitate your entry into a renewed relationship with yourself and the world, long after you have ingested them, whether in ceremony, as with ayahuasca, or in a therapeutic session, as with MDMA. In a real way, these experiences retune the brain's emotional apparatus. I was not surprised, for example, by a recent study showing that psychedelic use reduced the odds of men perpetrating intimate-partner violence.[2]

All that said, I am no psychedelic evangelist. Contrary to the fond imaginings of some enthusiasts, neither plant-based nor manufactured psychedelic medicines will, on their own, transform health care or human consciousness at large. That will have to await vast-scale social change, not least the broadening of the mainstream medical ideology. For all they can offer, at present psychedelic treatments are esoteric, expensive, and time-intensive. They are bound to remain beyond most people's reach for both practical and cultural reasons. But we would be negligent to exclude them, to ignore their healing potential for many endemic conditions in the face of which Western medicine finds itself largely helpless.[†]

Wondrous as their effects can be, for our purposes plant medicines and other mind-manifesting substances are not only interesting in themselves but also powerful ambassadors for the bodymind principles that modern science is only now catching

---

[†]   Like many others, I'm confident that the studies now being pursued will prove that, even on strict economic grounds, such treatments can be cost-effective—consider, for example, the lifetime expense of keeping someone on medication for something like PTSD.

up to. The lessons they transmit testify to the indomitability of the human spirit and the possibility of unlocking its potency, with or without substances and no matter what life has thrown at us. We now know that on every continent, seemingly in every recorded era, people have availed themselves of the apothecary called Earth to promote healing, wisdom, and spiritual realization, and indeed to transmit culture down through the generations.

Psychedelic medicine came to exert a major influence in the life of one of the last great Native American warrior leaders to challenge the relentless, genocidal expansion of settler colonialism in the American Southwest. After his inevitable defeat and his people's humiliating confinement to ever-shrinking reservations, the brilliant Comanche chief Quanah Parker turned to spiritual pathways for solace. He worked with the desert cactus peyote, as a forerunner of what later became the Native American Church. Typical of Indigenous practices, he wasn't interested in religion but in spirituality. "The white man goes into his church and talks *about* Jesus," he once said, "but the Indian goes into his tipi and talks *to* Jesus."[3]

After my "communion with God" in the Peruvian jungle, I had a felt sense of what Quanah Parker had meant.

Chapter 32

My Life as a Genuine Thing: Touching Spirit

Ultimately your greatest gift to the world is being who you are—both your gift and your fulfillment.

—A. H. Almaas, *Being and the Meaning of Life*

Until my clear-blue-sky moment in the Peruvian jungle in 2019, spirituality had existed for me mostly as rumor, theory, or concept—or as a vague longing, both wistful and wishful. Though I had consumed shelves of books, and could even speak articulately on the subject, I had never myself been subject to a direct encounter with such storied states as wonder, mystery, or "the peace that passeth all understanding." My faith in humanity's potential for genuine, revelatory transformation, while sincere, had come to me largely secondhand; I could not trace this faith to any experience of my own. It certainly didn't derive from any deistic belief or devotional practices of the organized religious kind. That said, what I learned in Peru gave experiential substance to these inklings of possibility. It went beyond belief and spoke to the essence of healing.

Literal beliefs aside, to the shaman's unsurprised observation that "Dr. Gabor was communing with God," I can only say amen. Something transcendent *did* take place that morning: an overdue rendezvous with that in me which is beyond the "me" I've subscribed to for so long. I touched into a space where I was aware of myself as an expanse of consciousness, unmoored from my identity's self-confining biographical ballast. The medicine under the shaman's guidance—and, just as important, my days of inner preparation—had left me open to information so outside my usual frames of reference that I didn't imagine I could ever access it. Shakespeare's Hamlet knew this kind of knowledge: "There are more things in heaven and Earth, Horatio, / Than are dreamt of in your philosophy."†

Looking back, I see that the experience did not so much instill new beliefs in me, as it did relax and unfasten my personality's militant *un*belief, which can be every bit as fundamentalist as the theistic certainties of ultra-religious sects. The actor and activist Ashley Judd has a terrific phrase for this leap of nonliteral faith: "surrendering to a God you don't believe in."

The first thing I learned in Peru—and here I mean direct learning, not stacking more facts on the woodpile of knowledge—is that healing is outside the thinking mind's wheelhouse. For one thing, the mind by its nature is a house divided: our personalities contradict themselves constantly. In my case, part of me always held out hope, even if a theoretical kind, that I might someday, somehow, have an "enlightenment" moment, the big-ticket aha, while another part was stowed away, stoking cynicism and pessimism. Spirit, by contrast, is one with itself. Our minds, our learned knowledge, can store healing principles worth remembering and can even help lead us toward experiences that heal. There will come a time, if we wish to go "all the way," when these trusty protectors have to recuse themselves at the door and allow a less sophisticated, more vulnerable element, stripped of armored certainties, to enter.

---

† Act I, scene 5. In Shakespeare's time, "philosophy" could refer to rational, scientific thought.

Second, I learned that I could not have planned this. Quite the reverse: the entire set of events that brought me to that moment laid waste to every plan I'd made. My entry into the realm of spirit could take place only once I had given up the illusion of control and submitted completely to the way things were. My willingness to have my agenda undermined was my buy-in, the ante required of me to sit at the table of mystery.

Third, and closely related, was that I had to do several difficult things: surrender my identity as leader or healer; put aside my habit of helping others without sparing time or energy for my own transformation; and accept whatever personal diminishment I feared would result from stepping away from my expected role. The biggest challenge was to see past the resentful protests of my threatened ego: "I can't let these people down; they came all this way to work with *me*." My identity, the persona I had clung to all my life, had been subverted utterly. All it could do was negotiate its terms of surrender.

Life in its wisdom had put me in a position where I had no control. My only choice was to let go and trust—trust others, trust myself, and, most of all, trust the direction my life had suddenly taken—or not. Making the affirmative choice, which may not have been my selection in earlier moments, opened up the possibility of a powerful healing experience, a touch of grace. I won't say my letting go *caused* the healing—that's not how grace works, as far as I can tell—but it was a prerequisite. I just happened to finally be ready, at age seventy-five, to do so.

Not everyone will, or ought to, work with shamans or psychotropic plants; relatively few people are likely to even have such an opportunity. That doesn't matter. My particular experience, though under unusual circumstances, was suffused with the universal healing principles that guide this book's exploration, and which are available to all: the acceptance, the shedding of

identity, the choosing to trust the inner guidance against the re-
monstrations of the conditioned mind, and the genuine agency
that springs paradoxically from the willingness to give up rigid
control. If I can do it, I am convinced that anyone can—anyone,
that is, who commits to their healing and allows it to instruct
them rather than the other way around.

My experience with the shamans in Peru also taught me something about what healing is not. For years I had retained a fixed
idea that to heal I'd have to go through some monumental ca-
thartic release, as I've seen happen for others, or perhaps travel
back in time in some way, to relive or redeem the difficult past.
Yes, it can take that form, but not necessarily. Once again, it is
not the past that has to change (or can change), only our present
relationship to ourselves. As I lay prone on the mat—I'm told I
both laughed and sobbed at various times—I was profoundly
aware that my infancy had occurred in just the way it had, that
nothing will ever alter that, that my grandparents will never not
have gone to their deaths. I also knew that none of that could interfere with or diffuse the peace that was my birthright and essence, ever present and ever possible. Not just mine: everyone's.
It was beyond acceptance. In that moment, present to how it is
and must be, I knew there was nothing to accept—except in the
sense of gladly receive.

―――――――――

Even before Peru, it had dawned on me, if only through observation and intuition, that there is more to being human than
meets the eye—or as the spiritual master Eckhart Tolle has
quipped, "than meets the I." We are part of, and endowed with,
something greater than the egoic mind, with its baked-in sense
of separateness, can comprehend, much less prove. "No one
has ever touched a soul or seen one in a test-tube," the founder

of behaviorist psychology John Watson wrote in 1928—and so far as the five senses are concerned, he was correct. But we in the West are playing with a less-than-full sensory deck: our senses have been stripped, to borrow from Dylan,[†] of more subtle ones that spiritual adepts and Indigenous cultures have always cultivated. "We live in a world that is split," the Buddhist meditation teacher Jack Kornfield told me, "and so our psyche is split. We make money by going to work, and we take care of our bodies in the gym, and we maybe take care of our psyche a little bit in therapy, and we do the arts when we go to a concert, and we do the sacred by going to church or synagogue or mosque or something like that. They're all in compartments, as if the sacred was somehow separate from the work that we do, or the music that we make."

One of the earliest and, for many, most challenging steps in programs like Alcoholics Anonymous is to entrust one's life to the care of a higher power, whatever one understands that term to mean. Whether we know it or not, we all seek our higher power. The longing manifests in many ways: our desire to belong; our drive to know our purpose in life; the urge to escape the limitations of our conditioned, self-centered personalities; our taste for transcendent experiences. Unfortunately, in our culture we are taught to seek fulfillment by filling ourselves with evanescent externals. It cannot be done, for what we are missing within cannot be replaced from without. The emptiness dogging us emanates from the places where we have lost contact with our deepest selves. A. H. Almaas, whom I'm fortunate to call a mentor, calls these broken connections "holes." "Allowing ourselves to tolerate the holes and go through them on the other side is more difficult now, because everything in society is against this.

---

†   In his 1965 song "Mr. Tambourine Man."

Society is against essence. Everybody around you, wherever you go, is trying to fill holes, and people feel very threatened if you don't try to fill yours the same way."[1]

"I don't see society as an enemy," he clarified when we spoke. "It's more like society is asleep. It just doesn't know. Some knowledge of it may arise through religion, where there is at least an awareness that there is more to us than the usual physical thing. The spiritual drive wakes up in a human being at some point. It's mysterious when it wakes up: sometimes it wakes up by itself; sometimes it's triggered by something happening outside, by listening to somebody or reading a book. When the spiritual drive or curiosity wakes up, that's when one yearns to find out more about what a human being is beyond the limitations society normally understands, recognizes, and tries to enforce."

Spirituality defies both description and prescription. Countless pathways are out there; some of these resonate more than others for different people. I've tried as much extended meditation as my restless mind can tolerate. One time I sat in speechless contemplation for ten days; never again. It turns out it's not my way, even though I experienced some benefits at the time. Yoga, brief meditation sessions, the occasional psychedelic experience, contemplative silence, reading the spiritual classics of many faiths and disciplines, and listening to the contemporary masters have all helped as I stumble my way toward deeper truths. Some seekers choose none of the above, finding their way to their rapprochement with spirit via wholly self-mapped, even accidental byways. The point is not the big aha, but the arising— sudden or gradual, however it comes—of the consciousness that holds the mind but doesn't mistake itself for its contents. My colleague the physician Will Cooke, who in his work with addicted people in the Appalachian-adjacent region of Southern Indiana has seen his share of spiritual openings, described to me "this spark inside of everyone, that shimmering self waiting to be re-vealed, that's just cluttered and stacked with all this stuff that life has stuck to them, and they can't shine. But if we pull that away a little bit at a time and reveal who they are, it's always something beautiful."

The yearning for spirit was summed up by the American jour-nalist and broadcaster Michael Brooks shortly before his un-timely death at age thirty-six in the summer of 2020. Brooks, who has been widely mourned for his heart, humor, and commitment to truth and justice at home and internationally, had been delv-ing more deeply into spiritual work. His sister, Lisha, has quoted him as having remarked, the day before he died, on a growing awareness of spirit: "I am feeling a spaciousness inside me, like outer space or the ocean." In words that crystallize the endeavor of getting real and returning to ourselves, he then stated his com-mitment to nurturing and expanding this felt sense. "I'd like to work in the coming weeks," he wrote, "on the mechanics of what it means to continue *separating myself from the stuff that separates me from me.* I want to remember the inner."

Ashley Judd has forged her own unique path to healing. One of the first women to call out the film mogul Harvey Weinstein for his inveterate sexual predations, Judd had long carried the early imprints of life in a family rife with alcoholism and unpro-cessed grief. For her, the grace that allowed her to surrender to a God she "didn't believe in" arose in part from an intimate en-counter with the natural world. "I was sitting in a creek in the Great Smoky Mountains National Park," she recalled when we talked, "and all the butterflies were coming down the creek, and the sun was glinting off the water, and I just knew that everything was okay. It was one of those epiphanic moments where time was suspended and I was okay, and I was alone, and I might always be alone, but everything was all right." Even when old stuff arises,

Judd says the memory of that moment remains alive for her in a way that fortifies her dedication to the healing path, and can even lighten the proceedings. "There can be some humor," she said, chuckling. "I kicked its ass before. I'll be okay."

"I'll be okay" is also the message the Canadian Olympic cyclist and skater Clara Hughes found in her encounter with Nature. Having been the only athlete in history to win multiple medals at both the Summer and Winter Olympics—six altogether—Hughes had created for herself a new and busy career as a speaker and teacher, and a new identity as the bearer of healing and inspirational messages to others. Following her own painful struggles with deep depression, she came to an awakening. "I realized I was getting stuck," the vibrant forty-seven-year-old told me. "I was repeating everything. 'This is not healthy,' I felt. It's not me. I needed to get a life . . . In 2017, March 22, I quit everything. I stopped public speaking, I quit the board of directors that I was on, I just stopped, and started walking." Following her inner voice, she embraced a new passion: long-distance hiking, a pursuit that gives a whole new meaning to the title of this final section, "Pathways to Wholeness." She has spent about six months of each year in the last three years walking.

Among their many salutary effects, these extended pilgrimages bring Hughes into the present moment in a way that aligns perfectly with the will to heal. "When I walk," she said vibrantly, "there is no tomorrow. Yesterday is gone . . . there is only here, now. I listen to the forest speak, the mountains, the water. I hear their voices. Trees become family. Rocks become living beings that you know, and you're happy to see." Walking has also instilled in her a new sense of what it means to be resilient. "I know without a doubt that I can breathe through anything, every single difficult thing that surfaces. In whatever headspace that may come to me in my day . . . I can sit, and I can write, I can draw,

I can garden, I can do the dishes. I can bring myself back to my breath, and I'm okay. And I'm going to be okay, and it's me." I was glad she said the part about drawing and gardening, since few of us will ever journey into the wild in quite so epic a way as she has. But any activity that brings us back to our own nature— which is, of course, but one expression of Nature writ large— unencumbered by gadgets and digital obsessions, can be a fount of refreshment.

Nature played a major role in V's recovery from metastatic uterine cancer, following multiple surgeries and chemotherapy. "I used to be horrified by Nature," the writer and activist told me, "until I got very, very sick, and then I heard—I heard the Mother calling me to come to the country. It was like, 'you need to come.'" It began with a solitary potted tree outside the window of her hospital room. "I fell in love with that tree," she said, smiling at the recollection. "I was so sick at that point. I had lost thirty pounds, I didn't know if I was going to make it, and I was looking at that tree, saying to myself, 'Oh my God, I'm going to have to look at this tree every day as I anticipate death?' And that first day that tree just started to speak to me . . . And I was like, *Wow! I don't think I've ever seen what leaves are* . . . And the next day it was like, *Bark!* And the next day it was like, *Trunk!* Literally, I didn't want people to talk to me anymore, I didn't want people to come near me—just let me be with this tree; this tree and I are having something amazing happen here. The last day that I was in that room, the tree blossomed, white blossoms. That was the beginning of my transformation."

None of this is news to the world's Indigenous peoples; oneness with Nature has been a pillar of such cultures since forever. Even through the brutal displacement of North America's original

Nations from the life-giving lands that were part and parcel of their identities, the awareness of belonging to this planet has never been lost. In fact, according to the Navajo activist, artist, and ceremonial leader Pat McCabe, known as Woman Stands Shining, it is a lifeline, a fount of resilience and strength. "The first thing that comes to my heart," she told me, "is that we have a commitment to Earth. It's not just a commitment, though—it's a mad love affair with this Earth. And we have a capacity and a role in helping Her and all the rest of the life to thrive. It's not part of the modern world paradigm. Everything is so individualistic, individual achievement, and even anthropocentric, right? Totally self-oriented. When you are part of that larger community, Earth, and you are accountable to this mad romance with birds and fish and trees and mountains and sky, you have more to compel you, to guide you."

In my interviews for this book, I was struck by how often people would bring up their experience with and reverence for Indigenous traditions—an esteem I have come to share through my interactions with Native healers and elders in both South and North America, whether sitting in ceremony in a Peruvian maloca, a Colombian hut, or in a sweat lodge in Alberta. I am grateful to the communities who have welcomed me, an outsider from the "settler" side of the neocolonial divide, into their places and given me a taste of their ways—as much of a taste as one dropping in from the dominant culture can be given, anyway.

If we see Native wisdom not as something to be consumed but rather as a rich trove of traditions about ways of living and dying that deserve and demand our humble curiosity and respect, its broad, unitary perspective could round out the dualistic, biological focus of the Western medical mentality. Indigenous traditions are themselves fighting for survival, but they can still offer a salutary, equal complement to Western medicine's scientific wizardry. They can also be a necessary corrective to the latter's failure to honor our emotional, social, communal, and spiritual needs.

Helen Knott likens being in the sweat lodge to returning to the womb. "Our healing," she told me, "must include that piece of humility where you ask for help and recognize that you can't do everything on your own, that just on your own you could be a pitiful creature as a human being. Suffering from this human condition, trying to find our way, that sweat lodge takes us back to our origins—in the belly of our Mother Earth. Being able to let things go, and to lie on the earth and to just *be* there. The lodge is always a powerful place." When the large, heated rocks are hauled into the pit in the middle of the sweat lodge, participants welcome them as "grandmothers and grandfathers." This is not metaphor; it is profound understanding and clear seeing, far clearer and wiser than most of us are schooled in. Do we not all come from the earth that spawned those rocks, as from the water that is poured over them before the prayers and the chants begin? Would we not, if we could see things that way, think twice before despoiling and pillaging that which creates and sustains us? In the Western world, at great cost to ourselves, we have long lost touch with this unity that Indigenous cultures recognize and honor.

The part-Lakota psychiatrist and physician Lewis Mehl-Madrona[†] is experienced in both high-tech emergency medicine and in the traditional healing methods of his people. In his view, both have their place, and he would not want to do without either one. Like me, he has seen the miracles both can bestow. "For a Native American, a healing is a spiritual journey," he writes. "As most people intuitively grasp (except maybe doctors, who are

---

[†] Former medical director at the Center for Complementary Medicine, University of Pittsburgh Medical Center, and currently on the faculty of the family medicine residency program at Eastern Maine Medical Center, affiliated with the University of New England.

trained to disbelieve the idea), what happens to the body reflects what is happening in the mind and the spirit. People *can* get well. But before a person can do so, he or she must often undergo a transformation—of lifestyle, emotions, and spirit—besides making the necessary shifts in the physical body."[2]

"In the Lakota idea," Mehl-Madrona told me when we met to discuss this book and the possibility of collaborating in some healing events, "we need to celebrate and support people who are ill because they're the canaries in the mine. They're the ones who are showing us that our society is out of balance, and we need to thank them for taking that on and doing it for the rest of us. All of us need to participate in their healing, because if not for them, where would we be? We're all responsible for whatever ails them. We have the responsibility to contribute to their healing for everybody's benefit." What a bracing old/new thought: a society in which all have responsibility for the health of all, where the illness is seen as the manifestation of shared experience. A culture like ours has much to learn from ones that take our biopsychosocial nature as a given.

I had to laugh when Mehl-Madrona then pointed out another distinction between Western medical attitudes and his grandparents' Indigenous tradition. One of his teachers, a famed American physician, lectured to his coed medical school class: " 'Boys,' he said—he couldn't get around the idea that there were women in the class—'Boys, life is a relentless progression toward death, disease, and decay. The job of a physician is to slow the rate of decline.' And I was really shocked, because my great-grandmother always taught us that you should die healthy 'so you can party on the other side.' She didn't really believe that you had to be sick to die. She didn't connect sickness and death. For her, death was like your time is up, and sickness is just something you may have to go through."

"How old was she when she died?" I asked.

"In her mid-nineties, and in good health. It's a funny story: one evening she told everyone that she was going to die that night. And she said, 'It's my time. My time is up.' Then my mother, who was trying very hard to be modern, said, 'Nonsense, you're very healthy.' 'That has nothing to do with dying,' my great-grandmother replied. And in the morning, she was dead."

It's not a question of romanticizing Native ways, nor of aping Indigenous practices. But we can and must overcome what Wade Davis furiously calls "cultural myopia," the sense that "other peoples are failed versions of ourselves. Or that they are ancient, vestigial creatures, destined to fade away, quaint and colorful humans who wear feathers. These are living, dynamic people who have something to say."

Although my own experience of healing took place in the jungle, and Clara Hughes's in wide-open spaces, I have seen people coming home to themselves even in the claustrophobically confined and, far too often, less-than-humane precincts of prisons. Some of the gentlest people I've met have been lifers in Canadian or American prisons who have courageously confronted their past. Many others working with such people have shared with me that same heartfelt impression.

Thanks to my work in addiction, I have been invited to speak to incarcerated populations—in other words, to the most traumatized and marginalized in our culture. I will not forget what Rick, a lifer in California's notorious San Quentin State Prison, told me. He had been through a volunteer-led transformational program that took him for a deep dive into the self, beginning with a childhood that featured every category of adverse childhood experience: an alienated and violent adolescence, and a drug-addled young adulthood that culminated in a killing. He was now thirty years older, a smallish, thin Black man with gray stubble and thinning hair. He was hoping to apply for parole. We were sitting in a meeting room, along with about a dozen of his confreres, of various ages. "This group," he said, "made me think about my actions and helped me to stop running, to stand up and face those inner demons I had always run away from. I have learned to love myself and to know that there are people who care out there."

I wondered what he would want the parole board to know about him. "Well," Rick pondered, "at that time in my life I was separated from me. I didn't even know who I was. I didn't respect myself, so I couldn't respect no one else. I didn't love myself, so I didn't have no love for anybody else. But after doing this time, really stopping and looking at my life as a genuine thing, and with the love for myself and understanding that for me love is everything... love is opening me up to everything outside of me. What I'm doing for myself, learning about me, I'm learning about everyone else, too. I'm not different from everybody else. If I touch spirit, I'm not separated. If you do let me out of here, this is the kind of work I want to do when I get out. I'm ready. I want to go home, but even if they don't let me go home, I already know who I am and what I want to do." Every one of the five compassions we looked at earlier was shimmeringly present in Rick's words.

———

"There is only one common rule valid in finding your special truth. It is to learn to listen patiently to yourself, to give yourself a chance to find your own way which is yours and nobody else's," wrote the psychologist and visionary Wilhelm Reich.[3]

Listening for our "special truth" is among the most daunting of challenges amid the clamor of our increasingly noisy world—

a world that isolates even as it discourages healthy solitude. The quest is age-old. George Bernard Shaw's play *Saint Joan* depicts the heroic life and death of the young peasant girl Joan of Arc, whose visions and "voices" inspired her to lead the armed revolt against the English occupation of fifteenth-century France. "Oh, your voices, your voices," the French king Charles VII says at one point to Joan with envy and frustration. "Why don't the voices come to me? I am king, not you." "They do come to you," Joan replies, "but you do not hear them. You have not sat in the field in the evening listening for them. When the angelus rings you cross yourself and have done with it; but if you prayed from your heart and listened to the thrilling of the bells in the air after they stop ringing, you would hear the voices as well as I do."

Among the challenges of healing ourselves personally and of bringing healing to our troubled world is being still long enough to allow our true selves, that "still small voice" we read of in the King James Bible, or as the Hebraic Tanakh describes it, that "soft murmuring sound," to be heard.† The ancient and modern practices of mindfulness encourage and allow space for that voice to emerge, by separating us from and enabling us to observe the cacophonous traffic in our minds without being seduced, overwhelmed, or intimidated by it.

Mindfulness practices have also had the documented benefits of reducing inflammation, reprogramming epigenetic functioning, promoting the repair of telomeres, reducing stress hormone levels, and encouraging the development of healthier brain circuitry.[4] Mindfulness even reduced the disease progression in patients with ALS:[5] the mind-body unity in action once again.

When we observe ourselves with compassionate curiosity instead of judgment, perhaps we can also learn to drop our

---

† I Kings 19:12.

prejudgments—also known as prejudices—against others. A most encouraging study comes from Israel/Palestine, site of ongoing hatred and conflict. Over three hundred Jewish students from grades three to five were exposed to a mindfulness and compassion-based social-emotional program. Six months later, and despite a flare-up of violent hostilities, these students showed "significantly reduced" prejudice toward and negative stereotyping of Palestinians.[6]

I interviewed several leading mindfulness practitioners; each attested that their practice has led them, and others, to greater compassion and acceptance of fellow humans. "I would never bet against the human heart," the psychologist and Buddhist meditation teacher Rick Hanson[†] told me.

The present book's title employs the word "myth" in its everyday, contemporary sense. "That's just a myth," we might say to an agitated friend peddling the conspiracy theory du jour. "There's no proof." But this pejorative use of the word actually puts us at odds with most of cultural history. Until very recently, myth was seen as a fount of knowledge, a portal to spirit, and one of the fundaments of any healthy culture. It may well be that this original notion of myth can serve as a gateway into the world of healing, reconnecting us with eons of human wisdom and fostering a mindset where nothing is isolated happenstance and where meaning can be made from any of life's raw materials. It is a potent antidote to the dualistic thinking that fantasizes mind and body to be separable. In the world of myth, everything is connected: one of many real-world truths that mythic thinking can help us face.

Myth is a collective expression of one of the most uniquely

---

†   Author, most famously, of *Buddha's Brain: The Practical Neuroscience of Happiness, Love, and Wisdom.*

human qualities: imagination. Far from magical thinking or denialism, imaginative thinking allows us to see beyond appearances and tap into core insights into what wholeness and wellness mean. "When we lose myth," the American storyteller, author, and *Living Myth Podcast* host Michael Meade told me, "we know less. We know less about ourselves, we know less about illness, and thus we know less about healing." What, then, I asked, could a return to mythic imagination tell us about wholeness and healing? "An illness stops us in our course, and then can be a wake-up call, if we allow the body to teach us what's going on," he replied. We have witnessed that in these chapters many a time.

The mythic and the prophetic are closely linked. On the societal scale, we could move toward wholeness if we were willing to heed the warnings our collective afflictions, from cancer to COVID-19, are sounding about how we live. Mythic thinking might help us enshrine and enact the scientific principle that our health derives from connection—to our essence, to each other, and to a culture that honors these interrelationships.

Older understandings of myth also spring from a deep connection to (or oneness with) Nature, which is perhaps why myth-making in the positive sense comes to us so naturally. As Wade Davis put it when we spoke, "For most of human history, our relationships with the natural world had been based on metaphors." Mountains are symbols of strength and constancy; rivers embody change, flow, even life itself. These meanings have profound consequences for how we live, for how we see the world and our place in it. They are the marks of a culture that knows how to read, and heed, Nature's signs.

Michael Meade has a beautiful phrase for the kind of collective knowing that dates back as long as we've been around: "a thought in the heart." My own heart resonates with the thought that—despite all apparent evidence to the contrary—there is in all of us an essential aspect that cannot be extinguished. This society, in its spiritually dormant state of immaturity and denial, blocks our awareness of it, supplanting it instead with qualities, activities, goods, and beliefs that cannot possibly satisfy. As individuals we are unable to see our own beauty or perfection; as members of a collective, we miss how we are all made of, indeed interwoven within, the same divine fabric—if you prefer, you can substitute words like "eternal," "ancient," "more-than-human," or "soul" for "divine."

Touching spirit, to use the phrase of Rick from San Quentin, can only enliven the healing journey.

Chapter 33

Unmaking a Myth: Visioning a Saner Society

At intervals can be seen a glimpse of truth,
that daylight of the human soul.

—Victor Hugo, *Les Misérables*

What will it take to unmake the myth of normal? How can we possibly hope to disassemble such a vast agglomeration of culturally manufactured misperceptions, prejudices, blind spots, and health-killing fictions—especially when they serve the interests of a world order intent on its own continuance, even unto self-destruction?

The truth is, I don't know. In some ways I'm more comfortable describing the problem than charting a course out of it. I have my own convictions and hunches, especially about the obstacles to a better world, but that doesn't equal a detailed blueprint for something new. Even to the extent that I have strong beliefs about how things ought to look, it seems less than fitting to use the final chapter of this book on trauma and healing to get on a soapbox. And yet, as we bring this inquiry to its conclusion, I do feel a responsibility to offer some sort of alternate vision to the toxic culture I've been depicting.

What I can say with confidence, as a physician and healer, is that for our society to right itself and chart a course toward maximum health, certain conditions will have to be met. And it will take some key changes or shifts to create those conditions. They all derive from the core principles of this book: biopsychosocial medicine, disease as teacher, the primacy of both attachment and authenticity, and, above all, fearless self-inquiry, here on a social scale. None of these shifts is sufficient in itself, but as far as I can tell, they are all necessary. They may not fully come to pass without significant social-political transformation, but they are easy to grasp, and it is well within our power to work toward them.

A few years ago, as I was researching this book, I spoke with Noam Chomsky, father of modern linguistics, philosopher, activist, and cultural critic. I asked this intellectual luminary, who has called himself a "tactical pessimist and strategic optimist," if he still remains on the positive side of what is to come. Chomsky smiled. "You've got to be an optimist, otherwise you might just as well commit suicide. So yes, of course, I'm an optimist. You try to do what you can to correct things; whether it can be done or not, we don't know. It's the slogan Gramsci made famous: 'pessimism of the intellect, optimism of the will.'† There is no other choice." I would also call it the optimism of heart and soul, which are the birthplace of will. These nonrational parts of ourselves know things about human potential and the nature of life that are untouchable by even the smartest intellect.

Before engaging in any major reforms toward a more trauma-aware, health-friendly society, we'll want to look into our own hearts and minds to make sure we're approaching these daunting tasks from a place of possibility. The problems facing the world are challenging enough without adding our own stresses stemming from our habitual coping patterns. Are we seeing things *creatively* or *reactively*? Automatic reactions are, after all, the specialty of the traumatized personality, which is the ultimate

---

† Antonio Gramsci, the Italian philosopher, linguist, and antifascist activist.

hammer that only sees nails. Creativity, meanwhile, is about something more fundamental: it starts with seeing that we *can* create, and then has a feel for what *wants* to be created. It is a facet of authenticity, a close cousin of authorship.

One can create only from a perspective that says, "Something is possible here, no matter how things may look." There are plenty of grounds for this kind of optimism based on what we know about human nature and needs, and about the resilience and mysterious healing powers of the body and mind. We can also take sustenance from the knowledge that each of us is one of a growing community of people who are seeing through the status quo and envisioning alternatives to it.

Such an attitude necessarily involves patience and perspective, and a healthy tolerance for both the real and the ideal.

If we're out to see things as they are, we must be willing—even hungry—to shed our illusions. We have to welcome being disillusioned—perhaps even, as Alanis Morissette does in the chorus of one of her hit singles, thank it.‡ Commonly we speak of disillusionment ruefully as an experience to be avoided, akin to disappointment or a sense of having been betrayed. And it does carry a cost: we may have to let go of something we've come to value, or a perspective or attitude we've taken refuge in. What we see less easily, however, is the cost of refusing. As I often ask people, "Would you prefer to be *illusioned* or *dis*illusioned?" Would we rather engage with the world as it really is or only as we wish it were? Which approach brings more suffering in the end?

I grew up during the period of Stalinist oppression in my homeland, Hungary, though as an idealistic little Communist I was oblivious to its nature. I recall my heart swelling with pride to be living in a system dedicated to freedom, equality, and the

‡   The song is 1998's "Thank U."

kinship of humankind. At school assemblies I would leap to my feet on cue, eagerly joining my classmates in rhythmic applause and chants whenever the principal mentioned "Party" and "Leader." My parents and teachers knew better than to burst my ideological bubble: a careless dissenting word escaping a child's lips could mean harassment, loss of livelihood, even imprisonment. Then, one morning in late October 1956, our building shook to the thunder of artillery. A few days of liberty granted by the evanescent triumph of the Magyar uprising against the dictatorship, followed by its swift and bloody suppression, opened my twelve-year-old eyes. The Soviet Army I had long idolized, the fighting force that had saved my infant life, was suddenly the enemy. Not long after, on a rainy November night, my brother, parents, and I trudged across the muddy Austrian border, leaving behind our life in Hungary forever. That was my first disillusionment; more followed. In the wake of the horrors of the Vietnam War and the unconscionable lies used to justify it, I learned that the American empire, which in my adolescent mind had displaced the Soviet one as the new shining city on the hill, was as cruelly and rapaciously self-centered as its rival. I had to arrive as well at the heartrending realization that the dream that had been a balm to my soul, that of a triumphant Jewish national rebirth in my people's ancestral biblical home, had been achieved by imposing a nightmare on the Palestinian inhabitants of the land, a nightmare that continues to this day.[1] When the truth struck home, I was once again astonished that my imagined universe could have been such a distorted version of the real one. Visiting the West Bank and Gaza, I wept every day for two weeks.

I say all this not to enroll you, the reader, in my particular political views; only to indicate that, for each of us, there may be things about our "normal," including our sense of who we are and the nature of our society, that we are reluctant to let go of. My serial disillusionments were painful at the time, to be sure: they meant leaving something behind, something I had cherished and built a part of my world around. And yet I would not trade the freedom that has accompanied each relinquishing of illusion for the comforts I had to give up. When a false belief falls away, after the ache of loss and sense of being unmoored subsides, I have noticed that something in me relaxes, no longer tasked with squaring circles and holding together impossible contradictions. Ignorance may bring a blissed-out tranquility, but that is not true bliss; on the collective level, it can result in great and wide suffering. We do ourselves and the world a profound service when we endeavor to dissolve our illusions and open ourselves to the truths they conceal.

"Not everything that is faced can be changed," James Baldwin wrote, "but nothing can be changed until it is faced."[2]

A willingness to be disillusioned means confronting denial, one of the central buttresses of the status quo and a major barrier to imagining or seeking a transformed world. After all, were we to alter our worldview enough to see the state of things for what it is and what it is costing us, we would no longer consent to it so easily. "We live in a country in which words are mostly used to cover the sleeper, not to wake him up"—another penetrating observation from Baldwin that could accurately describe almost any place on earth.[3]

"The world forgets easily, too easily, what it does not like to remember," wrote Jacob Riis almost a hundred years earlier in *How the Other Half Lives*, his account of the squalidity of tenement life in late-nineteenth-century New York. This culture is a master at forgetting its past and obscuring the sordid aspects of its present.

Anyone anticipating that the global corporate capitalist system might one day face the truth of its own nature and fundamentally transform itself is in for a long and frustrating wait. Nor will its academic institutions or media be eager to give up their role as its ideological enablers. As Joan Didion remarked about the latter, for journalists "what 'fairness' has often come to mean is a scrupulous passivity, an agreement to cover the story not as it is occurring but as it is presented, which is to say as it is manufactured."[4] That leaves it up to each of us, as individuals and as groups, to seek out and support alternative sources of knowledge, to expose ourselves to uncertainty, to enter into the points of view of others, whether we agree with them or not, to listen to people doing hard activist work on the ground, to stay alert to the many tendrils the myth of normal extends to keep itself normalized. This would represent a new kind of citizenship, one arising from the needs and demands of the moment.

A Trauma-Conscious Society

It's hard to think of any collective domain where greater trauma awareness and insight into the nature of healing would not make a positive difference. I want to focus in these last pages on a few key ones.

The implications of a society being trauma-literate could be immense. Since trauma is the core dynamic undergirding so much ill health, we need to develop the eyes and ears to spot it to begin with. Some see encouraging signs: my colleague Bessel van der Kolk goes so far as to assert that "we are on the verge of becoming a trauma-conscious society."[5] I do not share that optimism in the short term, because that consciousness is still far from penetrating the decisive institutions of our culture. But I agree there is a recent sea change in the public's recognition of trauma's prevalence and significance in our lives. Many people, both lay and professional, are hungry to understand it. We see that in the long-term bestseller status of Bessel's foundational text and the gratifyingly impressive success of books like Dr. Bruce Perry's *What Happened to You?*, co-written with Oprah Winfrey. As too, if I may use it as an example, in the viral success of a film documenting my work, *The Wisdom of Trauma*, which was eye-opening in this regard even for me—it was seen by four million people in over 220 countries within two weeks of its release in June 2021.[†]

Trauma Awareness: Medicine

A trauma-informed medical system, for starters, could help heal and prevent suffering on a scale and in ways inspiring to envision. Such a system would revamp how health care is delivered, aligning itself with the latest scientific findings. Published almost every week in leading science journals, these findings have yet to make much of a dent in mainstream medical thinking. In this book we have cited many already, and more appear regularly.[6]

At present there remains powerful resistance to trauma awareness on the part of the medical profession—albeit a resistance more subliminal than deliberate, more passive than active. In the dozens of interviews I conducted with medical colleagues for this book, including recent graduates, virtually none of them recalled being taught about the mind-body unity or the profusely documented relationship between, for example, trauma and mental illness or addictions—let alone the links between adversity and physical disease. We doctors pride ourselves on what we call evidence-based practice while ignoring vast swaths of evidence that call into question central tenets of our dogma.

Then there is the highly stressed and often emotionally wounding or numbing impact of medical education, an experience reported by so many of my medical interviewees. "I was totally

---

† The film can be viewed at https://wisdomoftrauma.com.

traumatized in my first year of medical school," a well-known colleague told me. "It was teaching by terror, as in intimidating us to learn when we're already highly motivated to learn." "It's an abusive system; it's a traumatic system," my friend the Colorado psychiatrist Will Van Derveer said. "Residents [doctors] are killing themselves." His words brought to mind the study I mentioned in chapter 4 showing that the telomeres of physicians in training frayed more rapidly than those of other young people their age. Aside from the health dangers to these health care professionals themselves, trauma unawareness impedes them from recognizing the imprints of painful life experiences in others. Thus, unwittingly, they perpetuate a system that ignores and even compounds the real problem. A harried existence and the time constraints imposed, especially by fee-for-service models, inhibit physicians from delving into their patients' life histories, even when they are inclined to do so. Residents gave me heartbreaking accounts of listening to patients' personal stories with the effect of almost immediate symptom relief, only to be denigrated by their specialist mentors. Medical students find themselves criticized for not working fast enough. I interviewed Oregon physician Pamela Wible, whose own painful trajectory has led her to work in preventing suicide among doctors. "Never in my wildest dreams," Wible confessed, "did I think that after jumping through all the hoops of medical education I'd end up funneled into seven-minute office visits, and be treated as a factory worker, and be expected to treat my patients as widgets." A trauma-informed medical system would have care for the emotional health of its students and practitioners.

And yet, there are positive developments. Some medical schools are introducing elements of empathy training, and in Canada, there have been initiatives to acquaint medical students with

Indigenous history and traditions. Pediatrician Nadine Burke Harris, a well-known trauma awareness advocate and now the surgeon general of California, is introducing screening for adverse childhood experiences into public health programs in her state. In an interview held before her appointment to the post, she expressed an optimism that mirrors Bessel van der Kolk's. "Believe it or not," she told me, "it's going better than I'd hoped. I think we are looking at incremental milestones that need to happen over thirty or forty years' time, but a lot of groundwork is taking place." For his part, Will Van Derveer has initiated a popular trauma-focused training for fellow psychiatrists, subscribed to by colleagues from around the world. And Pam Wible has pioneered a community-based approach that respects the body-mind unity and helps empower people to be active agents in their health care. "Medicine," she told me, "is a calling and it's a soul's purpose." She has now created a way to follow that call.

Trauma Awareness: The Law

Can we next imagine a trauma-informed legal apparatus, one that could earn its title of "correctional system"? Such a system would have to dedicate itself to actually correcting things in a humane way, a far cry from what we have now. In North America, and in many parts of the world, the current model should more accurately be called a "trauma-punishing-and-inducing system." Despite the documented fact that a large number of prison inmates committed their crimes out of dynamics originating in severe childhood suffering, legal training leaves the average lawyer or judge even more woefully trauma-ignorant than their medical counterparts. True to its other customary name, morally speaking, ours is a *criminal* justice system.

A trauma-informed legal system would not justify or excuse

harmful behavior. Rather, it would replace nakedly punitive measures with programs designed to rehabilitate people and not to further traumatize them. "All us criminals start out as normal people just like anyone else, but then things happen in life that tear us apart, that make us into something capable of hurting other people," writes the academic and former inmate Jesse Thistle. "That's all any of the darkness really is. Love gone bad. We're just broken-hearted people hurt by life."[7] "Unlike in some other countries, here prison is not designed to rehabilitate you," he told me. "It's designed to mess you up so that you'll continue with high rates of recidivism, that's what I think."

Dr. Nneka Jones Tapia, a psychologist, is a former prison guard and currently the managing director of Chicago Beyond and Justice Initiatives. As a Black woman, she knows institutionalized racial trauma well. She spoke to me of resilience and the creation of a trauma-informed justice system. "We tend to reduce people to their behaviors: 'You're a murderer, you're a robber, you're a thief.' But we are not our worst behavior. I have had the blessing to see that everyone who is incarcerated has strengths and they have the capability of loving, if only we gave them the opportunity. It's not just people that need the healing. It's the system that has to be indicted and transformed."

Trauma Awareness: Education

Because trauma affects kids' ability to learn, a trauma-informed educational system would train teachers to be well versed in the science of development. Education in such a system would encourage an atmosphere where emotional intelligence is valued as highly as intellectual achievement. We would no longer evaluate kids based on performance goals that still mostly reflect and bestow social and racial advantage, but would provide settings where all were encouraged to thrive. "School programs could be designed to support healthy social and emotional development," writes teacher and school psychologist Maggie Kline. "When students feel safe, the regions of the brain for language, thinking, and reasoning are enhanced."[8] Teacher training would recognize signs and signals of children's "acting out" as pleas for help or markers of emotional pain, rather than viewing them as bad behaviors to be suppressed or as cause for punishment or exclusion.

Beyond schooling, the potential implications of my friend Raffi Cavoukian's vision of an entire society that honors the irreducible needs of children (see chapter 9) are both vast and simple. I leave it to you, the reader, to imagine what our world would look like if we placed young people's well-being in the forefront. What would it mean for parenting and for support for parenting, for childcare and education, for the economy, for what products we sell and buy, for what foods we sell and prepare, for the climate, for the culture? What if our intention, as parents, as educators, as a society, was to raise children in touch with their feelings, authentically empowered to express them, to think independently and be prepared to act on behalf of their principles?

A healthy society would also strive to close the largely artificial generation gap that makes it difficult for parents to relate to their kids and vice versa. As discussed in an earlier section on peer orientation (chapter 13), the natural human arrangement has a strong communal dimension, and the adult community is meant to work together to hold space for the development of the young. That does not mean lording it over our kids, nor dictating every aspect of their lives, only that we reclaim responsibility for creating and maintaining the container for their growth. And we must also remember that parents need each other, and that we all need the presence of life-tested elders; in a world that's committed to health, child-rearing and intergenerational transmission of values and culture wouldn't be an isolating task.

In the last decades, in many countries around the world, people—adults and children in the millions—have mobilized to force into the political conversation critical issues such as environmental justice, Indigenous rights, women's rights, gender justice, racial equity, and police reform. One such person is Greta Thunberg, the teenage climate activist, who, describing her autism as her "superpower," has contributed greatly to her generation's awareness of climate change. "Many ignorant people still see it as an 'illness,' or something negative," she said on Twitter. "When the haters go after your looks and differences, it means they have nowhere left to go. And then you know you are winning." Her own example illustrates the healing power of meaningful engagement. Prior to her climate campaign, she divulged, she had "no energy, no friends and I didn't speak to anyone. I just sat alone at home, with an eating disorder."[9]

Inspired by figures like Thunberg and countless others whose names we may never know, we can revisit our list of the four *A*'s I laid out in chapter 26 that promote healing—*authenticity, agency, anger,* and *acceptance*—and add two more that are required for the pursuit of broad transformational change: *activism* and *advocacy*. The last two are socially meaningful ways of synthesizing the previous four, with some added ingredients—solidarity, collective thinking, and connection—to help counter capitalism's atomizing effects.

Part of advocacy is to use whatever privilege we may have to amplify the voices of those to whom society denies a voice; part of activism is organizing groups of people to demand necessary change. Both express a healthy, necessary "no," often accompanied by a resounding "yes"—for example, to a concrete policy goal like Medicare for All in the United States or long-overdue justice for First Nations people in Canada. These two bonus *A*'s are not, and cannot be, individual pursuits. I visited Zuccotti Park in New York City, in September 2011, the site of the Occupy Wall Street protests against inequality. Flawed and evanescent as that movement proved to be, I was struck by the enthusiasm, solidarity, and sheer energy of the crowd as they found a collective outlet for forwarding their vision of a just society. Often blocked from being expressed, that latent energy is within us all.

The photographer Nan Goldin, whose addiction to opiates we touched on in chapter 15, has waged more than a private struggle for recovery: she has engaged in both personal and collective activism against Purdue Pharma, the corporation that helped generate the opioid overdose crisis that has claimed hundreds of thousands of lives. Purdue reaped vast profits from its drug OxyContin, which it marketed as a less addictive opioid painkiller, suppressing evidence to the contrary. Goldin's friends in AA had advised against her going public, saying it would destroy her sobriety. "It turned out to be the best choice I ever made," she told me.

Her particular crusade has been directed against the Sacklers, the family that controls Purdue. Goldin's fame as an artist gave her a platform to raise her banner, especially since the Sacklers have cultivated a reputation as art benefactors. "I knew their names from going to museums," she said, "and I always thought of them as benevolent art philanthropists with great taste." Another salutary disillusionment, I thought. "And then I found out," Goldin continued, "about their involvement with the opiate crisis, their profiting off the suffering of hundreds of thousands of people, their complete callousness and inhumanity." Fueled by outrage at what she discovered, Goldin induced some of the world's most prestigious museums, including the Met in New York, to stop accepting money from the Sacklers and to eliminate their self-laundering logo from their buildings. The Sackler Institute of Graduate Biomedical Sciences at NYU's medical school has also dropped the family name.

I asked Goldin why she saw her decision to engage in public activism as the best choice she ever made. Her answer speaks to the health rewards of the two added A's of *activism* and *advocacy*. "You need something bigger than yourself," she replied without hesitation. "For me what's bigger than myself is other people suffering. And that's a situation I can help rectify. The politics of this moment are bigger than any individual, the way the world is right now. Trying to find a way to impact that, that's my power, that's what I fight about. It helps keep me sober." As Goldin found, standing up to a toxic system can help us find a place to stand within ourselves.

———————

It is never redundant to remind ourselves that the Chinese phrase for "crisis" is a compound of symbols for "danger" and "opportunity."

We have seen how people with debilitating and even life-threatening pathology can learn from their illnesses and transform their lives. If the same principle were applied on a societal scale, the climate crisis would be an opportunity to examine the dominant perceptions and practices of a culture on a path of self-destruction. The COVID-19 experience, which, ironically enough, has done much to *unmask* many unflattering facts about our ways of life, is a powerful reminder of the interconnections between all life-forms; of our true nature rooted in our relationship to one another; of the inequities of a system in which the most socially vulnerable are left most open to attack by a deadly virus; of how the slogan "We are all in this together" is a sad fiction when it comes to the economic ravages and windfalls of the public health catastrophe that has marked this decade for all time.

And speaking of crises, there could be no more damning indictment of a system than that its young people, stalked as they are by anxieties about human-made climate change, distrust adults and governments en masse.[10] The inimitable Greta Thunberg put it with devastating simplicity at a youth summit in Milan held in September 2021: "Build Back Better. Blah, blah, blah. Green economy. Blah blah blah. Net zero by 2050. Blah, blah, blah. This is all we hear from our so-called leaders. Words that sound great but so far have not led to action. Our hopes and ambitions drown in their empty promises."[11] Unfettered greed, inauthenticity, and disconnection have driven us to such a dark place that it falls to young people to wake us up to what this toxic culture has perpetrated and ignored for so long.

———

Prior to his trial for war crimes, the master engineer of Nazi genocide SS Lieutenant Colonel Adolf Eichmann was certified as "normal" by several psychiatrists—"more normal, at any rate than I am," one of them was said to have exclaimed according to Hannah Arendt's classic account.[12] "Another," Arendt reported, "had found that Eichmann's whole psychological outlook, including his relationship with his wife and children, his mother and father, his brothers and sisters and friends, was 'not only normal but most desirable.'"

This is what the American psychiatrist Robert J. Lifton has termed "malignant normality." Many of the greatest crimes have been and continue to be perpetrated by people in leadership positions who are deemed to be the epitome of normal in their respective societies, whether it's the production of toxic and climate-altering chemicals or, say, the imposition of policies that lead to mass starvation in countries far away. Hundreds of thousands of Iraqi children died of malnutrition in the 1990s because of U.S. sanctions.[13] America's then–U.N. ambassador Madeleine Albright declared that "the price is worth it," in an interview seen by millions. As we now know, and as anyone could have known then, there was no credible justification for such heartless cruelty. Albright subsequently became the first woman secretary of state and remains highly respected, especially in liberal circles.[†] One is reminded of Victor Hugo's withering phrase for such figures: "the barbarians of civilization."

As it turns out, it is often individuals who defy conventional normality who are the healthy ones. The psychologist Abraham Maslow made the investigation of self-actualization—the attainment of authentic satisfaction not based on external valuations—his life's work. "A study of people healthy enough to be self-actualized," he wrote in a widely read paper, "revealed that they were not 'well-adjusted' (in the naïve sense of approval of and identification with the culture)." These healthy people, suggested Maslow, had a complex relationship with their "much less healthy culture." Neither conformists nor automatically reflexive rebels, such men and women expressed their unconventionality in ways that kept them true to their inner values, without hostility but not without fight, when that was called for. "An inner feeling of detachment from the culture was not necessarily conscious but was displayed by almost all . . . They very frequently seemed to be able to stand off from it as if they did not quite belong to it."[14]

As we saw earlier, the antidote to the hypnotizing influence of

---

† Albright, who died in March 2022, would later publicly regret making that statement. She never did renounce the policies it justified.

normality is authenticity: finding meaning in one's inner experience, unobscured by societally promulgated fictions—prime among them what Daniel Siegel calls "the lie of the separate solo self." That falsehood is the ultimate abnormality. From where I stand, a life devoted to seeing through such a traumatizing nontruth, dwelling and creating outside its bounds, is a life lived well.

It all starts with waking up: waking up to what is real and authentic in and around us and what isn't; waking up to who we are and who we're not; waking up to what our bodies are expressing and what our minds are suppressing; waking up to our wounds and our gifts; waking up to what we have believed and what we actually value; waking up to what we will no longer tolerate and what we can now accept; waking up to the myths that bind us and the interconnections that define us; waking up to the past as it has been, the present as it is, and the future as it may yet be; waking up, most especially, to the gap between what our essence calls for and what "normal" has demanded of us.

We are blessed with a momentous opportunity. Shedding toxic myths of disconnection from ourselves, from one another, and from the planet, we can bring what is normal and what is natural, bit by bit, closer together. It is a task for the ages: one that can redeem the past, inspire the present, and point to a brighter, healthier future.

It is our most daunting challenge and greatest possibility.

Acknowledgments

No book springs forth fully formed from its author, like Athena from the head of Zeus. This one surely didn't. It bears the imprint of hundreds of scientists, researchers, physicians, thinkers, and authors, to say nothing of the many medical colleagues and professionals of various disciplines who generously shared with me their time and expertise, along with hundreds of ex-patients and other laypeople who openheartedly and trustingly spoke to me of their travails, struggles, and triumphs. While the interpretations, formulations, and presentation are fully my responsibility, along with any mistakes, I can claim no personal ownership of the truths I have tried to convey.

My New York literary super-agent, Laurie Liss, came along just as this book project emerged after a long period of near-frozen hibernation, and helped nurse it back to life, from proposal stage to fruition, through times of despondence to confident creativity. She also brought together the ideal team of English-language publishers in the U.S., U.K., and Canada. Much thanks to Megan Newman of Avery, Louise Dennys and Martha Kanya Forstner of Knopf in Toronto, and Joel Rickett of Ebury in London for enthusiastically seeing the possibilities in this work right from the beginning, and for continuing to do so despite some overreaching and trudging down blind alleys by the authors at times. I am grateful, too, for their incisive editing notes throughout and their forbearance as the authors repeatedly lurched from churlishness to appreciation as the truth of their bracing critiques hit home. The reader has much to thank them for. I must also acknowledge Rick Meier, Nina Shield, and Hannah Steigmeyer for their editorial contributions. Of this valiant crew my special thank-you to my dear friend

Louise Dennys, who took on the brunt of guiding the revision of the manuscript during its most crucial phase and with whom I was, on many days, in almost 24/7 communication.

Helping with the research in its crucial early states was the diligent Estella Kuchta, in which regard I must also mention the unfailingly helpful staff at the Library of the College of Physicians and Surgeons of B.C., most particularly Karen Shaw-Karvelson. I owe gratitude as well to Professor Peter Prontzos, who for years steered essential research data in my direction. Katherine Abegg and Jordan Stanger-Ross were kind enough to cast early eyes on the book proposal, sharpening it with their astute reflections.

Laura Kassama of Virtual Squirrel and Elsa DeLuca transcribed hundreds of hours of interviews. Thank you both.

Stephanie Lee, my ever-considerate and efficient manager, kept me grounded as best she could by saying no on my behalf, organizing my many activities, and protecting time to work on this book.

For my acknowledgment of the indispensable collaboration of my co-writer Daniel, please see the Author's Note at the beginning of this volume. What is not described there is the sheer pleasure of working with my son on this, the first of two books we have contracted to write together. The next one, *Hello Again: A Fresh Start for Adult Children and Their Parents*, will be even more of a partnership, one I look forward to.

Finally, I return to the person to whom this work is dedicated: my wife, Rae, who, well beyond moral and emotional support through thick and thin—and often the stress was thick while the confidence was thin—provided, through many hours and through many repeated iterations of each chapter, much-needed critique and the most honest feedback, not always graciously received but eventually, almost always heeded. Much to the reader's benefit.

Gratitude to all.

Gabor Maté

DANIEL THANKS: Mom, Aaron, and Hannah, for thinking I could do it and insisting I should—I'm as lucky a son and sibling as they come; Laurie Liss, for your solidarity and sagacity from the first to the last; Eric Adams, Stan Byrne, Jeremy Gruman, Anna Guest, Katie Halper, Michael R. Jackson, Dashaun Justice Simmons, and Jordan and Ilana Stanger-Ross and family, for loving friendship and encouragement under every imaginable circumstance and some unimaginable ones; my brilliant musical theater collaborators—especially but not limited to Will Aronson, Victoria Clark, Max Friedman, Hannah Kohl, Fred Lassen, Kent Nicholson, and Marshall Pailet—for teaching me everything I know about playing nice with others (now let's get these dang musicals made, dang it!); my theater agent Sarah Douglas for believing in my voice all these years; Scott Kouri, for hearing me better than I ever could. Much appreciation as well to a couple of supremely incisive cultural commentators, Stephen Jenkinson and Matt Christman, whose eloquent irreverence in speaking faithfully to the moment's many madnesses was both a balm during the plague times and an invigorating invitation to clearer thought and bolder delivery.

Special thanks to all those I met at Estación Migratoria Las Ajugas in Mexico City. The kindness and fortitude of these men—hailing from Cuba, Ecuador, Haiti, Uganda, Venezuela, and throughout the "Global South"—got me through an unexpected, COVID-extended stay in summer 2021 that forever reconfigured my sense of normal. I also owe a huge debt of thanks to my heroes and angels "on the outside," including: Roberto Banchik at Penguin Random House México; Louise Dennys at Knopf Canada; John Ralston Saul; and Jorge Kanahuati and Katherine Abegg, most especially.

Kat, beyond those harrowing few weeks, I can't express how much your insight, companionship, allegiance, and unsparing truthfulness have meant to me throughout this book's long lifespan, and nourished what ended up on these pages. Thank you.

Finally, thanks to Dad: for inviting me to play with you, for sticking with it through the more-than-occasional bump, and for trusting me with your magnum-est opus yet while giving me space to contribute to your contribution to the world. It's been the opportunity of my lifetime to finally get to put words in your mouth, and a true joy besides. Proud of you, Pop.

Notes

Introduction

1. Respectively, *Scattered Minds: The Origins and Healing of Attention Deficit Disorder*; *When the Body Says No: The Cost of Hidden Stress*; *In the Realm of Hungry Ghosts: Close Encounters with Addiction*; and, with Dr. Gordon Neufeld, *Hold On to Your Kids: Why Parents Need to Matter More Than Peers*. These are the Canadian and U.K. titles. In the U.S. the ADD book is titled *Scattered: How Attention Deficit Disorder Originates and What You Can Do About It*, and *When the Body Says No* is subtitled *Exploring the Stress-Disease Connection*.

2. Morris Berman, *The Twilight of American Culture* (New York: W. W. Norton, 2001), 64–65.

3. Thom Hartmann, *The Last Hours of Ancient Sunlight: The Fate of the World and What We Can Do About It Before It's Too Late* (New York: Three Rivers Press, 2000), 164.

4. Christine Buttorff et al., *Multiple Chronic Conditions in the United States* (Santa Monica, CA: RAND Corporation, 2017).

5. "Nearly 7 in 10 Americans Take Prescription Drugs, Mayo Clinic, Olmsted Medical Center Find," Mayo Clinic, news release, June 19, 2013, https://newsnetwork.mayoclinic.org/discussion/nearly-7-in-10-americans-take-prescription-drugs-mayo-clinic-olmsted-medical-center-find/.

6. Carly Weeks, "Up to Half of Baby Boomers Will Have High Blood Pressure Soon, Report Warns," *Globe and Mail*, April 3, 2013.

7. Alvaro Alonso and Miguel Hernán, "Temporal Trends in the Incidence of Multiple Sclerosis: A Systematic Review," *Neurology* 71, no. 2 (July 8, 2008), doi: 10.1212/01.wnl.0000316802.35974.34.

8. Calum MacLeod, "Obesity of China's Kids Stuns Officials," *USA Today*, January 9, 2007, https://usatoday30.usatoday.com/news/world/2007-01-08-chinese-obesity_x.htm.

9. "Mental Health by the Numbers," National Alliance on Mental Illness, https://www.nami.org/mhstats.

10. "The Size and Burden of Mental Disorders in Europe," ScienceDaily, September 6, 2011, https://www.sciencedaily.com/releases/2011 /09/110905074609.htm. Source: European College of Neuropsycho-pharmacology.

11. Brett Burstein et al., "Suicidal Attempts and Ideation Among Children and Adolescents in US Emergency Departments, 2007–2015," *JAMA Pediatrics* 173, no. 6 (April 2019): 598–600, https://doi.org/10.1001 /jamapediatrics.2019.0464, cited in Carly Cassella, "Child Suicide Attempts Are Skyrocketing in the US, and Nobody Knows Why," ScienceAlert, April 11, 2019, https://www.sciencealert.com/us-children-are -facing-a-mental-health-crisis-as-suicidal-ideations-climb.

12. Samira Shackle, "'The Way the Universities Are Run Is Making Us Ill': Inside the Student Mental Health Crisis," *Guardian*, September 27, 2019.

13. Hui Cao et al., "Prevalence of Attention-Deficit/Hyperactivity Disorder Symptoms and Their Associations with Sleep Schedules and Sleep-Related Problems Among Preschoolers in Mainland China," *BMC Pediatrics* 18, no. 1 (February 19, 2018): 70.

14. Caroline Hickman et al., "Young People's Voices on Climate Anxiety, Government Betrayal and Moral Injury: A Global Phenomenon," preprint submitted to the *Lancet*, September 2021, https://papers.ssrn .com/sol3/papers.cfm?abstract_id=3918955.

15. "CDC Continues to Support the Global Polio Eradication Effort," Centers for Disease Control and Prevention, March 18, 2016, https://www.cdc .gov/polio/updates/?s_cid=cs_404.

Chapter 1: The Last Place You Want to Be

1. As summarized by Dr. Bessel van der Kolk in his foreword to Peter Levine, *Trauma and Memory: Brain and Body in a Search for the Living Past* (Berkeley, CA: North Atlantic Books, 2015), xi.

2. Levine, *Trauma and Memory*, xx.

3. John Bowlby, *Separation: Anxiety and Anger* (New York: Basic Books, 1973), 12.

4. Bessel van der Kolk, *The Body Keeps the Score: Brain, Mind, and Body in the Healing of Trauma* (New York: Penguin, 2014), 43.

5. Levine, *Trauma and Memory*, xxii.

6. Peter Levine, *Healing Trauma Study Guide* (Boulder, CO: Sounds True, 1999), 5.

7. Clyde Hertzman and Tom Boyce, "How Experience Gets Under the Skin to Create Gradients in Developmental Health," *Annual Review of Public Health* 31 (April 21, 2010): 329–47.

8. Mark Epstein, *The Trauma of Everyday Life* (New York: Penguin, 2013), 17.

9. Levine, *Healing Trauma Study Guide*, 7.

10. Levine, *Healing Trauma Study Guide*, 7.

11. Tara Westover, *Educated: A Memoir* (New York: HarperCollins, 2018), 111.

12. Rollo May, *The Courage to Create* (New York: W. W. Norton, 1975), 100.

13. Gershen Kaufman, *Shame: The Power of Caring* (Rochester, VT: Schenkman Books, 1980), 20.

14. Elizabeth Wurtzel, "Elizabeth Wurtzel Confronts Her One-Night Stand of a Life," *New York*, January 6, 2013.

15. *Dhammapada: The Sayings of the Buddha*, trans. Thomas Cleary (New York: Bantam Books, 1995), 7.

16. Eva Hoffman, *Time* (London: Profile Books, 2009), 7–8.

Chapter 2: Living in an Immaterial World

1. Candace Pert, *Molecules of Emotion: Why You Feel the Way You Feel* (New York: Touchstone, 1997), 30.

2. M. Wirsching et al., "Psychological Identification of Breast Cancer Patients Before Biopsy," *Journal of Psychosomatic Research* 26, no. 1 (1982): 1–10.

3. S. Greer and T. Morris, "Psychological Attributes of Women Who Develop Breast Cancer: A Controlled Study," *Journal of Psychosomatic Research* 19, no. 2 (April 1975): 147–53.

4. Sandra P. Thomas et al., "Anger and Cancer: An Analysis of the Linkages," *Cancer Nursing* 23, no. 5 (November 2000): 344–48.

5. A. J. Wilbourn and H. Mitsumoto, "Why Are Patients with ALS So Nice," presented at the ninth International ALS Symposium on ALS/MND, Munich, 1998.

6. Theresa Mehl, Berit Jordan, and Stephan Zierz, " 'Patients with Amyotrophic Lateral Sclerosis (ALS) Are Usually Nice Persons'—How Physicians Experienced in ALS See the Personality Characteristics of Their Patients," *Brain Behavior* 7, no. 1 (January 2017).

7. Frank J. Penedo et al., "Anger Suppression Mediates the Relationship Between Optimism and Natural Killer Cell Cytotoxicity in Men Treated for Localized Prostate Cancer," *Journal of Psychosomatic Research* 60, no. 4 (April 2006): 423–27.

8. Edna Maria Vissoci Reiche, Sandra Odebrecht Vargas Nunes, and Helena Kaminami Morimoto, "Stress, Depression, the Immune System, and Cancer," *Lancet Oncology* 5, no. 10 (October 2004): 617–25. The authors write: "These notions could explain the increased occurrence of lymphatic and hematological malignant diseases, and of melanomas seen in a cohort of 6,284 Jewish Israelis who lost an adult son. The incidence of cancer was increased in the parents of accident victims and in war-bereaved parents, compared with that in non-bereaved members of the population. Accident-bereaved parents also had an increased risk of respiratory cancer."

9. J. Li et al., "The Risk of Multiple Sclerosis in Bereaved Parents: A Nationwide Cohort Study in Denmark," *Neurology* 62, no. 5 (March 9, 2004: 726–29.

10. A. Roberts et al., "PTSD Is Associated with Increased Risk of Ovarian Cancer: A Prospective and Retrospective Longitudinal Cohort Study," *Cancer Research* 79, no. 19 (October 1, 2019): 5113–120. September 5, 2019, https://doi.org/10.1158/0008-5472.CAN-19-1222.

11. Premal H. Thekar et al., "Chronic Stress Promotes Tumor Growth and Angiogenesis in a Mouse Model of Ovarian Carcinoma," *Nature Medicine* 12, no. 8 (August 12, 2006): 939–44; published online July 23, 2006, https://doi.org/10.1038/nm1447.

12. Saskia L. Mol et al., "Symptoms of Post-Traumatic Stress Disorder After Non-Traumatic Events: Evidence from an Open Population Study," *British Journal of Psychiatry* 286 (June 2005): 494–99.

13. S. Weiss, "The Medical Student Before and After Graduation," *Journal of the American Medical Association* 114 (1940): 1709–18.

14. Dr. Jeff Rediger, medical director at McLean Hospital, Harvard, personal communication.

15. Ahmed Tawakol et al., "Relation Between Resting Amygdalar Activity and Cardiovascular Events: A Longitudinal and Cohort Study," *Lancet* 389, no. 10071 (February 25, 2017): 834–45.

16. N. Slopen et al., "Job Strain, Job Insecurity, and Incident Cardiovascular Disease in the Women's Health Study: Results from a 10-Year Prospective Study," *PLoS ONE* 7, no. 7 (2012): e40512, https://doi.org/10.1371/journal .pone.0040512.

17. Esme Fuller-Thomson et al., "The Link Between Childhood Sexual Abuse and Myocardial Infarction in a Population-Based Study," *Child Abuse and Neglect* 36, no. 9 (September 2012): 656–65, https://doi.org/10.1016/j .chiabu.2012.06.001.

18. D. Baumeister et al., "Childhood Trauma and Adulthood Inflammation: A Meta-Analysis of Peripheral C-Reactive Protein, Interleukin-6 and Tumor Necrosis Factor-α," *Molecular Psychiatry* 21, no. 5 (May 2016): 642–49.

Chapter 3: You Rattle My Brain

1. George L. Engel, "The Clinical Application of the Biopsychosocial Model," *American Journal of Psychology* 137, no. 5 (May 1980): 535–44.

2. George L. Engel, "The Need for a New Medical Model: A Challenge for Biomedicine," *Science* 196, no. 4286 (April 8, 1977): 129–36.

3. Bessel van der Kolk, *The Body Keeps the Score: Brain, Mind, and Body in the Healing of Trauma* (New York: Penguin, 2014), 80.

4. Richard Grant, "Do Trees Talk to Each Other?," *Smithsonian*, March 2018, https://www.smithsonianmag.com/science-nature/the-whispering -trees-180968084.

5. Daniel Siegel, *Pocket Guide to Interpersonal Neurobiology: An Integrative Handbook of the Mind* (New York: W. W. Norton, 2012), xviii.

6. N. J. Johnson et al., "Marital Status and Mortality: The National Longitudinal Mortality Study," *Annals of Epidemiology* 10, no. 4 (May 2000): 224–38.

7. J. C. Coyne and A. DeLongis, "Going Beyond Social Support: The Role of Social Relationships in Adaptation," *Journal of Consulting and Clinical Psychology* 54, no. 4 (August 1986): 454–60, cited in T. E. Robles and J. K. Kiecolt-Glaser, "The Physiology of Marriage: Pathways to Health," *Physiology and Behavior* 79, no. 3 (August 2003): 409–16.

8. "There's quite a bit of research linking relationship conflict to different types of physiological responses, such as increased release of stress hormones, inflammation, changes in appetite regulation, and immune functioning," said Veronica Lamarche, a professor of social psychology at the University of Essex. "A Bad Marriage Can Seriously Damage Your Health, Say Scientists," *Guardian*, July 16, 2018, https://www.theguardian.com/lifeandstyle/2018/jul/16/a-bad-marriage-is-as-unhealthy-as-smoking-or-drinking-say-scientists.

9. J. M. Gottman and L. F. Katz, "Effects of Marital Discord on Young Children's Peer Interaction and Health," *Developmental Psychology* 25, no. 3 (1989): 373–81.

10. Constance M. Weil and Shari L. Wade, "The Relationship Between Psychosocial Factors and Asthma Morbidity in Inner City Children with Asthma," *Pediatrics* 104, no. 6 (December 1999): 1274–80.

11. N. Yamamoto and J. Nagano, "Parental Stress and the Onset and Course of Childhood Asthma," *BioPsychoSocial Medicine* 9, no. 7 (March 2015), https://doi.org/10.1186/s13030-015-0034-4.

12. P. F. Coogan et al., "Experiences of Racism and the Incidence of Adult-Onset Asthma in the Black Women's Health Study," *CHEST Journal* 145, no. 3 (March 2014): 480–85.

13. T. E. Seeman and B. S. McEwen, "Impact of Social Environment Characteristics on Neuroendocrine Regulation," *Psychosomatic Medicine* 58, no. 5 (September–October 1996): 459–71.

14. A. Hughes et al., "Elevated Inflammatory Biomarkers During Unemployment: Modification by Age and Country in the UK," *Epidemiology and Community Health* 69, no. 7 (July 2015): 673–79, https://doi.org/10.1136/jech-2014-204404.

15. P. Butterworth et al., "The Psychosocial Quality of Work Determines Whether Employment Has Benefits for Mental Health: Results from a Longitudinal National Household Panel Survey," *Occupational and Environmental Medicine* 68, no. 11 (November 2011): 806–12, https://doi.org/10.1136/oem.2010.059030.

16. J. Holt-Lunstad et al., "Social Relationships and Mortality Risk: A Meta-analytic Review," *PLoS Medicine* 7, no. 7 (July 27, 2010), https://doi.org/10.1371/journal.pmed.1000316.

17. Thich Nhat Hanh, *Buddha Mind, Buddha Body* (Berkeley, CA: Parallax Press, 2007), 25.

Chapter 4: Everything I'm Surrounded By

1. As an editorial in the journal *Nature* acknowledged in 2010, "For all the intellectual ferment of the past decade, has human health truly benefited from the sequencing of the human genome? A startlingly honest response can be found [in the publication's current issue], where the leaders of the public and private efforts, Francis Collins and Craig Venter [American geneticist and physician who captained the Human Genome Project and director of the National Institutes of Health and leading biochemist and entrepreneur, respectively], both say 'not much.' " "Has the revolution arrived?" *Nature* 464 (March 31, 2010): 674–75.

2. Martha Henriques, "Can the Legacy of Trauma Be Passed Down the Generations?" *BBC Future*, March 26, 2019, https://www.bbc.com/future/article/20190326-what-is-epigenetics.

3. Moshe Szyf et al., "Maternal Programming of Steroid Receptor Expression and Phenotype Through DNA Methylation in the Rat," *Frontiers in Neuroendocrinology* 26, nos. 3–4 (October–December 2005): 139–62.

4. Frances A. Champagne et al., "Maternal Care Associated with Methylation of the Estrogen Receptor-1b Promoter and Estrogen Receptor-Alpha Expression in the Medial Preoptic Area of Female Offspring," *Endocrinology* 147, no. 6 (June 2006): 2909–15.

5. Lei Cao-Lei et al., "DNA Methylation Signatures Triggered by Prenatal Maternal Stress Exposure to a Natural Disaster: Project Ice Storm," *PLoS ONE* 9, no. 9 (September 19, 2014), https://doi.org/10.1371/journal.pone.0107653.

6. Wendy Leung, "Pregnancy Stress During 1998 Ice Storm Linked to Genetic Changes in Children After Birth, Study Suggests," *Globe and Mail*, September 30, 2014.

7. Ali B. Rodgers et al., "Paternal Stress Exposure Alters Sperm MicroRNA Content and Reprograms Offspring HPA Stress Axis Regulation," *Journal of Neuroscience* 33, no. 21 (May 2013): 9003–12.

8. Marilyn J. Essex et al., "Epigenetic Vestiges of Developmental Adversity: Childhood Stress Exposure and DNA Methylation in Adolescence," *Childhood Development* 84, no. 1 (January 2013): 58–57.

9. Nada Borghol et al., "Associations with Early-Life Socio-Economic Position in Adult DNA Methylation," *International Journal of Epidemiology* 41, no. 1 (February 2012): 62–74.

10. April D. Thames et al., "Experienced Discrimination and Racial Differences in Leukocyte Gene Expression," *Psychoneuroendocrinology* 106 (August 2019): 277–83.

11. April D. Thames, "Racism Shortens Lives and Hurts Health of Blacks by Promoting Genes That Lead to Inflammation and Illness," The Conversation, October 17, 2019, https://theconversation.com/study -racism-shortens-lives-and-hurts-health-of-blacks-by-promoting-genes -that-lead-to-inflammation-and-illness-122027.

12. Kathryn K. Ridout et al., "Physician-Training Stress and Accelerated Cellular Aging," *Biological Psychiatry* 86, no. 9 (November 1, 2019): 725–30.

13. Elissa S. Epel et al., "Accelerated Telomere Shortening in Response to Life Stress," *Proceedings of the National Academy of Sciences* 101, no. 49 (December 7, 2004): 17312–15, https://www.pnas.org/content/101/49 /17312.

14. Amanda K. Damjanovic et al., "Accelerated Telomere Erosion Is Associated with a Declining Immune Function of Caregivers of Alzheimer's Disease Patients," *Journal of Immunology* 179, no. 6 (September 15, 2007): 4249–54.

15. David H. Chae et al., "Discrimination, Racial Bias, and Telomere Length in African-American Men," *American Journal of Preventative Medicine* 46, no. 2 (February 2014): 103–11.

16. Arline T. Geronimus et al., "Do US Black Women Experience Stress-Related Accelerated Biological Aging?," *Human Nature* 21, no. 1 (March 10, 2010): 19–38.

17. Tonya L. Jacobs et al., "Intensive Meditation Training, Immune Cell Telomerase Activity, and Psychological Mediators," *Psychoneuroendocrinology* 36, no. 5 (June 2011): 664–81; Gene H. Brody et al., "Prevention Effects Ameliorate the Prospective Association Between Nonsupportive Parenting and Diminished Telomere Length," *Prevention Science* 16, no. 2 (February 2015): 171–80, https:// doi.org/10.1007/s11121-014-0474-2; and Dean Ornish et al., "Effect of Comprehensive Lifestyle Changes on Telomerase Activity and Telomere Length in Men with Biopsy-Proven Low-Risk Prostate Cancer: 5-Year

Follow-Up of a Descriptive Pilot Study," *Lancet Oncology* 14, no. 11 (October 2013): 1112–20, https://doi.org/10.1016/S1470-2045(13)70366-8.

Chapter 5: Mutiny on the Body

1. Karen Crouse, "Venus Williams Says She Struggled with Fatigue for Years," *New York Times,* September 1, 2011.

2. "Autoimmune Disease Rates Increasing," Medical News Today, https://www.medicalnewstoday.com/articles/246960.php; Jean-Francois Bach, "Why Is the Incidence of Autoimmune Diseases Increasing in the Modern World?," *Endocrine Abstracts* 16, S3.1 (2008).

3. Moises Velasquez-Manoff, "Educate Your Immune System," *New York Times,* June 3, 2016.

4. Sarah Knapton, "Crohn's Disease in Teens Jumps 300 Percent in 10 Years Fuelled by Junk Food," *The Telegraph,* June 18, 2014.

5. Eric I. Benchimol et al., "Trends in Epidemiology of Pediatric Inflammatory Bowel Disease in Canada: Distributed Network Analysis of Multiple Population-Based Provincial Health Administrative Databases," *American Journal of Gastroenterology* 112, no. 7 (July 2017): 1120–34, https://doi.org/10.1038/AJG.2017.97.

6. Grace Rattue, "Autoimmune Disease Rates Increasing," *Medical News Today,* June 22, 2012, https://www.medicalnewstoday.com/articles/246960.php.

7. Robin McKie, "Global Spread of Autoimmune Disease Blamed on Western Diet," *The Guardian,* January 9, 2022.

8. Arndt Manzel et al., "Role of 'Western Diet' in Inflammatory Autoimmune Disease," *Current Allergy and Asthma Reports* 14, no. 1 (January 2014): 404, doi: 10.1007/s11882-013-0404-6. ("The association between diet and the risk of developing inflammatory autoimmune diseases was proposed as early as 50 years ago . . . no definite associations between dietary factors and autoimmune diseases have so far been firmly established.")

9. In this condition not all the facts are unfavorable toward women; in men the same condition tends to be more severe and more likely to be fatal. Christine Peoples, "Gender Differences in Systemic Sclerosis: Relationship to Clinical Features, Serologic Status and Outcomes," *Journal of Scleroderma and Related Disorders* 1, no. 2 (May–August 2016): 177–240.

10. Sarah-Michelle Orton et al., "Effect of Immigration on Multiple Sclerosis Sex Ratio in Canada: The Canadian Collaborative Study," *Journal of Neurology, Neurosurgery and Psychiatry* 81, no. 1 (January 2010): 31–36.

11. Melinda Magyari, "Gender Differences in Multiple Sclerosis Epidemiology and Treatment Response," *Danish Medical Journal* 63, no. 3 (March 2016).

12. Paul H. Black, "Stress and the Inflammatory Response: A Review of Neurogenic Inflammation," *Brain, Behavior, and Immunity* 16, no. 6 (December 2002): 622–53.

13. C. H. Feldman et al., "Association of Childhood Abuse with Incident Systemic Lupus Erythematosus in Adulthood in a Longitudinal Cohort of Women," *Journal of Rheumatology* 46, no. 12 (December 2019): 1589–96.

14. R. Coelho et al., "Childhood Maltreatment and Inflammatory Markers: A Systematic Review," *Acta Psychiatrica Scandinavica* 129, no. 3 (March 2014): 180–92; Huang Song et al., "Association of Stress-Related Disorders with Subsequent Autoimmune Disease," *Journal of the American Medical Association* 319, no. 23 (June 19, 2018): 2388–400.

15. Andrea Danese et al., "Childhood Maltreatment Predicts Adult Inflammation in a Life-Course Study," *Proceedings of the National Academy of Sciences of the United States of America* 104, no. 4 (January 23, 2007): 1319–24.

16. George F. Solomon and Rudolf H. Moos, "The Relationship of Personality to the Presence of Rheumatoid Factor in Asymptomatic Relatives of Patients with Rheumatoid Arthritis," *Psychosomatic Medicine* 27, no. 4 (July 1965): 350–60.

17. C. E. G. Robinson, "Emotional Factors and Rheumatoid Arthritis," *Canadian Medical Association Journal* 77, no. 4 (August 15, 1957): 344–45.

18. Alex J. Zautra et al., "Examination of Changes in Interpersonal Stress as a Factor in Disease Exacerbations Among Women with Rheumatoid Arthritis," *Annals of Behavioral Medicine* 19, no. 3 (Summer 1997): 279–86.

19. G. S. Philippopoulos et al., "The Etiologic Significance of Emotional Factors in Onset and Exacerbations of Multiple Sclerosis," *Psychosomatic Medicine* 20, no. 6 (November 1958): 458–73.

20. Varda Mei-Tal et al., "The Role of Psychological Process in a Somatic Disorder: Multiple Sclerosis," *Psychosomatic Medicine* 32, no. 1 (January–February 1970): 67–85.

21. Gary M. Franklin et al., "Stress and Its Relationship to Acute Exacerbations in Multiple Sclerosis," *Journal of Neurologic Rehabilitation* 2, no. 1 (March 1, 1988): 7–11.

22. L. Briones et al., "The Influence of Stress and Psychosocial Factors in Multiple Sclerosis: A Review," conference paper, in *Psychotherapy and Psychosomatics* 82, suppl. 1 (September 2013): 1–134.

23. "In the last half-century, the prevalence of autoimmune disease . . . has increased sharply in the developed world," reported Moises Velasquez-Manoff in "Educate Your Immune System" (*New York Times*, June 5, 2016). "Many, like Type 1 diabetes and celiac disease, are linked with specific gene variants of the immune system, suggesting a strong genetic component. But their prevalence has increased much faster—in two or three generations—than it's likely the human gene pool has changed."
   Many theories have been advanced for the sharp rise in autoimmune cases, including the so-named hygiene hypothesis. According to this notion, industrialization and prosperity have led to lifestyles that prevent human beings from being exposed to microorganisms that would have trained our immune systems to be hardier, more resilient. "The implication is that, by delaying exposure to once-common infections, improvements in societal hygiene may increase the prevalence of autoimmune diseases." Velasquez-Manoff, "Educate Your Immune System." For all we know, there may be some truth to that view—but surely it cannot explain the dramatic rise over a few decades: Has the hygienic state of Danish women, for example, really changed that much in the past quarter century?

24. Huang Song et al., "Association of Stress-Related Disorders with Subsequent Autoimmune Disease," *Journal of the American Medical Association* 319, no. 23 (June 19, 2018): 2388–400.

25. Idam Harpaz et al., "Chronic Exposure to Stress Predisposes to Higher Autoimmune Susceptibility in C57BL/6 Mice: Glucocorticoids as a Double-Edged Sword," *European Journal of Immunology* 43, no. 3 (March 2013): 258–769.

26. Deborah Talbot, "What's It Like Living with Lupus," Elemental, July 13, 2018, https://elemental.medium.com/what-its-like-living-with-lupus-8doc2efcbe5e.

Chapter 6: It Ain't a Thing

1. Except for some specific malignancies, no major breakthroughs have been made in cure or prevention. Little has changed since Gina Kolata reported in 2009 that in over half a century, cancer death rates had "barely budged," falling by only 5 percent between 1950 and 2005. The major improvements were the results of smoking cessation, not medical advances as such. Gina Kolata, "Advances Elusive in the Drive to Cure Cancer," *New York Times*, April 21, 2009.

2. Gabor Maté, *When the Body Says No: The Cost of Hidden Stress* (Toronto: Knopf Canada, 2003; published in the United States with the subtitle *Exploring the Stress-Disease Connection*), chapter 18.

3. Michelle Kelly-Irving et al., "Childhood Adversity as a Risk for Cancer: Findings from the 1958 British Birth Cohort Study," *BMC Public Health* 13, no. 1 (August 19, 2013): 767, https://bmcpublichealth .biomedcentral.com/articles/10.1186/1471-2458-13-767.

4. Holly R. Harris et al., "Early Life Abuse and Risk of Endometriosis," *Human Reproduction* 3, no. 9 (September 2018): 1657–68.

5. M. Watson et al., "Influence of Psychological Response on Breast Cancer Survival: 10-Year Follow-Up of a Population-Based Cohort," *European Journal of Cancer* 41, no. 12 (August 2005): 1710–14.

6. Janine Giese-Davis et. al., "Decrease in Depression Symptoms Is Associated with Longer Survival in Patients with Metastatic Breast Cancer," *Journal of Clinical Oncology* 29, no. 4 (February 1, 2011): 413–20.

7. This cervical cancer study is cited in Jane G. Goldberg, ed., *Psychotherapeutic Treatment of Cancer Patients* (New York: Routledge, 1990), 45.

8. Frank J. Penedo et al., "Anger Suppression Mediates the Relationship Between Optimism and Natural Killer Cell Cytotoxicity in Men Treated for Localized Prostate Cancer," *Journal of Psychosomatic Research* 60, no. 4 (April 2006): 423–27.

9. Ann L. Coker et al., "Stress, Coping, Social Support, and Prostate Cancer Risk Among Older African American and Caucasian Men," *Ethnicity and Disease* 16, no. 4 (Autumn 2006): 978–87.

10. Meghan O'Rourke, "What's Wrong with Me?" *New Yorker*, August 19, 2013.

11. Paige Green McDonald et al., "A Biobehavioral Perspective of Tumor Biology," *Discovery Medicine* 5, no. 30 (December 2005): 520–26.

12. David Smithers, "Cancer: An Attack on Cytologism," *Lancet* 279, no. 7228 (March 10, 1962): 493–99.

Chapter 7: A Traumatic Tension

1. Susan Sontag, *Illness as Metaphor and AIDS and Its Metaphors* (New York: Picador, 2001), 55. The essay originally appeared in the *New York Review of Books* in 1978.

2. Jonathon Cott, *Susan Sontag: The Complete Rolling Stone Interview* (New Haven: Yale University Press, 2013). The original interview was published October 1979.

3. Marcia Angell, "Disease as a Reflection of the Psyche," *New England Journal of Medicine* 312 (June 13, 1985): 1570–72.

4. "From Irritated to Enraged: Anger's Toxic Effect on the Heart," Harvard Heart Health, December 6, 2014, https://www.health.harvard.edu/heart -health/from-irritated-to-enraged-angers-toxic-effect-on-the-heart.

5. Geoffrey H. Tofler et al., "Triggering of Acute Coronary Occlusion by Episodes of Anger," *European Heart Journal: Acute Cardiovascular Care*, February 2015, https://doi.org/10.1177/2048872615568969.

6. "Keep Calm, Anger Can Trigger a Heart Attack!," ScienceDaily, February 24, 2015, https://www.sciencedaily.com/releases/2015/02 /150224083819.htm.

7. I cite this verbatim from a first-person account of her breast cancer diagnosis by a Montreal woman, published in the *Globe and Mail*. I no longer have the date of the article, which appeared sometime between 2004 and 2007. It's exactly the dynamic noted by Lydia Temoshok.

8. Andrew W. Kneier and Lydia Temoshok, "Repressive Coping Reactions in Patients with Malignant Melanoma as Compared to Cardiovascular Disease Patients," *Journal of Psychosomatic Research* 28, no. 2 (1984): 145–55, https://doi.org/10.1016/0022-3999(84)90008-4.

9. James J. Gross and Robert W. Levenson, "Emotional Suppression: Physiology, Self-Report, and Expressive Behavior," *Journal of Personality and Social Psychology* 64, no. 6 (June 1993): 970–86.

10. Lydia Temoshok, Letter to the Editor, *New York Times*, September 6, 1992.

11. Susan Sontag, *As Consciousness Is Harnessed to Flesh: Journals and Notebooks, 1964–1980*, ed. David Rieff (Farrar, Straus and Giroux, 2012), 313.

Chapter 8: Who Are We Really?

1. Alfie Kohn, *No Contest: The Case Against Competition*, rev. ed. (Boston: Houghton Mifflin, 1992), 13.

2. Marshall Sahlins, *The Western Illusion of Human Nature* (Chicago: Prickly Paradigm Press, 2008), cited by Darcia Narvaez in "Are We Losing It? Darwin's Moral Sense and the Importance of Early Experience," in *The Routledge Handbook of Evolution and Philosophy*, ed. Richard Joyce (New York: Routledge, 2017), 328.

3. Jack D. Forbes, *Columbus and Other Cannibals: The Wétiko Disease of Exploitation, Imperialism, and Terrorism* (New York: Seven Stories Press, 1992), 49.

4. François Ansermet and Pierre Magistretti, *Biology of Freedom: Neural Plasticity, Experience, and the Unconscious*, trans. Susan Fairfield (New York: Other Press, 2007), 8.

5. Jean Liedloff, *The Continuum Concept: In Search of Happiness Lost*, rev. ed. (1985; Boston: Da Capo Press, 1975), 24.

6. "Probably all humans lived in such bands until at least a few tens of thousands of years ago, and probably most still did as recently as 11,000 years ago." Jared Diamond, *The World Until Yesterday: What We Can Learn from Traditional Societies* (New York: Penguin Books, 2012), 14.

7. Frans de Waal, *The Age of Empathy: Nature's Lessons for a Kinder Society* (New York: Broadway Books, 2010), 25.

Chapter 9: A Sturdy or Fragile Foundation

1. Cavoukian has worked with some of the world's leading developmental experts to create the Raffi Foundation for Child Honouring. Officially, the foundation may have been Raffi's first foray into advocacy, but it was far from the first time he had contemplated what children require and deserve, as his famous 1980 song about the need for love in a family illustrates.

2. Antonio R. Damasio, *Descartes' Error: Emotion, Reason and the Human Brain* (New York: G. P. Putnam's Sons, 1994), 128.

3. Jean Liedloff, *The Continuum Concept: In Search of Happiness Lost*, rev. ed. (1985; Boston: Da Capo Press, 1975), 37.

4. Jack P. Shonkoff et al., "An Integrated Scientific Framework for Child Survival and Early Childhood Development," *Pediatrics* 129, no. 2 (February 2012): 1–13.

5. The seminal psychologist and researcher Allan Schore writes: "The mother is implicitly shaping her infant's unconscious mind, which as Freud observed develops before the conscious mind"; and "the essential adaptive right-brain functions of interdependence, social connection, and emotion regulation emerge out of early attachment experience." Allan Schore, *The Development of the Unconscious Mind* (New York: W. W. Norton, 2019), 33, 57.

6. Stanley I. Greenspan and Stuart Shankar, with Beryl I. Benderly, "The Emotional Architecture of the Mind," in Raffi Cavoukian et al., *Child Honouring: How to Turn This World Around* (Homeland Press, 2006), 5.

7. Gordon Neufeld, "The Keys to Well-Being in Children and Youth: The Significant Role of Families," keynote address, delivered at the European Parliament, Brussels, November 13, 2012, https://neufeldinstitute.org /wp-content/uploads/2017/12/Neufeld_Brussels_address.pdf.

8. Maia Szalavitz and Bruce D. Perry, *Born for Love: Why Empathy Is Essential—and Endangered* (New York: William Morrow, 2011), 5.

9. J. Maselko et al., "Mother's Affection at 8 Months Predicts Emotional Distress in Adulthood," *Journal of Epidemiology and Community Health* 65, no. 7 (2011): 621–25.

10. Jordan Peterson, *12 Rules for Living: An Antidote to Chaos* (Toronto: Random House Canada, 2018), 141.

11. Jaak Panksepp and Lucy Biven, *The Archaeology of Mind: Neuroevolutionary Origins of Human Emotions* (New York: W. W. Norton, 2012), 386.

Chapter 10: Trouble at the Threshold

1. Thomas Verny, *Pre-Parenting* (New York: Simon and Schuster, 2003), 159–60.

2. In the 2011 documentary *Zeitgeist III: Moving Forward*, directed by Peter Joseph.

3. In the 2016 documentary *In Utero*, directed by Kathleen Man Gyllenhaal, https://www.inuterofilm.com/stephen_gyllenhaal.

4. Laurie Tarkian, "Tracking Stress and Depression Back to the Womb," *New York Times*, December 4, 2004.

5. Catherine Lebel et al., "Prepartum and Postpartum Maternal Depressive Symptoms Are Related to Children's Brain Structure in Preschool," *Biological Psychiatry* 80, no. 11 (December 1, 2016): 859–68.

6. Claudia Buss et al., "High Pregnancy Anxiety During Mid-Gestation Is Associated with Decreased Gray Matter Density in 6–9-Year-Old Children," *Psychoneuroimmunology* 35, no. 1 (January 2010): 141–53.

7. D. Kinney et al., "Prenatal Stress and Risk for Autism," *Neuroscience and Biobehavioral Reviews* 32, no. 8 (October 2008): 1519–32.

8. Sonja Entringer et al., "Fetal Programming of Body Composition, Obesity, and Metabolic Function: The Role of Intrauterine Stress and Stress Biology," *Journal of Nutrition and Metabolism* 2012: 632548; published online May 10, 2012, https://doi.org/10.1155/2012/632548.

9. Sonja Entringer et al., "Prenatal Stress, Development, Health and Disease Risk: A Psychobiological Perspective," *Psychoneuroendocrinology* 62 (December 2015): 366–75.

10. Sonja Entringer et al., "Stress Exposure in Intrauterine Life Is Associated with Shorter Telomere Length in Young Adulthood," *Proceedings of the National Academy of Sciences* 108, no. 33 (August 16, 2011).

11. Jill M. Goldstein, "Impact of Prenatal Maternal Cytokine Exposure on Sex Differences in Brain Circuitry Regulating Stress in Offspring 45 Years Later," *Proceedings of the National Academy of Sciences* 118, no. 15 (April 13, 2021), https://doi.org/10.1073/pnas.2014464118.

12. Maartie Zijlman et al., "Maternal Prenatal Stress Is Associated with the Infant Intestinal Microbiota," *Psychoneuroendocrinology* 53 (March 2015): 233–45.

13. C. Liu et al., "Prenatal Parental Depression and Preterm Birth: A National Cohort Study," *BJOG: An International Journal of Obstetrics and Gynecology* 123, no. 12 (November 2016): 1973–82, https://doi.org/10.1111/1471-0528.13891.

14. "Fetal Scans Confirm Maternal Stress Affects Babies' Brains,"

MediBulletin Bureau, March 27, 2018, https://medibulletin.com/fetal
-scans-confirm-maternal-stress-affects-babies-brains/.

15. Frederica P. Perera et al., "Prenatal Polycyclic Aromatic Hydrocarbon
(PAH) Exposure and Child Behavior at Age 6–7 Years," *Environmental
Health Perspectives* 120, no. 6 (June 1, 2012): 921–26.

16. Jane E. Allen, "Prenatal Pollutants Linked to Later Behavioral Ills,"
ABC News, March 12, 2012, https://abcnews.go.com/Health/w
_ParentingResource/prenatal-pollutants-linked-childhood-anxiety-adhd
/story?id=15974554.

17. Of course, environmental pollution affects virtually everyone, through
chemicals in our food and daily environment whose effects have not
been adequately investigated, if at all. What news we do have is far from
reassuring, as a large number of potentially harmful chemicals have
been identified in the umbilical cord blood samples in both Canada and
the United States, as in Europe and Asia. Moreover, in a sane society, it
would not be up to underfunded researchers to prove that some chemical
is harmful to fetus, child, and adolescent—it would be up to those who
introduce such substances into our air, earth, food supply, and the very
bloodstreams of pregnant women to show that it is not.

18. See, for example, Malidoma Patrice Somé, *Ritual, Magic and Initiation in
the Life of an African Shaman* (New York: G. P. Putnam's Sons, 1994), 20.
See also the documentary *What Babies Want*, https://www.youtube.com
/watch?v=-3mtFRjEVWc.

Chapter 11: What Choice Do I Have?

1. Susan J. McDonald et al., "Effect of Timing of Umbilical Cord
Clamping of Term Infants on Maternal and Neonatal Outcomes,"
Cochrane Database of Systemic Reviews 7 (July 11, 2013), https://doi
.org/10.1002/14651858.CD004074.pub3.

2. Anne Fadiman, *The Spirit Catches You and You Fall Down: A Hmong Child,
Her American Doctors, and the Collision of Two Cultures* (New York: Farrar,
Straus and Giroux, 1997; paperback edition, 2012), 74.

3. See, for example, Michael Klein et al., "Relationship of Episiotomy to
Perineal Trauma and Morbidity, Sexual Dysfunction, and Pelvic Floor
Relaxation," *American Journal of Obstetrics and Gynecology* 171, no. 3
(October 1994): 591–98.

4. Ties Boerma et al., "Global Epidemiology of Use of and Disparities in Caesarean Sections," *Lancet* 392, no. 10155 (October 2018): 1341–48.

5. Boerma, "Global Epidemiology."

6. Obstetric Care Consensus, "Safe Prevention of the Primary Cesarean Delivery," *Obstetrics and Gynecology* 123, no. 3 (March 2014): 693–711.

7. Cited by Suzanne Hope Suarez, "Midwifery Is Not the Practice of Medicine," *Yale Journal of Law and Feminism* 5, no. 2 (1992).

8. Sarah J. Buckley, "Hormonal Physiology of Childbearing: Evidence and Implications for Women, Babies, and Maternity Care," Childbirth Connection Programs, National Partnership for Women and Families, Washington, D.C., January 2015.

9. Ilana Stanger-Ross, *A Is for Advice: The Reassuring Kind* (New York: William Morrow, 2019), 23–24.

10. Buckley, "Hormonal Physiology of Childbearing."

11. World Health Organization, "Evidence Shows Significant Mistreatment of Women During Childbirth," news release, October 9, 2019, https://www.who.int/news/item/09-10-2019-new-evidence-shows-significant-mistreatment-of-women-during-childbirth.

12. Jesse Feith, "Indigenous Woman Records Slurs by Hospital Staff Before Her Death," *Montreal Gazette,* September 30, 2020, https://montrealgazette.com/news/local-news/indigenous-woman-who-died-at-joliette-hospital-had-recorded-staffs-racist-comments.

13. Jean Liedloff, *The Continuum Concept: In Search of Happiness Lost*, rev. ed. (1985; Boston: Da Capo Press, 1975), 58.

Chapter 12: Horticulture on the Moon

1. Emily Oster, "The Data All Guilt-Ridden Parents Need," *New York Times*, April 19, 2019, https://www.nytimes.com/2019/04/19/opinion/sunday/baby-breastfeeding-sleep-training.html (published as "Baby's First Data" in the print edition on April 20, section SR 1).

2. Lloyd deMause, ed., *The History of Childhood: The Untold Story of Child Abuse* (New York: Peter Bedrick Books, 1988), 53.

3. Jordan R. Peterson, *12 Rules for Life: An Antidote to Chaos* (Toronto: Random House Canada, 2018), 144.

4. Ashley Montagu, *Touching: The Human Significance of Skin*, 3rd ed. (New York: Harper and Row, 1986), 296.

5. D. W. Winnicott, *Through Pediatrics to Psycho-Analysis: Collected Papers* (Abingdon, UK: Brunner-Routledge, New York: 1992), 99.

6. Montagu, *Touching*, 42.

7. Adrienne Rich, *Of Woman Born: Motherhood as Experience and Institution* (New York: W. W. Norton, 1995), 31.

8. Lane Strathearn et al., "What's in a Smile? Maternal Brain Responses to Infant Facial Clues," *Pediatrics* 122, no. 1 (July 2008): 40–51.

9. John H. Kennell et al., "Maternal Behavior One Year After Early and Extended Post-Partum Contact," *Developmental Medicine and Child Neurology* 16, no. 2 (April 1974): 172–79.

10. Darcia Narvaez, *Neurobiology and the Development of Human Morality: Evolution, Culture, and Wisdom* (New York: W. W. Norton, 2014), 29–30.

11. Jean Liedloff, *The Continuum Concept: In Search of Happiness Lost*, rev. ed. (1985; Boston: Da Capo Press, 1975), 97.

12. As documented, for example, by Charles C. Mann in his bestselling book *1491: New Revelations of the Americas Before Columbus* (New York: Knopf, 2005).

13. Stacy Schiff, *The Witches: Salem, 1692* (London: Weidenfeld and Nicholson, 2015), 45.

14. Peterson, *12 Rules for Life*, 139.

15. Robert D. Sage and Benjamin S. Siegel, "Effective Discipline to Raise Healthy Children," *Pediatrics* 142, no. 6 (December 2018).

16. Manisha Aggarwal-Schifellite, "How Spanking May Affect Brain Development in Children," *Harvard Gazette*, April 12, 2021, https://news.harvard.edu/gazette/story/2021/04/spanking-children-may-impair-their-brain-development/.

17. "Breastfeeding: Achieving the New Normal," editorial, *Lancet* 387 (January 30, 2016): 404.

18. Craig A. McEwen and Bruce S. McEwen, "Social Structure, Adversity, Toxic Stress, and Intergenerational Poverty: An Early Childhood Model," *Annual Review of Sociology* 43, no. 1 (August 2017): 445–72.

19. Allan Schore, *Affect Regulation and the Origin of the Self: The Neurobiology of Emotional Development* (Mahwah, NJ: Lawrence Erlbaum Associates, 1994), 378.

20. Claire Cain Miller, "The Relentlessness of Modern Parenting," *New York Times*, December 25, 2018, A1.

21. Emily Oster, "Don't Worry, Baby," *New Yorker*, June 3, 2019.

22. Miranda Bryant, " 'I Was Risking My Life': Why One in Four US Women Return to Work Two Weeks After Childbirth," *Guardian*, January 27, 2020.

23. Colin M. Turnbull, *The Forest People* (London: Chatto and Windus, 1961), 113.

24. Darcia Narvaez, "Allomothers: Our Evolved Support Systems for Mothers," *Psychology Today*, May 12, 2019, https://www.psychologytoday.com/ca/blog/moral-landscapes/201905/allomothers-our-evolved-support-system-mothers.

25. NBC News, May 15, 2020.

26. Robert D. Putnam, *Bowling Alone: The Collapse and Revival of the American Community* (New York: Simon and Schuster, 2000), 27.

27. Rich, *Of Woman Born*, 53–54.

Chapter 13: Forcing the Brain in the Wrong Direction

1. James Garbarino, *Raising Children in a Socially Toxic Environment* (San Francisco: Jossey-Bass, 1995), 2.

2. Garbarino, *Raising Children in a Socially Toxic Environment*, 5.

3. Natalie Angier, "Ideas and Trends: The Sandbox; Bully for You—Why Push Comes to Shove," *New York Times*, May 20, 2001.

4. D. Clark, "Frequency of Bullying in European Countries, 2018," Statista, October 7, 2021, https://www.statista.com/statistics/1092217/bullying-in-europe/.

5. Cited in Timothy Singham, "Concurrent and Longitudinal Contribution of Exposure to Bullying in Childhood Mental Health: The Role of

Vulnerability and Resistance," *JAMA Psychiatry*, published online October 4, 2017, https://doi.org/10.1001/jamapsychiatry.2017.2678.

6. Bridgette Watson, "They Killed Him for Entertainment: Carson Crimeni's Father Speaks Out Against Bullying," CBC News, February 26, 2020, https://www.cbc.ca/news/canada/british-columbia/darrel-crimeni -bullying-awareness-1.5477247.

7. Gordon Neufeld, "The Keys to Well-Being in Children and Youth: The Significant Role of Families," keynote address, delivered at the European Parliament, Brussels, November 13, 2012.

8. Joel Bakan, *Childhood Under Siege: How Big Business Targets Children* (New York: Free Press, 2011), 6.

9. Joel Bakan, "Kids and the Corporation," in *Child Honouring: How to Turn This World Around*, ed. Raffi Cavoukian and Sharna Olfman (Salt Spring Island, BC: Homeland Press, 2006), 190.

10. Georgia Wells et al., "Facebook Knows Instagram Is Toxic for Teen Girls, Company Documents Show," *Wall Street Journal*, September 14, 2021, https://www.wsj.com/articles/facebook-knows-instagram-is-toxic-for -teen-girls-company-documents-show-11631620739.

11. Shimi Kang, *The Tech Solution: Creating Healthy Habits for Kids Growing Up in a Digital World* (New York: Viking, 2020), ch. 1.

12. John S. Hutton et al., "Associations Between Screen-Based Media Use and Brain White Matter Integrity in Preschool-Aged Children," *JAMA Pediatrics* 174, no. 1 (2020).

13. Mari Swingle, *i-Minds: How and Why Constant Connectivity Is Rewiring Our Brains and What to Do About It* (New Society, 2019), 11, 185.

14. Allana Akhtar, "The World Health Organization Just Released Screen-Time Guidelines for Kids. Here's How Some of the World's Most Successful CEOs Limit It at Home," *Business Insider*, April 25, 2019, https://www.businessinsider.com/how-silicon-valley-ceos-limit-screen -time-at-home-2019-4.

15. James Garbarino, *Children and Families in the Social Environment* (New York: Routledge, 1992), 11.

16. Jasper Jackson, "Children Spending More Time Online Than Watching TV for the First Time," *Guardian*, January 26, 2012, https://www .theguardian.com/media/2016/jan/26/children-time-online-watching-tv.

17. William Doyle, "Why Finland Has the Best Schools," op-ed, *Los Angeles Times*, March 18, 2016, https://www.latimes.com/opinion/op-ed/la-oe -0318-doyle-finnish-schools-20160318-story.html.

18. Alfie Kohn, *No Contest: The Case Against Competition: Why We Lose in Our Race to Win* (Boston: Houghton Mifflin, 1992), 25.

Chapter 14: A Template for Distress

1. Siddhartha Mukherjee, "Same but Different: How Epigenetics Can Blur the Line Between Nature and Nurture," *New Yorker*, May 2, 2016.

2. Michael E. Kerr and Murray Bowen, *Family Evaluation: An Approach Based on Bowen Theory* (New York: W. W. Norton, 1988), 30.

3. Thomas Merton, *The Seven Storey Mountain: An Autobiography of Faith* (Boston: Mariner Books, 1999), 362.

4. Erich Fromm, *The Sane Society* (New York: Henry Holt, 1955), 79.

5. Aldous Huxley, *Brave New World* (New York: HarperCollins, 2014), 244.

6. Cited in Noelle McAfee, *Julia Kristeva* (New York: Routledge, 2004), 108.

7. Merton, *The Seven Storey Mountain*, 148.

8. Neil Postman, *Amusing Ourselves to Death: Public Discourse in the Age of Show Business*, 20th anniversary ed. (New York: Penguin Books, 2008), 128.

9. Ezra Klein, "Noam Chomsky's Theory of the Good Life," transcript, April 23, 2021, https://www.nytimes.com/2021/04/23/opinion/ezra-klein -podcast-noam-chomsky.html.

Chapter 15: Just Not to Be You

1. "Overdose Death Rates," National Institute on Drug Abuse, https://www .drugabuse.gov/drug-topics/trends-statistics/overdose-death-rates.

2. Roni Caryn Rabin, "Overdose Deaths Reached Record High as the Pandemic Spread," *New York Times*, November 17, 2021, https://www .nytimes.com/2021/11/17/health/drug-overdoses-fentanyl-deaths.html.

3. Nora D. Volkow and T. K. Li, "Drug Addiction: The Neurobiology of Behavior Gone Awry," *Neuroscience* 5 (December 2004): 963–70.

4. F. Zhou et al., "Orbitofrontal Gray Matter Deficits as Marker of Internet Gaming Disorder: Converging Evidence from a Cross-Sectional and

Prospective Longitudinal Design," *Addiction Biology* 24, no. 1 (January 2019): 100–109, https://doi.org/10:1111/adb.12750.

5. Kyle S. Burger and Eric Stice, "Frequent Ice Cream Consumption Is Associated with Reduced Striatal Response to Receipt of an Ice Cream–Based Milkshake," *American Journal of Clinical Nutrition* 94, no. 4 (April 2012): 810–17, https://doi.org/10.3945/ajcn.111.027003.

6. "Definition of Addiction," American Society of Addiction Medicine, https://www.asam.org/quality-care/definition-of-addiction.

7. Keith Richards with James Fox, *Life* (New York: Back Bay Books, 2011), 322.

8. P. A. Harrison, J. A. Fulkerson, and T. J. Beebe, "Multiple Substance Use Among Adolescent Physical and Sexual Abuse Victims," *Child Abuse and Neglect* 21, no. 6 (June 1997): 529–39.

9. Hannah Carliner et al., "Childhood Trauma and Illicit Drug Use in Adolescence: A Population-Based National Comorbidity Survey Replication," *Journal of the American Academy of Child and Adolescent Psychiatry* 55, no. 8 (August 2016): 701–8.

Chapter 16: Show of Hands

1. Vincent J. Felitti et al., "The Relationship of Adult Health Status to Childhood Abuse and Household Dysfunction," *American Journal of Preventive Medicine* 14 (1998): 245–58.

2. Vincent J. Felitti and Robert Anda, "The Lifelong Effects of Adverse Childhood Experiences," chapter 10, in *Chadwick's Child Maltreatment: Sexual Abuse and Psychological Maltreatment*, vol. 2, 4th ed. (St. Louis, MO: STM Learning, 2014), 207.

3. Gene H. Brody et al., "Parenting Moderates a Genetic Vulnerability Factor in Longitudinal Increases in Youths' Substance Use," *Journal of Consulting and Clinical Psychology Association* 77, no. 1 (February 2009): 1–11; among other studies, such as, for example, Marcello Solinas et al., "Prevention and Treatment of Drug Addiction by Environmental Enrichment," *Progress in Neurobiology* 92, no. 4 (December 2010): 572–92.

4. I first cited this statement by Dr. Perry in my book on addiction, *In the Realm of Hungry Ghosts*.

5. Gail Dines, *Pornland: How Porn Has Hijacked Our Sexuality* (Boston: Beacon Press, 2010), 57.

6. Jaak Panksepp et al., "The Role of Brain Emotional Systems in Addictions: A Neuro-Evolutionary Perspective and New 'Self-Report' Animal Model," *Addiction* 97, no. 4 (May 2002): 459–69.

7. Louis Cozolino, *The Neuroscience of Human Relationships: Attachment and the Developing Social Brain* (New York: W. W. Norton, 2006), 115.

Chapter 17: An Inaccurate Map of Our Pain

1. Kay Redfield Jamison, *Touched with Fire: Manic-Depressive Illness and the Artistic Temperament* (New York: Free Press, 1994), 193.

2. I dispensed fully with this issue of twin and adoption studies in an appendix to my book on addiction. In short, I argue that these ostensibly pristine cases of "different environments, same health problems" are so blind to the environmental factors *contained in their experimental design*— maternal stress during pregnancy and the trauma of separation from birth mother, to cite two obvious examples—as to be invalid, no matter what mental or physical condition we are talking about. A link to that appendix is posted at this book's website, https://drgabormate.com/book/the-myth -of-normal, for the benefit of the curious or unconvinced. The professional reader may further consult the psychologist Jay Joseph's comprehensive work *The Trouble with Twin Studies: A Reassessment of Twin Research in the Social and Behavioral Sciences* (Routledge, 2016).

3. "Because the troubled mind has been perceived in terms of diverse religious, scientific, and social beliefs of discrete cultures, the forms of madness from one place and time in history often look remarkably different from the forms of madness in another," notes Ethan Watters in his book *Crazy Like Us: The Globalization of the American Psyche* (New York: Free Press, 2020), 5.

4. Cited in Robert Whitaker, *Anatomy of an Epidemic: Magic Bullets, Psychiatric Drugs, and the Astonishing Rise of Mental Illness in America* (New York: Broadway Books, 2010), 274.

5. American Psychiatric Association, "Chair of DSM-5 Task Force Discusses Future of Mental Health Research," press release, May 3, 2013.

6. For example, by the psychologist Irvin Kirsch, recently associate director of the program in placebo studies and a lecturer in medicine at the Harvard Medical School. "It now seems beyond question that the traditional account of depression as a chemical imbalance in the brain is

simply wrong," Kirsch wrote in his own extensive review of the scientific literature, *The Emperor's New Drugs: Exploding the Antidepressant Myth*, cited in Marcia Angell, "The Epidemic of Mental Illness: Why?," *New York Review of Books*, June 23, 2011. (Dr. Angell is the former editor of the *New England Journal of Medicine*.)

7. Richard L. Morrow et al., "Influence of Relative Age on Diagnosis and Treatment of Attention-Deficit/Hyperactivity Disorder in Children," *Canadian Medical Association Journal* 184, no. 7 (April 17, 2012): 755–62.

8. "Oppositional Defiant Disorder," Mayo Clinic, https://www.mayoclinic .org/diseases-conditions/oppositional-defiant-disorder/symptoms-causes /syc-20375831.

9. J. E. Khoury et al., "Relations Among Maternal Withdrawal in Infancy, Borderline Features, Suicidality/Self-Injury, and Adult Hippocampal Volume: A 30-Year Longitudinal Study," *Behavioral Brain Research* 374 (November 18, 2019): 112139, https://doi.org/10.1016/j.bbr.2019.112139.

10. John Read et al., "Child Maltreatment and Psychosis: A Return to a Genuinely Integrated Bio-Psycho-Social Model," *Clinical Schizophrenia and Related Psychoses* 2, no. 3 (October 2008): 235–54.

11. Thomas Bailey et al., "Childhood Trauma Is Associated with Severity of Hallucinations and Delusions in Psychotic Disorders: A Systematic Review and Meta-Analysis," *Schizophrenia Bulletin* 44, no. 5 (2018): 1111–22.

12. Richard Bentall, "Mental Illness Is a Result of Misery, Yet Still We Stigmatize It," *Guardian*, February 26, 2016.

13. Martin H. Teicher and Jacqueline A. Samson, "Annual Research Review: Enduring Neurobiological Effects of Childhood Abuse and Neglect," *Journal of Child Psychology and Psychiatry* 57, no. 3 (March 2016): 241–66.

14. R. C. Lewontin, *Biology as Destiny: The Doctrine of DNA* (New York: Harper Perennial, 1991), 30.

15. W. Thomas Boyce, *The Orchid and the Dandelion: Why Some Children Struggle and How All Can Thrive* (London: Allen Lane, 2019), 11.

16. E. Fox and C. B. Beevers, "Differential Sensitivity to the Environment: Contribution of Cognitive Biases and Genes to Psychological Wellbeing," *Molecular Psychiatry* 21, no. 12 (2016): 1657–62.

17. Louis Menand, "Acid Reflux: The Life and High Times of Timothy Leary," *New Yorker*, June 26, 2006.

Chapter 18: The Mind Can Do Some Amazing Things

1. A. H. Almaas, *The Freedom to Be* (Berkeley, CA: Diamond Books, 1989), 85.

2. Douglas F. Watt and Jaak Panksepp, "Depression: An Evolutionarily Conserved Mechanism to Terminate Separation Distress? A Review of Aminergic, Peptidergic, and Neural Network Perspectives," *Neuropsychoanalysis* 11, no. 1 (January 1, 2009): 7–51.

3. Noël Hunter, *Trauma and Madness in Mental Health Services* (New York: Palgrave Macmillan, 2018), 5.

4. The psychologist and research scientist Stephen Porges posits the concept of *neuroception*, the brain's unconscious assessment of security. "This automatic process," he writes, "involves brain areas that evaluate cues of safety, danger, and life threat." "The perception of safety," he suggests, "is the turning point in the development of relationships for most mammals." This is particularly true for human beings, with our long formative period of helpless dependency. Stephen W. Porges, *The Pocket Guide to the Polyvagal Theory: The Transformative Power of Feeling Safe* (New York: W. W. Norton, 2017), 19; and Stephen W. Porges, *The Polyvagal Theory: Neurophysiological Foundations of Emotions, Attachment, Communication, Self-Regulation* (New York: W. W. Norton, 2011), see especially chapter 1.

5. Helen Knott, *In My Own Moccasins: A Memoir of Resilience* (Saskatchewan, Canada: University of Regina Press, 2019), 96.

6. This quote by Robin Williams was reported to have been sourced from a video interview I have not been able to view directly. But he reveals much about his childhood loneliness and inner torments in almost similar words in this YouTube interview with James Lipton: https://www.dailymotion.com/video/x64ojf8.

7. In a Swedish study looking at hundreds of thousands of subjects, the risk of Parkinson's disease was nearly three times as great in those who had experienced depression, and even greater in those with severe depression. Helena Gustafsson et al., "Depression and Subsequent Risk of Parkinson Disease," *Neurology* 84, no. 24 (June 16, 2015): 2422–29. Another review concluded that chronic emotional stress also elevates the risk for the disease, possibly by damaging dopamine cells in certain parts of the brain:

Atbin Djamshidian and Andrew Lees, "Can Stress Trigger Parkinson's Disease?," *Journal of Neurology, Neurosurgery, and Psychiatry* 85, no. 8 (August 2014): 879–82.

8. Schizophrenia Working Group, "Biological Insights from 108 Schizophrenia-Associated Genetic Loci," *Nature* 511 (2014): 421–27.

9. "Dissociation," writes the psychiatrist Mark Epstein, "offers immediate protection from the traumas of life." Mark Epstein, *The Trauma of Everyday Life* (New York: Penguin, 2014), 84.

10. Knott, *In My Own Moccasins*, 24.

11. Theo Fleury, *Playing with Fire* (New York: HarperCollins, 2010), 25.

12. A recent study showed that prolonged use of antipsychotics in *adults* results in a diminished thickness of the cerebral cortex, the brain's executive apparatus. "The prefrontal cortex doesn't get the input it needs and is being shut down by drugs," a leading researcher told the *New York Times*. "That reduces the psychotic symptoms. It also causes the prefrontal cortex to slowly atrophy." Aristotle N. Voineskos et al., "Effects of Antipsychotic Medication on Brain Structure in Patients with Major Depressive Disorder and Psychotic Features: Neuroimaging Findings in the Context of a Randomized Placebo-Controlled Clinical Trial," *JAMA Psychiatry* 77, no. 7 (July 1, 2020): 674–83.

13. Russell A. Barkley, *Attention-Deficit Hyperactivity Disorder: A Handbook for Diagnosis and Treatment* (New York: Guilford Press, 1990), 103.

14. Jaak Panksepp, "Can PLAY Diminish ADHD and Facilitate the Construction of the Social Brain?," *Journal of the Canadian Academy of Child and Adolescent Psychiatry* 16, no. 2 (May 2007): 57–66.

15. For example, Liliana J. Lengua et al., "Pathways from Early Adversity to Later Adjustment: Tests of the Additive and Bidirectional Effects of Executive Control and Diurnal Cortisol in Early Childhood," *Development and Psychopathology*, 2019, https://doi.org/10.1017/S0954579419000373; also Jens C. Pruessner et al., "Dopamine Release in Response to a Psychological Stress in Humans and Its Relationship to Early Maternal Care: A Positron Emission Tomography Study Using [11C]Raclopride," *Journal of Neuroscience* 24, no. 11 (March 17, 2004): 2825–31.

16. Bruce D. Perry and Maia Szalavitz, *The Boy Who Was Raised as a Dog (And Other Stories from a Child Psychiatrist's Notebook): What*

Traumatized Children Can Teach Us About Loss, Love, and Healing (New York: Basic Books, 2006), 51.

17. The study by Nicole M. Brown, M.D., and her colleagues analyzed data from the 2011 National Survey of Children's Health and was presented on May 6, 2014, at the Pediatric Academic Societies' annual meeting in Vancouver, B.C. It was reported in ScienceDaily, May 6, 2014: "Study Finds ADHD and Trauma Often Go Hand in Hand."

18. Stanley Coren, "Can Dogs Suffer from ADHD?," *Psychology Today*, January 9, 2018, https://www.psychologytoday.com/us/blog/canine-corner/201801/can-dogs-suffer-adhd.

19. John Bowlby, *Attachment*, 2nd ed. (New York: Basic Books, 1982), 377.

20. Bruno Etain et al., "Childhood Trauma Is Associated with Severe Clinical Characteristics of Bipolar Disorders," *Journal of Clinical Psychiatry* 74, no. 10 (October 2013): 991–98.
       The study does not imply, and neither do I, that childhood adversity "causes" bipolar disorder. It is, however, a contributing factor, especially to the condition's severity.

Chapter 19: From Society to Cell

1. János Selye, *The Stress of Life*, rev. ed. (New York: McGraw-Hill, 1978), 370.

2. Zachary M. Harvanek et al., "Psychological and Biological Resilience Modulates the Effects of Stress on Epigenetic Aging," *Translational Psychiatry* 11 (2021), https://doi.org/10.1038/s41398-021-01735-7.

3. E. R. De Kloet, "Corticosteroids, Stress, and Aging," *Annals of the New York Academy of Sciences* 663 (1992): 357–71.

4. Yuval Noah Harari, *Sapiens: A Brief History of Humankind* (Toronto: McClelland & Stewart, 2014), 314.

5. BBC interview, "Blair Calls for Lifestyle Change," 2006, cited in Ted Schrecker and Clare Bambra, *How Politics Makes Us Sick: Neoliberal Epidemics* (New York: Palgrave Macmillan, 2015), 29.

6. Phillip Inman, "IMF Boss Says Global Economy Risks Return of Great Depression," *Guardian*, January 17, 2020.

7. David Lao, "Almost 9 out of 10 Canadians Feel Food Prices Are Rising Faster Than Income: Survey," *Global News*, December 16, 2019.

8. Vancity, "Report: B.C. Women Are Financially Stressed, Stretched and Under-Resourced," press release, March 17, 2018, based on the province-wide survey "Money Troubled: Inside B.C.'s Financial Health Gender Gap."

9. Schrecker and Bambra, *How Politics Makes Us Sick*, 42.

10. John Ralston Saul, "The Collapse of Globalism," *Harper's*, March 2004.

11. Ashild Faresjö et al., "Higher Perceived Stress but Lower Cortisol Levels Found Among Young Greek Adults Living in a Stressful Social Environment in Comparison with Swedish Young Adults," *PLoS ONE* 8, no. 9 (September 16, 2013), https://doi.org/10.1371/journal.pone.0073828.

12. Sonia J. Lupien et al., "Child's Stress Hormone Levels Correlate with Mother's Socioeconomic Status and Depressive State," *Biological Psychiatry* 48, no. 10 (November 15, 2000): 976–80.

13. Tara Siegel Bernard and Karl Russell, "The Middle-Class Crunch: A Look at 4 Family Budgets," *New York Times*, October 3, 2019.

14. Wade Davis, "The Unravelling of America," *Rolling Stone*, August 6, 2020, https://www.rollingstone.com/politics/political-commentary/covid-19-end-of-american-era-wade-davis-1038206/.

15. Morris Berman, *The Twilight of American Culture* (New York: W. W. Norton, 2001), 64–65.

16. Bernard and Russell, "The Middle-Class Crunch."

17. William T. Gallo et al., "Involuntary Job Loss as a Risk Factor for Subsequent Myocardial Infarction and Stroke: Findings from the Health and Retirement Survey," *American Journal of Industrial Medicine* 45, no. 5 (May 2004): 408–16; and W. T. Gallo et al., "The Impact of Late Career Job Loss on Myocardial Infarction and Stroke: A 10 Year Follow Up Using the Health and Retirement Survey," *Journal of Occupational and Environmental Medicine* 63, no. 10 (October 2006): 683–87.

18. Matthew E. Dupre et al., "The Cumulative Effect of Unemployment on Risks for Acute Myocardial Infarction," *Archives of Internal Medicine* 172, no. 22 (December 2012): 1731–37.

19. Louis Uchitelle, "Job Insecurity of Workers Is a Big Factor in Fed Policy," *New York Times*, February 27, 1997.

20. Schrecker and Bambra, *How Politics Makes Us Sick*, 53.

21. Ben Stein, "In Class Warfare, Guess Which Class Is Winning," *New York Times*, November 26, 2006, https://www.nytimes.com/2006/11/26/business/yourmoney/26every.html.

22. David Marchese, "Ben and Jerry's Radical Ice Cream Dreams," *New York Times*, July 29, 2020.

23. Joseph E. Stiglitz, *The Price of Inequality: How Today's Divided Society Endangers Our Future* (New York: W. W. Norton, 2013), xlviii–xlix.

24. Rupert Neate, "Billionaires' Wealth Rises to $10.2 Trillion amid Covid Crisis," *Guardian*, October 7, 2020.

25. *Star* editorial board, "Billionaires Get Richer While Millions Struggle. There's a Lot Wrong with This Picture," *Toronto Star*, September 21, 2020.

26. Martin Gilens and Benjamin I. Page, "Testing Theories of American Politics: Elites, Interest Groups, and Average Citizens," *Perspectives on Politics* 12, no. 3 (September 2014): 564–81.

27. Paul Krugman, "Why Do the Rich Have So Much Power?," *New York Times*, July 8, 2020.

28. James Reid, *Alienation* (University of Glasgow Publications, 1972), 5.

Chapter 20: Robbing the Human Spirit

1. David Brooks, "Our Pathetic Herd Immunity Failure," *New York Times*, May 6, 2021.

2. Karl Marx, *Economic and Philosophical Manuscripts*, trans. T. B. Bottomore, in Erich Fromm, *Marx's Concept of Man* (London: Continuum, 2004), 83.

3. Bruce Alexander, *The Globalization of Addiction: A Study in Poverty of the Spirit* (New York: Oxford University Press, 2008), 58.

4. Tony Schwartz and Christine Porath, "Why You Hate Work," *New York Times*, June 1, 2014.

5. Charles Duhigg, "Wealthy, Successful, and Miserable," *New York Times*, February 21, 2019, https://www.nytimes.com/interactive/2019/02/21/magazine/elite-professionals-jobs-happiness.html.

6. Awais Aftab, "Meaning in Life and Its Relationship with Physical, Mental, and Cognitive Functioning: A Study of 1,042 Community-Dwelling Adults Across the Lifespan," *Journal of Clinical Psychiatry* 81, no. 1 (2020).

7.   John T. Cacioppo and Stephanie Cacioppo, "The Growing Problem of Loneliness," *Lancet* 391, no. 10019 (February 3, 2018): 426–27.

8.   American Psychological Association, "Social Isolation, Loneliness, Could Be Greater Threat to Public Health Than Obesity," ScienceDaily, August 5, 2015, www.sciencedaily.com/releases/2017/08/170805165319.htm.

9.   Denise Aydinonat et al., "Social Isolation Shortens Telomeres in African Gray Parrots," *PLoS ONE* 9, no. 4 (2014): e93839, https://doi.org/10.1371/journal.pone.0093839.

10. Nicole K. Valtorta et al., "Loneliness and Social Isolation as Risk Factors for Coronary Heart Disease and Stroke: Systematic Review and Meta-analysis of Longitudinal Observational Studies," *Heart* 102, no. 13 (2016), https://heart.bmj.com/content/102/13/1009.

11. Dhruv Kullur, "Loneliness Is a Health Hazard, but There Are Remedies," *New York Times*, December 22, 2016.

12. Vivek H. Murthy, *Together: The Healing Power of Human Connection in a Sometimes Lonely World* (New York: Harper Wave, 2020), 98.

13. Tim Kasser et al., "Some Costs of American Corporate Capitalism: A Psychological Exploration of Value and Goal Conflicts," *Psychological Inquiry* 18, no. 1 (March: 2007): 1–22.

Chapter 21: They Just Don't Care If It Kills You

1.   Russell Brand, "Edward Snowden: The Worst Conspiracies Are in Plain Sight," YouTube video, April 16, 2021, https://www.youtube.com/watch?v=eozAJfbP3gg&t=23s.

2.   Belinda S. Lennerz et al., "Effects of Dietary Glycemic Index on Brain Regions Related to Reward and Craving in Men," *American Journal of Clinical Nutrition* 98, no. 3 (September 2013): 641–47.

3.   Ashkan Afshin et al., "Health Effects of Dietary Risks in 195 Countries, 1990–2017: A Systemic Analysis for the Global Burden of Disease Study 2017," *Lancet* 393, no. 10184 (May 11, 2019): 1958–2017.

4.   American Heart Association, "180,000 Deaths Worldwide May Be Associated with Sugary Soft Drinks, Research Suggests," ScienceDaily, March 19, 2013, https://www.sciencedaily.com/releases/2013/03/130319202144.htm.

5. "Mexico Obesity: Oaxaca Bans Sales of Junk Food to Children," BBC News, Aug. 6, 2020, https://www.bbc.com/news/world-latin -america-53678747.

6. "Mexico Takes Title of 'Most Obese' from America," *Global Post*, July 28, 2013, https://www.cbsnews.com/news/mexico-takes-title-of-most-obese -from-america.

7. Susan Greenhalgh, "Making China Safe for Coke: How Coca-Cola Shaped Obesity Science and Policy in China," *British Medical Journal* 364 (January 9, 2019): k5050, https://doi.org/10.1136/bmj.k5050.

8. "Statistics on Obesity, Physical Activity, Diet, England, 2020," National Health Service, May 5, 2020, https://digital.nhs.uk/data-and-information /publications/statistical/statistics-on-obesity-physical-activity-and-diet /england-2020.

9. Ted Schrecker and Clare Bambra, *How Politics Makes Us Sick: Neoliberal Epidemics* (New York: Palgrave Macmillan, 2015), 32.

10. Nicholas Kristof, "Drug Dealers in Lab Coats," *New York Times*, October 18, 2017.

11. In 2014, on the fiftieth anniversary of the U.S. surgeon general's landmark report exposing the ill effects of manufactured tobacco, the same office issued an update. "The tobacco epidemic was initiated and *has been sustained* by the aggressive strategies of the tobacco industry, which has deliberately misled the public on the risks of smoking cigarettes."

12. "Smoking and Tobacco Use: Fast Facts," Centers for Disease Control and Prevention, https://www.cdc.gov/tobacco/data_statistics/fact_sheets /fast_facts/index.htm.

13. Sheila Kaplan, "Biden Plans to Ban Cigarettes with Menthol," *New York Times*, April 29, 2021.

14. Milton Friedman, "Your Greed or Their Greed?," *Phil Donahue Show*, YouTube, uploaded July 14, 2007, https://www.youtube.com/watch ?v=RWsx1X8PV_A.

15. Milton Friedman, "The Social Responsibility of Business Is to Increase Its Profits," *New York Times*, September 13, 1970.

16. Andrea Wulf, *The Invention of Nature: The Adventures of Alexander von Humboldt, the Lost Hero of Science* (London: John Murray, 2015), 5.

17. William J. Ripple et al., "World Scientists' Warning of a Climate Emergency," *BioScience* 70, no. 1 (January 2020): 8–12.

18. Nick Watts et al., "The 2018 Report of the *Lancet* Countdown on Health and Climate Change: Shaping the Health of Nations for Centuries to Come," *Lancet* 392, no. 10163 (December 8, 2018): 2479–514.

19. "More Than 200 Health Journals Call for Urgent Action on Climate Crisis," *Guardian*, September 6, 2021; and Robert Lee Holtz, "Action on Climate Change Is Urged by Medical Journals in Unprecedented Plea," *Wall Street Journal*, September 6, 2021.

Chapter 22: The Assaulted Sense of Self

1. Malcolm X, as told to Alex Haley, *The Autobiography of Malcolm X* (1964; New York: Ballantine Books, 2015), 56.

2. Jean-Paul Sartre, *Anti-Semite and Jew: An Exploration of the Etiology of Hate* (1948; New York: Schocken Books, 1995), 53–54.

3. "Ken Hardy on the Assaulted Sense of Self," Psychotherapy Networker, YouTube video, 2016, https://www.youtube.com/watch?v=i26A50ec UWM.

4. Helen Knott, *In My Own Moccasins: A Memoir of Resilience* (Saskatchewan, Canada: University of Regina Press, 2019), 200–201.

5. David H. Chae et al., "Racial Discrimination and Telomere Shortening Among African-Americans: The Coronary Artery Risk Development in Young Adults (CARDIA) Study," *Health Psychology* 39, no. 3 (March 2020): 209–19.

6. Ta-Nehisi Coates, *Between the World and Me* (New York: Spiegel & Grau, 2015), 27–28.

7. Clyde Hertzman and Tom Boyce, "How Experience Gets Under the Skin to Create Gradients in Developmental Health," *Annual Review of Public Health* 31, no. 1 (April 2010): 329–47.

8. David T. Lackland, "Racial Differences in Hypertension: Implications for High Blood Pressure Management," *American Journal of the Medical Sciences* 348, no. 2 (August 2014): 135–38.

9. American Academy of Allergy, Asthma, and Immunology, "Black Children Six Times More Likely to Die of Asthma," press release, March

4, 2017, https://www.aaaai.org/about-aaaai/newsroom/news-releases/black-children-asthma.

10. The Baldwin citation is from a panel discussion moderated by Nat Hentoff, broadcast in 1961 on WBAI-FM radio and subsequently published with the title "The Negro in American Culture," in *CrossCurrents* 11, no. 3 (Summer 1961): 205–224.

11. Amy Roeder, "America Is Failing Its Black Mothers," *Harvard Public Health,* Winter 2019, https://www.hsph.harvard.edu/magazine/magazine_article/america-is-failing-its-black-mothers.

12. Brad N. Greenwood et al., "Physician-Patient Racial Concordance and Disparities in Birthing Mortality for Newborns," *Proceedings of the National Academy of Sciences* 117, no. 35 (September 1, 2020): 21194–200, https://doi.org/10.1073/pnas.1913405117.

13. Cristina Nova and Jamila Taylor, "Exploring African Americans' High Maternal and Infant Death Rates," Center for American Progress, February 1, 2018, https://www.americanprogress.org/issues/early-childhood/reports/2018/02/01/445576/exploring-african-americans-high-maternal-infant-death-rates.

14. Arline Geronimus et al., " 'Weathering' and Age Patterns of Allostatic Load Scores Among Blacks and Whites in the United States," *American Journal of Public Health* 96, no. 5 (May 2006): 826–33.

15. "Lifespan of Indigenous People 15 Years Shorter Than That of Other Canadians, Federal Documents Say," Canadian Press, January 23, 2018, https://www.cbc.ca/news/health/indigenous-people-live-15-years-less-philpott-briefing-1.4500307.

16. Roland Dyck et al., "Epidemiology of Diabetes Mellitus Among First Nations and Non–First Nations Adults," *Canadian Medical Association Journal* 182, no. 3 (February 23, 2010): 249–56.

17. L. Kirmayer, "Suicide Among Canadian Aboriginal People," *Transcultural Psychiatric Research Review* 31 (1994): 3–57.

18. Michael Marmot, *The Health Gap: The Challenge of an Unequal World* (New York: Bloomsbury, 2015), 12.

19. Sonia J. Lupien et al., "Child's Stress Hormone Levels Correlate with Mother's Socioeconomic Status and Depressive State," *Biological Psychiatry* 48, no. 10 (November 15, 2000): 976–80.

20. In Dennis Raphael, ed., *Social Determinants of Health: Canadian Perspectives*, 3rd ed. (Canadian Scholars Press, 2016), xiii.

21. Alex Soth, "The Great Divide," *New York Times*, September 5, 2020, https://www.nytimes.com/interactive/2020/09/05/opinion/inequality -life-expectancy.html.

22. M. Lemstra et al., "Health Disparity by Neighborhood Income," *Canadian Journal of Public Health* 97, no. 6 (November 2006): 435–39.

23. For example, Joan Luby et al., "The Effects of Poverty on Childhood Brain Development: The Mediating Effect of Caregiving and Stressful Life Events," *JAMA Pediatrics* 167, no. 12 (December 2013): 1135–42.

24. J. R. Swartz et al., "An Epigenetic Mechanism Links Socioeconomic Status to Changes in Depression-Related Brain Function in High-Risk Adolescents," *Molecular Psychiatry* 22, no. 2 (February 2017): 209–224.

25. Dennis Raphael et al., *Social Determinants of Health*, 2nd ed., 13. (Raphael here is recycling facetious advice that has been circulating for some years.) https://thecanadianfacts.org/The_Canadian_Facts -2nd_ed.pdf.

26. Michael Marmot and Eric Brunner, "Cohort Profile: The Whitehall II Study," *International Journal of Epidemiology* 34, no. 2 (April 2005): 251–56; and Aline Dugravot et al., "Social Inequalities in Multimorbidity, Frailty, Disability, and Transitions to Mortality: A 24-Year Follow-Up of the Whitehall II Cohort Study," *Lancet Public Health* 5, no. 1 (January 1, 2020): e42–50.

27. Richard Wilkinson, *The Impact of Inequality: How to Make Sick Societies Healthier* (New York: New Press, 2005), 58.

28. Robert Sapolsky, "The Health-Wealth Gap," *Scientific American*, November 2018, https://www.scientificamerican.com/index.cfm /_api/render/file/?method=inline&fileID=123ECD96-EF81-46F6 -983D2AE9A45FA354.

Chapter 23: Society's Shock Absorbers

1. Haider J. Warraich, "Why Men and Women Feel Pain Differently," *Washington Post*, May 15, 2021.

2. "Female Smokers Are Twice as Likely as Male Smokers to Develop Lung

Cancer," ScienceDaily, December 2, 2003, https://www.sciencedaily.com
/releases/2003/12/031202070515.htm.

3. Margaret Altemus et al., "Sex Differences in Anxiety and Depression
    Clinical Perspectives," *Frontiers in Neuroendocrinology* 35, no. 3 (August
    2014): 320–30.

4. Franck Mauvois-Jarvis et al., "Sex and Gender: Modifiers of Health,
    Disease, and Medicine," *Lancet* 396, no. 10250 (August 22, 2020): 565–82.

5. In the United States, for example, being Black or Hispanic and being
    female create more risk for autoimmune disease than either factor alone.
    A 1964 study on systemic lupus in New York in the *American Journal of
    Public Health* reported that "the morbidity and mortality rates were highest
    among Negroes, followed in descending order by the rates for Puerto
    Ricans and other whites" (Morris Siegel, "Epidemiology of Systemic
    Lupus Erythematosus: Time Trend and Racial Differences, *American
    Journal of Public Health* 54, no. 1 [January 1964]: 33–43). Fifty years later,
    that racial differential persisted. "By and large, SLE is more frequent and
    more severe with higher disease activity and more damage accrual in
    non-Caucasian populations (Hispanics, African descendants and Asians)
    than in Caucasians" (L. A. Gonzalez et al., "Ethnicity in Systemic Lupus
    Erythematosus [SLE]: Its Influence on Susceptibility and Outcomes,"
    Lupus 22, no. 12 [October 2013]: 1214–24). Being female and Indigenous
    on either side of the 49th parallel also elevates the risk—in Canada, for
    example, rheumatoid arthritis affects Indigenous people at a rate three
    times higher than the national average (Stephen Hunt, "Arthritis Affects
    Indigenous People at a Rate Three Times Higher Than Average," CBC
    News, November 5, 2018, https://www.cbc.ca/news/canada/calgary
    /indigenous-rates-arthritis-higher-than-average-1.4892319). Women,
    of course, predominate in these statistics: among Aboriginal women,
    the rheumatoid arthritis ratio is not three but *six* times elevated over
    men ("Rheumatoid Arthritis and the Aboriginal Population—What
    the Research Shows," JointHealth Insight, September 2006, https://
    jointhealth.org/programs-jhmonthly-view.cfm?id=19&locale=en-CA).

6. A 2021 World Health Organization study reported that one in four
    women and girls around the world have been assaulted by a male partner.
    If nonpartner violence is factored in, the WHO estimates that "about a
    third of women aged 15 or older—between 736 million and 852 million—
    will experience some form of sexual or physical violence in their lifetime."

The rates, according to the WHO paper, would be significantly higher were other forms of abuse factored in, such as online violence and sexual harassment. Liz Ford, "Quarter of Women and Girls Have Been Abused by a Partner, Says WHO," *Guardian*, March 9, 2021.

7. Melanie A. Hom et al., "Women Firefighters and Workplace Harassment: Associated Suicidality and Mental Health Sequelae," *Journal of Nervous and Mental Disease* 205, no. 12 (December 2017): 910–17.

8. Catherine E. Harnois and João L. Bastos, "Discrimination, Harassment, and Gendered Health Inequalities: Do Perceptions of Workplace Mistreatment Contribute to the Gender Gap in Self-Reported Health?," *Journal of Health and Social Behavior* 59, no. 2 (2018): 283–99.

9. Julie Holland, *Moody Bitches* (New York: Penguin Press, 2015), 30.

10. Elaine D. Eaker et al., "Marital Status, Marital Strain, and Risk of Coronary Heart Disease or Total Mortality: The Framingham Offspring Study," *Psychosomatic Medicine* 69, no. 6 (July–August 2007): 509–13.

11. Suzanne G. Haynes et al., "Women, Work and Coronary Heart Disease: Prospective Findings from the Framingham Heart Study," *American Journal of Public Health* 70, no. 2 (February 1980): 133–41.

12. Gillian Friedman, "Jobless, Selling Nudes Online, and Still Struggling," *New York Times*, January 12, 2021, https://www.nytimes.com/2021/01/13/business/onlyfans-pandemic-users.html.

13. Gail Dines, *Pornland: How Porn Has Hijacked Our Sexuality* (Boston: Beacon Press, 2010), xi.

14. Emer O'Hanlon, "Porn Lies Behind Cuts and Bruises of Rough Sex Fad," *Irish Independent*, August 2, 2020, https://www.independent.ie/opinion/comment/porn-lies-behind-cuts-and-bruises-of-rough-sex-fad-39416367.html.

15. Mary Wollstonecraft, *A Vindication of the Rights of Woman* (New York: Vintage Classics, 2014), 65.

16. Andrea Dworkin, *Intercourse* (1987; New York: Basic Books, 2007), 112.

17. Janice K. Kiecolt-Glaser et al., "Spousal Caregivers of Dementia Victims: Longitudinal Changes in Immunity and Health," *Psychosomatic Medicine* 53 (1991): 345–62.

18. Rachel M. Radin et al., "Maternal Caregivers Have Confluence of Altered Cortisol, High Reward-Driven Eating, and Worse Metabolic Health,"

PLoS ONE 14, no. 5 (May 10, 2019): e0216541, https://doi.org/10.1371 /journal.pone.0216541.

19. Jessica Grose, "Mothers Are the 'Shock Absorbers' of Our Society," *New York Times*, October 14, 2020, https://www.nytimes.com/2020/10/14 /parenting/working-moms-job-loss-coronavirus.html.

20. Caroline Criado Perez, *Invisible Women: Exposing Data Bias in a World Designed for Men* (London: Chatto & Windus, 2019), 73.

21. Kate Manne, *Down Girl: The Logic of Misogyny* (New York: Oxford University Press, 2018), 130.

Chapter 24: We Feel Their Pain

1. Anthony Brooks and Grace Tatter, "Surviving Family Politics at Thanksgiving," *On Point*, WBUR, November 27, 2019, https://www.wbur .org/onpoint/2019/11/27/family-politics-thanksgiving.

2. Kevin B. Smith et al., "Friends, Relatives, Sanity, and Health: The Costs of Politics," *PLoS One* 14, no. 9 (September 2019), https://journals.plos .org/plosone/article?id=10.1371/journal.pone.0221870.

3. Elissa Epel, "Stressed Out by Politics? It Could Be Making Your Body Age Faster, Too," *Quartz*, March 16, 2017, https://qz.com/931355/telomeres -and-cell-aging-nobel-prize-for-medicine-winner-elizabeth-blackburn -and-elissa-epel-explain-how-trump-is-aging-our-cells/.

4. Steven Stosny, "He Once Called It 'Election Stress Disorder.' Now the Therapist Says We're Suffering from This," *Washington Post*, February 6, 2017, https://www.washingtonpost.com/news/inspired-life /wp/2017/02/06/suffering-from-headline-stress-disorder-since-trumps -win-youre-definitely-not-alone/?noredirect=on.

5. Alice Miller, *For Your Own Good: Hidden Cruelty in Child-Rearing and the Roots of Violence* (1983; New York: Farrar, Straus and Giroux, 1990), 65.

6. Sue Gerhardt, *The Selfish Society* (London: Simon and Schuster, 2011), 46.

7. Jim Coyle, "For Stephen Harper, a Stable Upbringing and an Unpredictable Path to Power," *Toronto Star*, October 8, 2015, https://www .thestar.com/news/insight/2015/10/04/for-stephen-harper-a-stable -upbringing-and-an-unpredictable-path-to-power.html.

8. "An Emotional Justin Trudeau Cries Discussing the Death of Gord

Downie," *Global News*, YouTube, October 18, 2017, https://www
.youtube.com/watch?v=YMCaDvah6No.

9. Jonathan Kay, "The Justin Trudeau I Can't Forget," *Walrus*, September
    29, 2015.

10. Claudia Wallis, "Of Psychopaths and Presidential Candidates,"
    Scientific American Mind, guest blog, August 12, 2016, https://blogs
    .scientificamerican.com/mind-guest-blog/of-psychopaths-and
    -presidential-candidates/.

11. Jane Mayer, "Trump's Boswell Speaks," *New Yorker*, July 26, 2016.

12. Amy Chozick, "Clinton Father's Brusque Style, Mostly Unspoken but
    Powerful," *New York Times*, July 20, 2015.

13. Megan Twohey, "Her Husband Accused of Affairs, a Defiant Clinton
    Fought Back," *New York Times*, October 3, 2016.

14. David Brooks, "The Avalanche of Distrust," *New York Times*, September
    13, 2016.

15. George Lakoff, *The Political Mind* (New York: Penguin Books, 2008), 76.

16. Randy Rainbow (@randyrainbow), "G'night, mom and dad. See you in
    the morning. ♥," Twitter, August 11, 2020, 10:17 p.m., https://twitter.com
    /randyrainbow/status/1293386210388381696.

17. See, for example, "Stephen Kicks Off a *Late Show*'s Obama-Rama
    Extravagama with a Special Obamalogue," *The Late Show with Stephen
    Colbert*, CBS, YouTube video, https://www.youtube.com
    /watch?v=RmtCV-U8wwo.

Chapter 25: Mind in the Lead

1. Aeschylus, *Agamemnon*, in *The Orestia*, translated by Robert Fagles (New
    York: Penguin, 1979), 109.

2. Edith Eva Eger, *The Choice: Embrace the Possible* (New York: Scribner,
    2017), 280.

Chapter 26: Four A's and Five Compassions

1. Kelly Turner, *Radical Remission: Surviving Cancer Against All Odds* (New
    York: HarperOne, 2014), 45.

2. Henning Krampe et al., "The Influence of Personality Factors on Disease Progression and Health-Related Quality of Life in People with ALS," *Amyotrophic Lateral Sclerosis* 9, no. 2 (May 2008): 99–107.

3. Henriët van Middendorp et al., "Effects of Anger and Anger Regulation Styles on Pain in Daily Life of Women with Fibromyalgia: A Diary Study," *European Journal of Pain* 14, no. 2 (February 2010): 176–82.

4. Helen Knott, *In My Own Moccasins: A Memoir of Resilience* (Saskatchewan, Canada: University of Regina Press, 2019), 240.

5. Thomas Merton, *The Seven Storey Mountain: An Autobiography of Faith* (Boston: Mariner Books, 1999), 362.

Chapter 27: A Dreadful Gift

1. Nancy A. Shadick et al., "A Randomized Controlled Trial of an Internal Family Systems–Based Psychotherapeutic Intervention on Outcomes in Rheumatoid Arthritis: A Proof-of-Concept Study," *Journal of Rheumatology* 40, no. 11 (November 2013): 1831–41.

2. Aleksandr Solzhenitsyn, *Cancer Ward* (New York: Vintage Classics, 2017), 89.

Chapter 28: Before the Body Says No

1. Richard C. Schwartz, *Introduction to the Internal Family Systems Model* (Trailheads Publications, 2001), 54.

2. A. H. Almaas, *The Freedom to Be* (Diamond Books, 1989), 12.

3. Cited in Thich Nhat Hanh, *The Heart of the Buddha's Teaching* (New York: Broadway Books, 1998), 45.

4. János Selye, *The Stress of Life*, rev. ed. (New York: McGraw-Hill, 1978), 419.

Chapter 29: Seeing Is Disbelieving

1. Bruce H. Lipton and Steve Bhaerman, *Spontaneous Evolution: Our Positive Future (And a Way to Get There from Here)* (Carlsbad, CA: Hay House, 2009), 38–39.

2. Jeffrey M. Schwartz and Sharon Begley, *The Mind and the Brain: Neuroplasticity and the Power of Mental Force* (New York: ReganBooks, 2002).

Chapter 30: Foes to Friends

1. Richard Schwartz, *Introduction to the Internal Family Systems Model* (Trailheads Publications, 2001), 67–68.

2. Edith Eger, *The Gift* (New York: Scribner, 2020), 156.

Chapter 31: Jesus in the Tipi

1. For example, on ayahuasca: José Carlo Bouso et al., "Ayahuasca, Technical Report 2021," International Center for Ethnobotanical Education, Research and Service, December 2021, https://www.iceers.org/ayahuasca -technical-report/.

2. Michelle S. Thiessen et al., "Psychedelic Use and Intimate Partner Violence: The Role of Emotion Regulation," *Journal of Psychopharmacology*, 2018, https://doi.org/10.1177/0269881187.

3. S. C. Gwynne, *Empire of the Summer Moon: Quanah Parker and the Rise and Fall of the Comanches* (New York: Scribner, 2010), 314.

Chapter 32: My Life as a Genuine Thing

1. A. H. Almaas, *Elements of the Real in Man* (Diamond Books, 1987), 26.

2. Lewis Mehl-Madrona, *Coyote Medicine: Lessons from Native American Healing* (New York: Simon and Schuster, 1997), 16–17.

3. Wilhelm Reich, *The Murder of Christ: The Emotional Plague of Mankind* (New York: Farrar, Straus and Giroux, 1953), 174–75.

4. For example, Quinn A. Conklin et al., "Meditation, Stress Processes, and Telomere Biology," *Current Opinion in Psychology* 28 (2019): 92–101; D. Bergen-Cico et al., "Reductions in Cortisol Associated with Primary Care Brief Mindfulness Programs with Veterans with PTSD," *Med Care* 52, no. 12, suppl. 5 (December 2014): S25–31; and A. M. Gallegos et al., "Mindfulness-Based Stress Reduction to Enhance Psychological Functioning and Improve Inflammatory Biomarkers in Trauma-Exposed Women: A Pilot Study," *Psychological Trauma* 7, no. 6 (November 2015): 525–32.

5. Francesco Pagnini et al., "Mindfulness, Physical Impairment and Psychological Well-Being in People with Amyotrophic Lateral Sclerosis," *Psychology and Health* 30, no. 5 (October 2014): 503–17, https://doi.org /10.1080/08870446.2014.982652.

6. Rony Berger et al., "Reducing Israeli-Jewish Pupils' Outgroup Prejudice with a Mindfulness and Compassion-Based Social Emotional Program," *Mindfulness* 9, no. 2 (December 2018), https://doi.org/10.1007/s12671-018 -0919-y.

Chapter 33: Unmaking a Myth

1. For people who might find this assertion surprising, I recommend the works of such Israeli historians as Ilan Pappe, Simha Flapan, Benny Morris, Tom Segev, and Avi Shlaim, or of American Jewish scholars like Norman Finkelstein; for example, Pappe's seminal work, *The Ethnic Cleansing of Palestine* (Oneworld, 2006). Or the reports of the indomitable Gideon Levy in the Israeli paper *Haaretz*. Or for a Palestinian view, the illuminating book of personal memoir and history by Rashid Khalidi, *One Hundred Years' War on Palestine: A History of Settler Colonialism and Resistance, 1917–2017* (New York: Picador, 2020).

2. James Baldwin, "As Much Truth as One Can Bear," *New York Times Book Review*, January 14, 1962.

3. Baldwin, "As Much Truth as One Can Bear."

4. The Joan Didion citations are from an obituary of the late writer: Sian Cain and Edward Helmore, "Joan Didion, American Journalist and Author, Dies at 87," *Guardian*, December 23, 2021.

5. Bessel van der Kolk, *The Body Keeps the Score: Brain, Mind, and Body in the Healing of Trauma* (New York: Penguin, 2014), 349.

6. For example, a study that crossed my desk just as I was writing this chapter: Nina T. Rogers, Christine Power, and Snehal M. Pinto Pereira, "Child Maltreatment, Early Life Socioeconomic Disadvantage and All-Cause Mortality: Findings from a Prospective British Cohort," *BMJ Open* 11 (2021): e050914, https://doi.org/10.1136/bmjopen-2021-050914.

7. Jesse Thistle, *From the Ashes* (Toronto: Simon & Schuster Canada, 2019), 260.

8. Maggie Kline, *Brain-Changing Strategies to Trauma-Proof Our Schools* (Berkeley, CA: North Atlantic Books, 2020), 2.

9. Alison Rourke, "Greta Thunberg Responds to Asperger's Critics: 'It's a Superpower,'" *Guardian*, September 2, 2019.

10. Caroline Hickman et al., "Young People's Voices on Climate Anxiety, Government Betrayal and Moral Injury: A Global Phenomenon,"

preprint submitted to the *Lancet*, September 2021, https://papers.ssrn
.com/sol3/papers.cfm?abstract_id=3918955.

11. Damian Carrington, " 'Blah, Blah, Blah': Greta Thunberg Lambasts
    Leaders over Climate Crisis," *Guardian*, September 28, 2021.

12. Hannah Arendt, "Eichmann in Jerusalem—I," *New Yorker*, February 16,
    1963.

13. According to an April 11, 2021, *New York Times* editorial, the number of
    Iraqi children who died as a result of U.S. sanctions in the 1990s was
    500,000. The interview in which Albright made the statement was aired
    on CBS's *60 Minutes*, May 12, 1996. Albright later wrote, "I had fallen
    into a trap and said something I did not mean, regretting having seemed
    'cold-blooded and cruel.' " Apart from her regret about how she came
    across, neither she nor any U.S. official responsible for the sanctions ever
    apologized for the deaths of the children.

14. Abraham Maslow, "Resistance to Acculturation," *Journal of Social Issues*
    1 (Fall 1951): 26–29.

Index

Page numbers in *italics* refer to illustrations.

abortion, 138
Abrams, Nancy, 398
acceptance, 380–82, 403–7, 474–75
ACE (Adverse Childhood Experiences)
    Study, 22, 230–31, 249, 270
acorn analogy, of human nature
    development, 117–18
acute myeloid leukemia, 401–3
addiction, 211–23, 224–34
    as an adaptation, 233–34
    advocacy and activism, 493–94
    background, 211–13
    "bad choices" paradigm, 213–14,
        219–20
    capitalism and, 295–96, 301–2,
        304–6
    child development and, 221–22,
        227–28, 227n, 230–32, 233–34
    definition (new), 224–26
    "disease" paradigm, 214–16, 215n,
        216n, 219, 224
    dopamine and endorphins, 232–34
    genetics of, 237n
    as healing journey teacher, 435–36,
        438–40
    misconceptions about, 213–16
    otherism and, 313–14
    personal stories, 261–62, 385–86
    to pleasure, 298–99
    pleasure and, 298–99
    sensitivity and, 261–62
    severity spectrum of, 226–27
    sobriety-abstinence comparison, 362
    to sugar, 299, 301–2
    toxic masculinity and, 341–42
    trauma facets of, 226–32
    what is right about addiction?
        216–20
    why the pain? 220–23, 227
ADHD (attention deficit hyperactivity
    disorder), 237n, 242–43, 264–67
Adiga, Aravind, 275
adrenal gland, 47–49, 62–63, 70

The Adventures of Augie March
    (Bellow), 255
Adverse Childhood Experiences (ACE)
    Study, 22, 230–31, 249, 270
advertising, 204–5, 298–300
advocacy and activism, 492–94
Aeschylus, 363
Afghanistan, 175
agency
    acceptance and, 381
    childbirth and, 148–49
    defined, 377–78
    disease as a teacher for, 395–99
    for healing, 74–75, 367–73,
        377–78, 381
    mental illness and, 236, 238
    self-examination and, 35–36
A Is for Advice (Stanger-Ross), 154
Albright, Madeleine, 496, 496n
alcohol. *See* addiction
Alcoholics Anonymous, 215–16,
    229, 467
Alexander, Bruce, 286, 288–89
alienation, 32–33, 172–73, 277–82, 285,
    290–93
allergies, 72
allomothers, 175
allostasis, 48
allostatic load, 48, 276, 319–20, 344
Almaas, A. H., 254, 383, 388, 409, 463,
    467–68
Alti, Zachary, 232
Alzheimer's disease, 60, 70, 330, 337
Amazing Grace (documentary), 356
American Academy of Pediatrics, 169
American College of Obstetricians and
    Gynecologists, 149, 174
American corporate capitalism (ACC),
    296. *See also* capitalism and
    corporate capitalism
American Heart Association, 301
American Psychiatric Association,
    240, 243

American Psychological Association, 293–94

Amusing Ourselves to Death (Postman), 205

amygdala, 46, 142, 326

amyotrophic lateral sclerosis (ALS), 41, 380, 402, 402n, 405–6, 477

The Anatomy of a Calling (Rankin), 94–95

Anatomy of an Epidemic (Whitaker), 241

Andrea, 271

Angell, Marcia, 97

anger
  for healing, 378–80, 381
  repression, 40–42, 77, 78, 79, 333–34, 379–80

Angier, Natalie, 183–84

Anné, Julie T., 271

anorexia, 270–72, 313–14

antidepressants, 82–83, 82n, 235, 245–46

antipsychotics, 235

anti-Semitism, 311, 314

ants, 197–98

anxiety, 172–73, 280, 295–96, 330

Arendt, Hannah, 495

The Art of the Deal (Trump), 350–51

asthma, 56–57, 64, 318

attachment and authenticity
  acceptance and authenticity, 381
  child development, 105–10, 128–32
  depression and, 254
  detachment and, 17–18
  disease as a teacher of, 395–99
  healing through authenticity, 375–76, 381, 387–88
  identity crises, 199–202
  mental illness and, 243–44
  peer orientation and, 181–83
  psychosocial integration of, 288

attention deficit hyperactivity disorder (ADHD), 237n, 242–43, 264–67

Austin, Jehannine, 251

authenticity. *See* attachment and authenticity

autism and autism-like symptoms, 191–92, 492

autoimmunity, 68–84. *See also specific conditions*
  antidepressants and, 82–83, 82n
  background, 70–72
  gender distribution, 73
  neurogenic inflammation and, 76–78
  personal stories, 68–71, 78–82
  process of, 90
  stress and, 74–84
  trends, 72–73, 82–84

autonomic nervous system, 45, 92, 365

ayahuasca, 448–54, 455–56, 458–59, 458n

Baby and Child Care (Spock), 162–63

Bakan, Joel, 187, 188–89, 306, 307, 310

Baldwin, James, 314–15, 318, 485

Bambra, Clare, 303

Banks, Russell, 160

Beautiful Boy (Sheff), 228

Being and the Meaning of Life (Almaas), 463

Bellow, Saul, 255

Bentall, Richard, 248, 253

Berman, Morris, 3, 281

Bezos, Jeff, 284

Bhagavad Gita, 52

Bianca, 81–82, 394–95

Biden, Hunter, 357

Biden, Joe, 306, 354

biological age, 65–66

biological embedding, 311–13, 331

biological regulation, 124–27

biopsychosocial approach to medicine, 53

bipolar disorder, 236, 237, 267–70

Blackburn, Elizabeth, 59–60

Blair, Tony, 277–78

blame
  gender gap, 352
  healing journey and, 112, 258–59, 432, 434, 437
  parenting and, 126, 139, 179–80
  self-blame, 30, 83–84, 86, 97–98, 100, 112
  trauma and, 34–35

Blessed with a Brain Tumor (Pye), 390–91, 404–5

bliss spot, 299

Bloch, Gary, 326–27

body disconnection, 23–24, 25–28, 33–35

bodymind, 39–46, 49–51, 96–97, 461–62

body politic, 346

body scanning and signals, 416–17

bodywide memory, 139

boldog, 453

borderline personality disorder, 247

Boston Globe, 241

Botox, 203

boundaries, 377–78

Bowlby, John, 17–18, 35
Boyce, Tom, 250
brain. *See* nervous system
Brand, Russell, 218, 300, 357
Brave New World (Huxley), 197, 201
breast cancer
  genetic inheritance, 60n
  mind-body unity and, 37–39, 40, 49
  personality traits and, 99, 111
  race and, 318
  stress and, 92–94
breastfeeding, 161, 165–66, 167,
    169–70, 175
British Journal of Psychiatry, 43
British Medical Journal, 309
Brody, Gene, 67
Brooks, David, 286, 353
Brooks, Michael, 469
Bruce, 211, 212, 221, 385–86
Buckley, Sarah, 150
Buddha and Buddhism, 31, 53, 58,
    365–66, 467
Buffett, Warren, 283
bulimia, 270–72, 313–14
bullying, 183–85, 323, 333
Bushmen of the Kalahari, 121
Business Insider, 192–93

Caap, Ulf, 199–200
Cacioppo, John, 293
Cacioppo, Stephanie, 293
cancer. *See also specific cancers*
  depression and, 43
  gender disparities, 330
  genetic inheritance, 60, 60n
  mind-body unity and, 37–46, 49–51
  personality traits and, 96–98, 99, 100,
    103–4, 110–12
  as a process, 85–87, 92–94
  racism and, 318
  stress and, 92–94
  as a teacher, 395–99
  war metaphors for, 87–88
Cancer Nursing, 40–41
Cancer Research, 42
Cancer Ward (Solzhenitsyn), 395
Canfield, Cheryl, 396, 403–4
capitalism and corporate capitalism,
    275–85, 297–310
  acculturation and, 6–8
  advertising, 204–5, 298–300
  agency of, 377

alienation and, 32–33, 290–91, 292
authenticity adaptations, 109–10
background, 3–6, 275–77
child development and, 187–93
climate change and, 308–10
criticisms of, 282–85
defined, 296
desocialization and, 277–82, 285
disconnection of society and, 295–96
ethic of, 277
goal of, 310
health and wellness fixation, 1
health impacts of, 280, 281–82,
    297–98, 301–6
human nature and, 121–22
loneliness and, 294
on personality traits, 409
pharmaceutical industry, 304–5,
    493–94
psychoanalysis of, 307
social character and, 200–207
tobacco industry, 305–6
unmaking of normalcy of, 485–86
capital-*T* trauma (big-*T* trauma), 21–22, 23
cardiovascular disease
  capitalism and, 281–82
  emotions and, 46
  healing journey, 95
  interpersonal biology and, 58
  personality traits and, 100
  process of, 94–95
  race and racism, 318
caregivers, 66, 105–6, 125–26, 129,
    337–38. *See also* child development
    and parenting
CARE system, 130–31
Carlene, 320–21
Caroline, 37–38, 37n, 40
Case, Anne, 289
Caterina, 267–70
Cavoukian, Raffi, 123, 124, 134–35, 491
CBS News, 302
celiac disease, 70, 72
Ceremony (Silko), 447
cesarean sections (C-sections), 143,
    152–54
character-building, 197–207
  background, 197–99
  consumption-hunger trait, 203–5
  hypnotic-passivity trait, 205–7
  identity crises, 199–202
  separation-from-self trait, 202–3
  social character, 200–207

Charcot, Jean-Martin, 80, 81
Charles VII (king), 477
Chekhov, Anton, 383
childbirth, 146–59
    agency and midwifery, 146–47, 150–55,
        158–59
    C-sections, 143, 152–54
    obstetrical trauma, 155–58
    race and, 319
    as sacred life passage, 159
    social culture and, 150
    socioeconomic status and, 157–58
    Western medicine and, 146–58
child development and parenting, 123–35,
        179–96
    addiction and, 221–22, 227–28,
        230–32, 233–34
    attachment and authenticity, 105–10,
        128–34
    autoimmunity and, 75, 76–77, 78, 81
    background, 160
    blame and, 126, 139, 179–80
    character-building, 197–207
    child honoring, 123–24, 127, 133–34
    digital technology use, 188–93, 194–95
    disease process rooted in, 85–87,
        88–89
    educational priorities, 193–96
    emotion development and,
        124–27, 134
    epigenetics and, 62–64
    free play, 134, 194–95
    gender gap in parenting, 337–39
    human nature and, 117–18
    instinct suppression for parents and,
        160–71
    interpersonal biology and, 56–57
    loneliness of parenting, 170, 174–78
    marketing and, 187–89
    maturation, 127–28, 131–34, 182,
        185–89
    mental illness and, 242–44, 247,
        248–49, 257, 267–70
    parental stress effects, 171–74
    peer orientation, 181–85, 187–88,
        491–92
    political culture and, 346–47
    social culture and, 126, 128, 134–35,
        175–77, 179–81, 183, 187–88,
        193–96
    trauma's impact on, 17–18, 21–23,
        33–35
    vulnerability and, 185–87

child honoring, 123–24, 127, 133–34, 491
Childhood Under Siege (Bakan), 187,
        188–89
Chinese medicine (traditional), 98
The Choice (Eger), 372
Chomsky, Noam, 115, 206, 482
The Chomsky-Foucault Debate
        (Chomsky), 115
A Chorus of Stones (Griffin), 13
chronic fatigue syndrome (myalgic
        encephalomyelitis; ME), 70, 101–2
circumcision, 167, 167n
climate change, 308–10
Clinton, Bill, 60, 352, 355
Clinton, Hillary, 349, 351–53
Coates, Ta-Nehisi, 314, 317
Cobain, Kurt, 356
Cohen, Ben, 283
Cole, Steven, 90–91, 92, 93–94, 282, 294
commercial culture. See capitalism and
        corporate capitalism
commercials and advertising, 204–5,
        298–300
community-mindedness
    benefits of, 287–88
    human nature and, 116, 120–21
    loss of, 286–96
    parenting and, 174–78
    pregnancy environment and, 144, 145
compassion
    autoimmunity and, 83–84
    of curiosity and understanding,
        384–85
    healing journey and, 83–84, 259,
        382–89
    ordinary human compassion, 272,
        383–84
    as personality trait, 102–3
    pity-compassion comparison, 384
    of possibility, 388–89
    of recognition, 385–86
    self-compassion, 83–84, 384, 391–95
    of truth, 386–88
Compassionate Inquiry (CI), 419–21,
        448–49
concussion analogy, 20
connection. See disconnection of society
conspiracy realism, 299–300
consumption-hunger trait, 203–5
The Continuum Concept (Liedloff), 119, 131
control adaptation, 260–62
Cooke, Will, 468–69
corporal punishment, 168–69

corporate capitalism. *See* capitalism and corporate capitalism

The Corporation (Bakan), 306

correctional system, 475–76, 489–90

cortisol, 70, 280, 280n

Courtney, 155–57

COVID-19 pandemic
  autoimmunity and, 84n
  capitalism and, 284
  gender disparities and, 338
  lessons from, 286
  race and, 317
  risk factors, 302–3
  as a teacher, 494–95

Coyle, Jim, 348

Cozolino, Louis, 233–34

Cracked Up! (documentary), 222, 236n

The Crack in the Cosmic Egg (Pearce), 359

Cree people, 163

Cribsheet (Oster), 161–62

Crimeni, Carson, 184–85

Crohn's disease, 49–50, 70, 72

Crow, Sheryl, 390

C-sections (cesarean sections), 143, 152–54

Cullis-Suzuki, Severn, 308–9

Cured (Rediger), 398–99

curing-healing comparison, 362

curiosity, 384–85

Curtis, Jamie Lee, 217–18, 357

Daily Gazette (Harvard University), 42–43

Damasio, Antonio, 124

Damon, Matt, 272

Danielle, 154

Danish Medical Journal, 73

Darlene, 382, 387–88

Davis, Wade, 281, 459–60, 475, 479

death, acceptance of, 403–7, 474–75

deaths by despair, 289

Deaton, Angus, 289

delta waves, 422–23

delusions, 268, 269–70

deMause, Lloyd, 162

denial and suppression, 27–28, 100–102, 441–46

depression
  biological approach to, 255–56
  cancer risk factor, 43
  capitalism and, 280, 295–96
  diagnostic approach to, 241, 253–54
  gender disparities, 330
  pharmaceutical approach to, 235, 247–48
  postpartum depression, 141, 142

Descartes' Error (Damasio), 124

desocialization. *See* disconnection of society

detachment. *See* attachment and authenticity

de Waal, Frans, 121

Dhammapada, 31

diabetes, 70, 72, 322–23

Diagnostic and Statistical Manual of Mental Disorders (DSM-5), 240, 243, 244

Dickinson, Emily, 209

Didion, Joan, 352, 486

digital technology use, 32–33, 188–93, 194–95

Dines, Gail, 233, 335

diplopia (double vision), 79, 81

disconnection from emotions, 23–28, 32–34, 111–12, 264–67

disconnection of society, 286–96
  alienation and, 32–33, 290–93
  capitalism and, 277–82, 285
  conclusion, 296
  dislocation and, 288–90
  loneliness and, 293–95
  loss of meaning and, 286–88, 291–92
  materialism and, 295–96
  spiritual, 467–68

disease as a process, 85–95
  addiction and, 225
  background, 85–87
  emotions and, 90, 96–97, 110–12
  healing journey centered on, 92, 94–95
  personality traits and, 96–112
  psychosomatic component to, 39
  as reframing approach to disease, 87–94
  self-compassion and, 83–84, 391–95

disease as a teacher, 390–407
  for acceptance of death, 403–7
  for authenticity development, 395–99
  background, 95, 390–91
  compassion and, 385–86
  COVID-19 pandemic, 494–95
  for emotional release, 399–403
  for self-compassion development, 83–84, 384, 391–95

"disease" paradigm
    of addiction, 214–16, 215n, 216n, 219, 224
    of mental illness, 235–41
dislocation, 288–90
dissociation adaptation, 250, 255–56, 262–64
Doblin, Rick, 460
dogs, 267
Dolman, Sherri, 151–53, 154
Donne, John, 52
dopamine, 190–91, 232–33, 241, 266
Dopamine Labs, 191
Doty, James, 382–83
double-mindedness, 433
double vision (diplopia), 79, 81
Down Girl (Manne), 340–41
Doyle, William, 195
drugs. See addiction and specific drugs
DSM-5 (Diagnostic and Statistical Manual of Mental Disorders), 240, 243, 244
Duhigg, Charles, 291
Dunham, Lena, 199, 217, 219, 222, 357
Dworkin, Andrea, 336–37
Dylan, Bob, 204

eating disorders, 270–72, 313–14
eczema, 70
Educated (Westover), 28
education system, 490–92
Eger, Edith, 371–73, 437–38
ego, 53–54, 104–7, 112
Eichmann, Adolf, 495
emotional labor, 337–41
emotions
    autoimmunity and, 75–76
    child development and, 124–27, 134, 188–89
    depression as absence of, 254–56
    disconnection from, 111–12
    disease as a teacher for release of, 399–403
    disease process and, 90, 96–97, 110–12
    gender gap and, 333–34, 336, 341–42
    hypnotic-passivity trait and, 205–7
    interpersonal biology and, 56–57
    machinery of stress, 46–49
    medical training and, 94–95
    mind-body unity, 38–46, 49–51
    personality traits and, 96–105, 110–12
    personal stories, 37–38, 49–51

pregnancy environment and, 138–43
    suppression of, 320
    survival instinct and, 28
employment, 57–58, 141, 290, 291–93
endocrine system (hormones)
    addiction and, 232–34
    childbirth and, 155
    digital technology use and, 190–91
    disease trends, 297–98
    infant-mother bond and, 165–66, 165n
    mental illness and, 241, 266
    mind-body unity and, 45, 47–49
endocrinologists, 297–98
endometriosis, 101–2
endorphins, 233–34
Engel, George, 53, 80
Ensler, Eve. See V
Epel, Elissa, 60, 65, 66, 67, 344
epigenetics, 59–67, 61n, 118, 134, 140, 142
Epstein, Mark, 15, 23
European Journal of Pain, 380
evolutionary theory, 62, 119–21
experience of experience, 33

Facebook, 189
Fadiman, Anne, 147
family life. See child development and parenting
family systems, 33–35, 393–94. See also child development and parenting
fat, 299
Feldman-Winter, Lori, 169
Felitti, Vincent, 109–10, 230–31, 270
feminine-coded goods and services, 340–41
fibromyalgia, 101–2, 380
fight, flight, and freeze responses, 27–28, 33–34
Fighting for Space (Lupick), 222
First Nations, 144, 320–21, 321–23
Fleury, Theoren, 221, 264
Floyd, George, 316–17
Food and Drug Administration, 306
Forbes, Jack, 116
The Forest People (Turnbull), 173–74
For Your Own Good (Miller), 347
Franklin, Aretha, 356
Franklin, Jon, 240
free play, 134, 194–95, 266
Freud, Sigmund, 460
Friedman, Milton, 307
Friedrichs, Ellen, 193

Fromm, Erich, 1, 200–201, 206, 403
From the Ashes (Thistle), 385

Garbarino, James, 178, 180–81, 194
Gautama, 53, 365–66
Gauthier, Mary, 420–21
Gelman, Karen, 88
gender gap, 329–42
    addiction and, 223
    of autoimmunity, 73
    emotional labor, 337–41
    epigenetics and, 66
    health impacts of, 329–38
    interpersonal biology and, 57
    patriarchal cycle, 313, 338–42
    self-realization for women, 336–41
    sexualization of women, 332, 334–36
    toxic masculinity, 341–42
genes and genetic inheritance
    of addiction, 215n, 231, 237n
    autoimmunity and, 72, 73
    of diseases, 60, 60n
    epigenetics, 59–67, 61n, 118, 134,
        140, 142
    gene expression, 62–63, 62n
    of human nature, 118
    loneliness and, 294
    of mental illness, 237–38, 240, 249–50,
        251–52, 262–63, 265
    of sensitivity, 249–50
genuineness. *See* attachment and
    authenticity
Georgieva, Kristalina, 278–79
Gerhardt, Sue, 347
Glenda, 49–51
The Globalization of Addiction
    (Alexander), 286, 288–89
Glover, Danny, 204–5
Goldin, Nan, 221–22, 435–36, 438–39,
    493–94
gonzo (pornography), 335
Good Will Hunting (film), 272
Göring, Bettina, 369–70
Göring, Hermann, 369–70
Gramsci, Antonio, 482, 482n
Greenspan, Stanley, 113, 126
grief, 42, 76, 77–78, 79–82, 129–31, 381
Griffin, Susan, 13
The Growth of the Mind (Greenspan), 113
Guardian, 310
guilt and regret, 97–98, 112, 432–35
gut instinct

disconnection from, 23–24, 27–28,
    33–34, 124, 160–71
    healing journey and, 395–99
    as second brain, 365
gut microbial flora, 142–43

Hamlet (Shakespeare), 464
Hammond, Darrell, 218–19, 222, 235–36,
    236n, 238, 259
Hanisch, Sue, 367–69
Hanson, Rick, 478
happiness, 298–99
"happy childhood," 227–28, 441–46
Harari, Yuval Noah, 277
Hardy, Kenneth, 315, 316, 332
Hare, R. D., 297
Hari, Johann, 247–48
Harper, Stephen, 348
Harrington, Anne, 235
Harris, Erica, 399–403, 443–45
Harris, Kamala, 354
Harris, Nadine Burke, 489
Hartmann, Thom, 4
headline stress disorder, 344
healing journey, 361–73, 430–46
    addiction as teacher for, 438–40
    background, 363–67, 430–32
    compassion overview, 83–84, 259,
        382–89
    conclusions, 373, 446
    curing-healing comparison, 362
    defined, 361–63
    disease as an agent of healing, 95,
        390–407. *See also* disease as a
        teacher
    "disease as a process" application to,
        92, 94–95
    guilt and regret as teacher for,
        432–35
    mental illness and, 238–39, 440–41
    ordinary human compassion, 383–84
    personality pattern modification, 98,
        104–5
    personal stories, 27, 256–60,
        367–73
    principle of acceptance, 380–82
    principle of agency, 74–75, 367–73,
        377–78, 381
    principle of anger, 378–80, 381
    principle of authenticity, 375–76, 381,
        387–88
    principle overview, 374–75

psychedelics and, 447–62
return-to-self practices, 408–12
self-accusation as teacher for,
435–38
self-inquiry exercise, 412–21
self-limiting beliefs release, 422–29
as spiritual journey, 463–80.
See also touching spirit
suppression and denial as teacher for,
441–46
unmaking the myth of normal for,
481–97. See also normal,
unmaking of
healthy anger, 378–80
heart, 365, 365n
heart attacks, 46. See also cardiovascular
disease
Hebraic Tanakh, 477
Henriques, Martha, 61
heroin. See addiction
Hertzman, Clyde, 312–13, 317
Hinduism, 52
Hippocrates, 98
Hitler, Adolf, 372, 437–38
Hmong immigrants, 147
Hoffman, Eva, 33
Holland, Julie, 329, 330, 333,
339–40
Hope Against Hope (Mandelstam), 363
Hope in the Dark (Solnit), 273
How the Other Half Lives (Riis), 485
How to Change Your Mind (Pollan),
456, 457
HPA axis, 47–49, 62–63, 275–76
Hughes, Clara, 470–71, 475
Hugo, Victor, 481, 496
human compassion, 383–84
human development. See character-
building; childbirth; child
development and parenting; human
nature and human needs; pregnancy
environment
Human Genome Project, 60
human nature and human needs, 115–22,
128, 134–35
Humboldt, Alexander von, 308
Hunter, Noël, 256–57
Huntington's disease, 60n
Huxley, Aldous, 197, 201
hypertension, 318. See also cardiovascular
disease
hypnotic-passivity trait, 205–7
hypothalamus, 47–49, 62–63, 91–92

Ibsen, Henrik, 32
Icaro, Mee Ok "Mandy," 68–72, 68n, 73,
74–76, 457–59, 458n
ice storm (Quebec, 1998), 63–64
idiopathic autoimmune diseases, 72
I Don't Want to Talk About It (Real), 342
illness. See addiction; disease as a process;
disease as a teacher; mental illness
and personality disorders
"Illness as Metaphor" (Sontag),
96–97, 111
i-Minds (Swingle), 191–92
immaterial (nonthings), 37, 40, 48, 51
immune system
autoimmune diseases, 68–84. See also
autoimmunity
epigenetics and, 64, 65
mind-body unity and, 41–43, 45,
50–51
immunosuppressants, 70
Indigenous cultures
addiction and, 222–23
"All my relations" greeting, 52
birth stories, 157–58
collective sphere of trauma for, 36
community-mindedness of, 121
compassion of understanding for, 385
medical training on, 489
parenting and, 164, 167–68, 174–75
pregnancy environment, honoring
of, 144
psychedelic practices, 447–54
racism and, 313–15, 320–24
social dislocation of, 289
spirituality of, 462, 467, 471–75
inequality. See otherism
inflammatory bowel disease (IBD),
49–50, 70, 72
inherent expectations, 119–21
In My Own Moccasins (Knott), 311,
315, 408
Instagram, 189
instincts. See gut instinct
interbeing, 58
interconnected natures. See attachment
and authenticity; autoimmunity;
disease as a process; emotions; genes
and genetic inheritance;
interpersonal biology; trauma facets
Internal Family Systems (IFS), 393–94
International Monetary Fund (IMF), 279
interpersonal biology, 52–58, 92
interpersonal compassion, 383–84

interpersonal neurobiology, 54–56
In the Body of the World (V), 85–86
In the Realm of Hungry Ghosts (Maté), 30, 212, 454
Invisible Women (Perez), 338
Iraq, 496, 496n
Irish Republican Army (IRA), 367–69
Israel-Palestine conflict, 478, 484
"It's not your fault," 272

Jagged (documentary), 335n
JAMA (*Journal of the American Medical Association*), 44, 82–83, 309
Jamison, Kay Redfield, 237–38
Janet, Pierre, 16
Jennings, Helen, 33–35
Jewel, 357, 374, 430
Ji Chengye, 5
Joan of Arc, 239–40, 477
Jobs, Steve, 193
Johnson, Boris, 302
Johnstone, Lucy, 241
Jones-Taylor, Myra, 173–74
Journal of the American Medical Association (*JAMA*), 44, 82–83, 309
Judd, Ashley, 357, 464, 469–70
Judith (author's mother), *14*, 17–18, 26, 130–31, 133
Julia, 78–79, 390–93
Jung, Carl, 238–39

Kaiser Permanente health care network, 230–31
Kang, Shimi, 190–91
Kasser, Tim, 295–96
Kaufman, Gershen, 30
Kazantzakis, Nikos, 361
Kerr, Michael, 198
Khazanov, Natasha, 123
King, Suzanne, 64
King James Bible, 477
Klein, Michael, 151
Klein, Naomi, 292
Kline, Maggie, 491
Knott, Helen
  on compassion of truth, 387
  on dissociation, 263
  In My Own Moccasins, 311, 315, 408
  on racism, 311, 315–16
  self-accusations of, 436–37

on self-harm, 259–60
on spirituality, 473
Kobor, Michael, 278
Kohn, Alfie, 116, 195–96
Kornfield, Jack, 467
Kotbi, Nabil, 236, 236n
Krishna, 52
Kristeva, Julia, 203–4
Kristof, Nicholas, 304, 305
Krugman, Paul, 284–85
Kupfer, David, 240

Ladd, Virginia, 72, 73
Lady Gaga, 357
Lakoff, George, 353
Lamott, Anne, 261
Lancet, 85, 149, 293, 301, 309
Lancet Oncology, 42
Landslide (Wolff), 343
Last Day podcast, 227–28
Leaves of Grass (Whitman), 52
legal system, 475–76, 489–90
Leslie, 257–59
Les Misérables (Hugo), 481
Letourneau, Nicole, 141–42, 145
Letters to a Young Poet (Rilke), 374
Levine, Peter
  on denial, 441
  on image, 203
  on self-limiting beliefs, 422
  on trauma, 16, 18, 21–22, 23–24
Lewis, Candace, 60
Lewontin, R. C., 250
Lewy body disease, 260
Liedloff, Jean, 119, 120, 124–25, 131, 158, 167–68
The Life and Opinions of Tristram Shandy, Gentleman (Sterne), 136
"life events," 43
Lifton, Robert J., 495–96
Lindstrom, Martin, 188–89
Lipton, Bruce, 422–23
Living Myth Podcast, 479
loneliness, 57–58, 170, 174–78, 293–95
Los Angeles Times, 195
loss of meaning, 286–88, 291–92
Lost Connections (Hari), 247–48
Lupick, Travis, 222
lupus, 70, 83, 330
Lustig, Rob, 297–98, 301, 310
lying, 350–51
lymphoma, 96

Mad Men (TV series), 298–99
Madness Explained (Bentall), 253
Madness: The Podcast, 307n
Malcolm X, 312
malignant normality, 495–97
Mandela, Nelson, 179
Mandelstam, Nadezhda, 363
Manne, Kate, 340–41
Marmot, Michael, 324–25, 328
Maron, Marc, 261
marriage status, 56–57
Martinez, Mario, 408, 422
Marx, Karl, 288, 290
Marxism, 283
masculine-coded perks and privileges,
    340–41
Maslow, Abraham, 496
Mason-John, Valerie (Vimalasara),
    313–14
Maté, Aaron, 182
Maté, Daniel, 128, 440–41
Maté, Gabor
    anti-Semitism and, 311
    childhood, *14*, 16, 17, 26, 130–31, 133,
        176, 254–56, 370–71, 372
    communing with God, 454,
        462, 463–66. *See also* touching
        spirit
    depression and, 254–56
    family life, 128, 136–39, *137*, 141, 143,
        145, 182, 339
    marriage life, 15–17, 18, 19, 29, 329–30,
        339, 340
    migration to Canada, 320–21
    mother (Judith), *14*, 17–18, 26,
        130–31, 133
    mother-in-law (Monica), 170
    painting of, *14*
    personal journey of unmaking normal,
        483–85
    psychedelic and healing journey of,
        447–54
    on Rae's childbirth experience, 158
    In the Realm of Hungry Ghosts, 30,
        212, 454
    trauma's effect on, 15–16, 18, 26, 133
    When the Body Says No, 374, 410
Maté, Rae
    childbirth experience, 158
    family life and pregnancy, 128, 136–39,
        141, 143, 145, 182, 339
    marriage life, 15–17, 18, 19, 29, 329–30,
        339, 340

paintings, *14*, *137*
    on sexualization of women, 332
materialism, 295–96
Matthew, 448, 450–51
maturation, 127–28, 131–34, 182, 185–89
May, Rollo, 29
Mayo Clinic, 243
McCabe, Pat (Woman Stands
    Shining), 472
McEwen, Bruce, 48, 57, 276
Meade, Michael, 479–80
Medicare for All, 493
medicine. *See* Western medicine
Mee Ok. *See* Icaro, Mee Ok "Mandy"
Mehl-Madrona, Lewis, 473–75
melanoma, 99, 100
Menand, Louis, 252
mental illness and personality disorders,
    235–52, 253–72. *See also specific
    conditions*
    adaptation of control as, 270–72
    adaptation of disconnection as,
        264–67
    adaptation of dissociation as, 255–56,
        262–64
    adaptation of power as, 267–70
    adaptation of sensitivity as, 249–51
    biological approach to, 235–41,
        255–56, 266
    child development and, 126, 134,
        242–44, 247, 248–49, 257, 267–70
    compassionate approach to, 272
    as a construct, 239–40
    diagnostic approach to, 241–45, 253–54
    digital technology use and, 191–92
    genetic approach to, 237–38, 240,
        249–50, 251–52, 262–63, 265
    healing journey and, 238–39
    as healing journey teacher, 440–41
    "It's not your fault," 272
    personal stories, 235–36, 254–62
    pharmaceutical approach to, 235,
        245–48, 264–65, 267, 267n
    pregnancy environment and,
        144, 145
    sensitivity and, 261–63, 265–67
Merton, Thomas, 200, 204, 389
midwifery, 146–47, 150–55, 158–59
migraine headaches, 101–2
Milburn, Michael, 346–47
Miller, Alice, 347, 370
The Mind and the Brain (Schwartz),
    423–24

The MindBody Code (Martinez), 408, 422
mind-body unity, 38–46, 49–51, 96–97, 461–62
mindfulness practices, 344, 382–83, 424, 477
mind-hacking, 299
Miray, 79
Molecules of Emotion (Pert), 37, 39–40
Monroe, Marilyn, 356
Montagu, Ashley, 163–64, 326
Moody Bitches (Holland), 329
Moorjani, Anita, 96, 110, 112, 375–76
Morissette, Alanis, 234, 335, 335n, 357, 483
Mork & Mindy (TV show), 262
Moss, Michael, 299
Mount Kilimanjaro, 367–69
Mount Sinai Hospital, 155–57
Mukherjee, Siddhartha, 197–98
multiple sclerosis (MS), 73, 79–82, 394–95
Murthy, Vivek, 295
muscular dystrophy, 60n
Musk, Elon, 284
myalgic encephalomyelitis (ME; chronic fatigue syndrome), 70, 101–2
mythic thinking, 478–80

Nader, Ralph, 285
narcissism, 30–31, 307, 436
Narcotics Anonymous, 215–16
Narvaez, Darcia, 120, 122, 131, 132n, 166–67, 168, 175
National Health Service (Great Britain), 303
Native American Church, 462
natural killer (NK) cells, 41–42
Nature, 469–71, 473, 479
Navarro, Dave, 218, 219, 357
Nazis, 17, 17n, 347, 370, 371–72, 437–38, 495–96
neoliberalism, 279–80, 279n
nervous system
    addiction and, 232–34
    autoimmunity and, 76–78, 79–82
    autonomic nervous system, 45, 92, 365
    child development and, 124–25, 134
    human nature and, 120–21
    mind-body unity and, 45
    pregnancy environment and, 141–42
    self-limiting beliefs and, 422–23
    socioeconomic status and, 326

Netsilik Inuit, 164
Neufeld, Gordon
    on acceptance, 381
    on attachment and authenticity, 105, 109, 181
    on child development, 126–28
    on free play, 194
    on maturation, 131–34, 132n
    on peer orientation, 181
    on sleep training, 170
    on vulnerability, 185–86
neural expectancy, 120–21
neurobiology (interpersonal), 54–56
neurogenic inflammation, 76–78
neuromarketing, 298–300
Never Broken (Jewel), 430
New England Journal of Medicine, 309
New Yorker, 91, 161, 169, 197–98, 252
New York Times, 72, 141, 161, 172, 183–84, 281, 283–86, 290, 295, 304, 306, 310, 335, 338
Nietzsche, Friedrich, 53, 350
"no," 413–16, 417–19
No Contest (Kohn), 195–96
No Logo (Klein), 292
nonthings, 37, 40, 48, 51
normal, myth of
    acculturation and, 6–8
    background, 1–6
    current medical paradigm of, 8–9
    human development. *See* character-building; childbirth; child development and parenting; human nature and human needs; pregnancy environment
    interconnected natures. *See* attachment and authenticity; autoimmunity; disease as a process; emotions; genes and genetic inheritance; interpersonal biology; trauma facets
    rethinking normal. *See* addiction; mental illness and personality disorders
    toxicities of culture, 3–5. *See also* capitalism and corporate capitalism; disconnection of society; gender gap; otherism; political culture; popular culture
    wholeness pathways. *See* disease as a teacher; healing journey; normal, unmaking of; touching spirit
normal, unmaking of, 481–97

COVID-19 experience and, 494–95
malignant normality, 495–97
personal journeys for, 481–86
trauma-conscious society
development, 486–94
North American Free Trade Agreement,
301–2
Northern Ireland, 367–69

Obama, Barack, 355
obesity, 270, 301–4
obituaries, 103–4
obsessive-compulsive disorder, 424
Occupy Wall Street protests, 493
Odent, Michel, 146, 148–49, 148n,
150, 158
Of Woman Born (Rich), 148
opioid epidemic, 304–7, 493–94
oppositional defiant disorder (ODD), 243
orchids (sensitive children), 250
Organisation for Economic Co-operation
and Development, 281, 302
originality. See attachment and
authenticity
Osborn, Bud, 218, 222
Osler, William, 77, 80, 98–99
Osmond, Humphry, 457
Oster, Emily, 161–62, 169–70, 172, 176
otherism, 311–28
addiction and, 222–23
alienation and, 290–93
assaulted sense of self and, 315–16
biological embedding of, 311–13
capitalism and, 283–85
gender gap, 329–42
Indigenous peoples and, 320–24
intersectionality of, 313
personal stories, 313–14
race and racism, 311–12, 313–24
socioeconomic status, 313, 319–20,
324–28
ovarian cancer, 42, 43, 89

Palestine-Israel conflict, 478, 484
panic disorder, 258–59
PANIC/GRIEF system, 129–31
Panksepp, Jaak
on addiction, 232n, 233
on ADHD, 265–66
on anger, 379
on depression, 255–56

emotional patterns of brain systems,
129–31, 130n, 134, 232n, 266, 333,
377–78
on free play, 194
on infant-mother bond, 165
on purpose of emotions, 28
paranoia, 235, 257
parenting. See child development and
parenting
Parkinson's disease, 60
paternal depression, 143
patriarchy, 313, 338–42
Pearce, Joseph Chilton, 359
Pediatrics, 125
peer orientation, 181–85, 187–88, 491–92
Perez, Caroline Criado, 338
Perry, Bruce
on addiction, 232
on child development, 249
on disconnection, 287
on maturation, 128
on mental illness, 244, 247
What Happened to You? 487
personality disorders. See mental illness
and personality disorders
personality traits
as adaptations, 409
attachment/authenticity conflict and
adaptations, 105–10
autoimmunity and, 77–78, 84
character-building, 197–207
emotions and, 96–105, 110–12
as habits, 102, 104–5
mind-body unity and, 96–98
personal stories, 96–98, 110–12
return-to-self practices and, 408–10
risk factors, 96–105
"type C," 99, 104–5
persuasive design, 191
Pert, Candace, 37, 39–40, 51, 83
Peterson, Jordan, 133, 163, 168–69
peyote, 456, 462
pharmaceuticals
industry, 304–5, 493–94
for mental illnesses, 235, 245–48,
264–65, 267
physical punishment, for children,
168–69, 346–47
pituitary gland, 47–49, 62–63
pity-compassion comparison, 384
PLAY system, 134, 266
pleasure, 298–99
Plotkin, Bill, 362, 431

Poe, Edgar Allan, 211
political character, 345
political culture
  alienation and, 291
  background, 343–45
  climate change and, 308–10
  conclusion, 357–58
  criticism of, 283–85
  intersectionality of, 354–57
  personal trauma manifestation and,
    353–54
  trauma manifestations in political
    leaders, 345–53
Pollan, Michael, 456, 457
popular culture, 183, 354–57
Porges, Stephen, 120, 194, 365
Pornland (Dines), 233
pornography, 232–33, 335–36
possession, of diseases, 88
possibility, compassion of, 388–89
Postman, Neil, 205
postpartum depression, 141, 142
post-traumatic stress disorder (PTSD),
  42, 43, 330, 331–32
poverty. See socioeconomic status and
  social stratification
power adaptation, 267–70, 335
pregnancy environment, 136–45
  emotion development and, 125
  epigenetics and, 64, 142
  Indigenous cultures honoring, 144
  maternal stress and, 136–43
  paternal stress and, 136–38, 143
  social culture and, 140–41, 144–45
  socioeconomic status and, 143–44
  support for, 144–45
prenatal environment, 64
Presley, Elvis, 356
The Price of Inequality (Stiglitz), 283–84
prisons, 475–76, 489–90
Profound Healing (Canfield), 396, 404
prostate cancer, 41–42, 67, 92–94, 318
proximate separation, 172
Prozac, 82–83, 82n, 245–46
Prozac Nation (Wurtzel), 246
psoriasis, 70
psychedelics, 447–62
  personal stories, 447–54, 457–59
  therapeutic uses, 454–57
  as transformational teachers, 459–62
Psychology Today, 267
psychoneuroimmunology, 45
psychosis, 235

psychosocial integration, 288
PTSD (post-traumatic stress disorder),
  42, 43, 330, 331–32
pulmonary fibrosis, 70
Purdue Pharma, 304–5, 493–94
Putnam, Robert D., 177
Pye, Will, 390–91, 402–3, 404–5,
  404n, 406
Pygmies, 174–75

Quanah Parker, 462
Quebec ice storm (1998), 63–64

RA (rheumatoid arthritis), 70, 73, 77–79,
  330, 391–93
race and racism
  addiction and, 222–23
  corporate capitalism and, 301
  epigenetics and, 65, 66–67
  toward Indigenous peoples, 320–24
  interpersonal biology and, 56–57
  intersectionality of, 313
  race as child of racism, 314–15
  as social determinant of health, 312,
    313–24
  telomeres and, 59–60
Radical Remission (Turner), 398
Rae. See Maté, Rae
RAGE system, 333, 377–78
Rainbow, Randy, 354
Rankin, Lissa, 94–95, 362
rape cancer, 85–87
Raphael, Dennis, 327
raw wound of trauma, 20–21
Reagan, Nancy, 213, 219
Real, Terry, 342
reattribution of self-limiting beliefs,
  425–26
recognition, compassion of, 385–86
re-creating self-limiting beliefs, 428–29
Rediger, Jeffrey, 398–99, 402
refocusing self-limiting beliefs, 426–27
Reich, Wilhelm, 476–77
Reid, Jimmy, 285, 290
Reisner, Steven, 307, 307n
relabeling self-limiting beliefs, 424–25
Report to Greco (Kazantzakis), 361
repression
  of anger, 40–42, 77, 78, 79, 333–34,
    379–80
  disease process and, 100, 101–2

response flexibility, 29
return-to-self practices, 408–12
revaluing self-limiting beliefs, 427–28
rheumatoid arthritis (RA), 70, 73, 77–79, 330, 391–93
Rich, Adrienne, 148, 165, 177
Richards, Keith, 220
Rick, 475–76
Riis, Jacob, 485
Rilke, Rainer Maria, 374
Robinson, C. E. G., 77–78
Rolling Stone, 281
Ruppert, Franz, 32

Sackler family, 304–5, 493–94
Sahlins, Marshall, 116
Saint-Exupéry, Antoine de, 364–65
Saint Joan (Shaw), 477
salt, 299
Salt Sugar Fat (Moss), 299
Sam, 405–6
Sanders, Bernie, 357
The Sane Society (Fromm), 1
San people, 121
San Quentin State Prison, 475–76
Sapiens (Harari), 277
Sapolsky, Robert, 117, 118, 140, 328
Sartre, Jean-Paul, 314
Saul, John Ralston, 280
saying "no," 413–16, 417–19
saying "yes," 420–21
scar of trauma, 20–21
schizophrenia, 241, 262–63
Schizophrenia Bulletin, 248
Schore, Allan, 172
Schrecker, Ted, 303
Schwartz, Jeffrey M., 423–24, 426
Schwartz, Richard "Dick," 393–94, 409, 430–31
Schwartz, Tony, 350–51
Scientific American, 349
scleroderma, 68–71, 73, 76
The Secret Life of the Unborn Child (Verny), 139
SEEKING apparatus, 232n
Seeman, Teresa, 57
selective serotonin uptake inhibitor (SSRI) medication, 82–83, 82n
self
    assaulted sense of, 315–16, 332
    return-to-self practices, 408–12
    shame-based view of, 30–31

self-abandonment, 205–7
self-accusation, 435–38
self-blame, 30, 83–84, 86, 97–98, 100, 112
self-compassion, 83–84, 384, 391–95
self-escape, 220–23, 229
self-estrangement, 23–24, 25–28, 33–35
self-examination, 35–36
self-fragmentation as adaptation, 250, 255–56, 262–64
self-harm, 259–60
self-inquiry exercise, 412–21
selfishness, 115–16, 121–22, 307, 434–35
self-limiting beliefs release, 422–29
self-pity, 384
self-realization, 336–41
self-silencing, 333–34
self-soothing, 259–60
self-sufficiency (superautonomous), 38–39, 40
self-worth, 271–72
Selye, János (Hans), 96, 275, 421
sense memory, 354
sensitivity, 23, 249–51, 261–63, 265–67
separation-from-self trait, 202–3
serotonin, 241, 245–46
Sessions, Jeff, 213, 219
The Seven Storey Mountain (Merton), 200
sex addiction, 232–33
sexual abuse. See trauma facets
sexualization of women, 334–36
shadow side, 239
Shakespeare, William, 464
shame, 30–31, 34–35
Shaw, George Bernard, 477
Sheff, David, 228
Shipibo shamans, 447–54
Shonkoff, Jack, 179
Sia, 357
Siegel, Daniel, 54–55, 354, 497
Silko, Leslie Marmon, 447
"the Sixties Scoop," 321–22
Sjögren's syndrome, 71
slavery, in United States, 36. See also race and racism
SLE (systemic lupus erythematosus), 70, 83, 330
"sleep-training," for babies, 170–71
small-t trauma, 22–23
Smithers, David, 85, 93
Smithsonian magazine, 54
Snowden, Edward, 300
social character, 200–207, 403

social culture. *See also* capitalism and
    corporate capitalism; disconnection
    of society; gender gap; otherism;
    political culture; popular culture
  acculturation and, 6–8
  background, 3–6
  character-building, 197–207
  child development and, 126, 128,
    134–35, 175–78, 179–81, 183,
    187–88, 193–96
  educational priorities, 193–96
  pregnancy environment and, 140–41,
    144–45
  spiritual disconnection of, 467–68
  trauma-conscious society
    development, 486–94
social dislocation, 288–90
social gradient, 327–28
socialization mode of parenting, 162–63
social media, 189, 344
socioeconomic status and social
    stratification
  addiction and, 222–23
  childbirth and, 157–58
  epigenetics and, 59–60, 64–65, 66–67
  health impacts of, 319–20, 324–28
  intersectionality of, 313
  parenting and, 172–74
  pregnancy environment and, 143–44
sociogenic brain damage, 326
Socrates, 35–36
Solnit, Rebecca, 273
Solzhenitsyn, Aleksandr, 395
"Song of Myself" (Whitman), 52
Sontag, Susan, 97–98, 110–12
spirituality. *See* touching spirit
spiritual openings, 466–71. *See also*
    touching spirit
Spock, Benjamin, 162–63
spontaneous remission, 398–99, 402–3
Stanger-Ross, Ilana, 154, 155, 159
Sterne, Laurence, 136
steroids, 70
Stiglitz, Joseph E., 283–84
stress
  ADHD and, 266
  autoimmunity and, 74–84
  as cancer "cause," 92–94
  of capitalism, 276–77, 278–82
  child development and, 129–31, 133
  epigenetics and, 62–66, 64n
  forms of, 46–47, 64, 64n
  interpersonal biology and, 56–57

  machinery of, 46–49
  mind-body unity and, 42–46
  overview of, 275–76
  parental, 171–74
  self-harm adaptation to, 259–60
  socioeconomic status and, 326
The Stress of Life (Selye), 96, 421
Study of Women's Health Across the
    Nation (SWAN), 66
substance use. *See* addiction
sugar, 299, 301–2
Sumrok, Dan, 229
superautonomous self-sufficiency,
    38–39, 40
suppression and denial, 27–28, 100–102,
    441–46
survival instinct, 27–28
Swan, Shanna, 144
The Sweet Hereafter (Banks), 160
Swingle, Mari, 191–92
systemic lupus erythematosus (SLE), 70,
    83, 330
systemic sclerosis, 68–71, 73, 76
Szalavitz, Maia, 128, 224
Szyf, Moshe, 62–63, 65, 66–67

Tailfeathers, Esther, 323–24
Tapia, Nneka Jones, 490
The Tech Solution (Kang), 190–91
telomeres, 59–67, 142
Temoshok, Lydia, 99, 99n, 104–5
Temple of the Way of Light, 447–54
"the Sixties Scoop," 321–22
Thich Nhat Hanh, 58
Thistle, Jesse, 217, 385, 439–40, 490
Thomas, April, 65
365 Days (film), 336
Thunberg, Greta, 308, 492, 495
Tide soap commercials, 204–5
tobacco industry, 305–6
tolerance-acceptance comparison, 381
Tolle, Eckhart, 466
Too Much and Never Enough
    (Trump), 350
Toronto Star, 284, 348
Touched with Fire (Jamison), 237–38
touching spirit, 463–80
  author communing with, 454, 462,
    463–66
  Indigenous cultures and, 462, 467,
    471–75
  mythic thinking, 11n, 478–80

Nature and, 469–71, 473, 479
personal special truth and, 476–78
in prisons, 475–76
spiritual openings, 466–71
toxicities of culture, 3–5. *See also*
capitalism and corporate capitalism;
disconnection of society; gender
gap; otherism; political culture;
popular culture
toxic masculinity, 332–33, 341–42
traditional Chinese medicine, 98
tranquilizer dependence. *See* addiction
Trauma and Madness in Mental Health Services (Hunter), 256–57
trauma awareness
activism and advocacy for, 492–94
education system development of, 490–92
legal system development of, 489–90
society development of, 486–92
Western medicine development of, 487–89
trauma facets, 15–36
adaptations to, 23–24
addiction and, 221–23, 226–32
background, 15–19
collective sphere of trauma, 36
definitions, 16
disconnection and, 25–28, 32–34, 265–66
dissociation and, 263–64
of mental illness, 236, 236n, 248–49
mind-body unity and, 49–51
multigenerational, 33–36, 320, 322
obstetrical trauma, 155–58
parenting and, 33–35
in political culture, 345–54
power as adaptation to, 269–70
present alienation, 32–33
response flexibility limited by, 29
self-harm as adaptation to, 259–60
shame-based view of self, 30–31, 34–35
social, 320, 322, 327–28
toxic masculinity, 341–42
types of, 21–24, 33–36
what it is and what it does, 19–24
what it is not, 24–25
world view distortion, 31–32
The Trauma of Everyday Life (Epstein), 15
trees, 53–54
Trudeau, Justin, 348–49
Trudeau, Pierre, 349
Trump, Donald J., 349–51, 352–53, 354

Trump, Fred, Jr., 350
Trump, Mary, 350
truth, 386–88, 476–78. *See also*
suppression and denial
truthfulness. *See* attachment and
authenticity
tuning out, 265
Turnbull, Colin, 173–74
Turner, Kelly, 377, 398, 403
Turner, Nina, 357
12 Rules for Life (Peterson), 163
twelve-step programs, 215–16, 229, 467
twin studies, 237–38, 237n
type I diabetes, 70, 72. *See also* diabetes
"type C" personality, 99, 104–5

UBS, 284
ulcerative colitis, 70
unions, 292–93
An Unquiet Mind (Jamison), 237
uterine cancer, 404–5

V (formerly known as Eve Ensler), 25, 27, 85–87, 88, 471
vaginal birth after cesarean section (VBAC), 152
Vagina Monologues (V), 85
van der Kolk, Bessel
on author's trauma, 370–71, 372
on character-building, 197
on ego, 53
on self-examination, 35–36
on trauma, 18, 21–22, 23, 35–36
on trauma-conscious society, 486–87
on Trump, 350
Van Derveer, Will, 488, 489
VBAC (vaginal birth after cesarean section), 152
vegetalismo, 448
Verny, Thomas, 139
Vietnam War, 484
A Vindication of the Rights of Woman (Wollstonecraft), 336
Virchow, Rudolf, 324
Volkow, Nora, 214–15
Volz-Boers, Ursula, 140
vulnerability, 185–87, 272, 341–42

Wallace, David Foster, 7
Wall Street Journal, 309

war metaphors, 87–88, 160, 213
Watson, John, 467
Webb, Eboni, 320
Weinstein, Harvey, 469
Weiss, Soma, 44
Western medicine. *See also* addiction;
    mental illness and personality
    disorders
  childbirth and, 146–58
  emotion suppression during training,
    94–95
  pharmaceutical industry, 304–5,
    493–94
  trauma-conscious medicine, 487–89
Westover, Tara, 28
What Happened to You? (Perry), 487
When the Body Says No (Maté), 374, 410
Whitaker, Robert, 240–41
The White Tiger (Adiga), 275
Whitman, Walt, 52
wholeness pathways. *See* disease
    as a teacher; healing journey;
    normal, unmaking of; touching
    spirit
Wible, Pamela, 488, 489

Wilbourn, Asa J., 41
Wilkinson, Richard, 328
Williams, Robin, 260–62, 272
Williams, Venus, 68, 71
Winehouse, Amy, 356
Winfrey, Oprah, 357, 487
Winnicott, D. W., 23, 164
The Wire (TV series), 293
The Wisdom of Trauma
    (documentary), 487
Wittels Wachs, Stephanie, 227–28
Wohlleben, Peter, 54
Wolff, Michael, 343
Wollstonecraft, Mary, 336
Wolynn, Mark, 34
Woman Stands Shining, 472
World Health Organization, 157, 184
worthlessness stories, 419–20
Wurtzel, Elizabeth, 31, 246

"yes," 420–21

Zmenak, Donna, 395–98, 399, 402